The ARRL's
FCC
Rule Book

Complete Guide to the
FCC Regulations

Edited by:
John Hennessee, N1KB

Published by:
ARRL
The national association for AMATEUR RADIO

Contents

Foreword

This new 12th edition of *The FCC Rule Book* includes many important changes. This edition of *The FCC Rule Book* is accurate and current as of April 15, 2000. An extensive amount of material has been added to guide you through the new Universal Licensing System regulations that took effect in 1998, the amateur license restructuring changes and other issues. As you can see from the "What's New" section, many Part 97 rule sections were affected. In fact, 35 of the 52 pages of Part 97 have changed since the last edition of this book. The complete Part 97 appears in Chapter 9; the rules that have changed since the last edition appear in **bold** type to make it easier to see exactly what has changed.

In addition, the changes brought on by license class restructuring have caused a significant increase in activity in the Amateur Radio Service. These changes, effective April 15, 2000, are reflected in this edition.

Through the FCC's Biennial Review—as well as proposals made by the ARRL, other organizations and individual amateurs—the Rules are in a constant state of refinement. These changes are designed to streamline the Rules by making them more efficient and eliminating those no longer pertinent or needed. At the same time, they continue to permit a great deal of operating flexibility in developing your operating skills and technical knowledge.

ARRL keeps amateurs abreast of any and all changes affecting the Amateur Radio Service each month in *QST*. Readers with Web access can find a tremendous amount of information on *ARRLWeb* at **http://www.arrl.org/**. ARRL Members can find additional information on the ARRL Members Only page at **http://www.arrl.org/members-only/**. If you're not already a member, why not consider joining today?

Have a suggestion for improving this book? Share it with us via the Feedback Form at the back, or send e-mail to **pubsfdbk@arrl.org**.

Now that the FCC is once again actively policing the Amateur Radio bands, it is more important than ever to make sure you are following *all* Part 97 rules at *all* times. The only way to be sure of doing that is by becoming familiar with the contents of this book!

David Sumner, K1ZZ
Executive Vice President
Newington, Connecticut
March 2000

Acknowledgments

The FCC Rule Book is always a work in progress and is the product of many individuals' expertise and hard work. Tracking FCC rules is a bit like following a moving vehicle. Tracking the changes brought on by the Universal Licensing System and the changes to the licensing structure is a bit like tracking a *speeding* vehicle!

Major contributors were Dale Clift, NA1L and Bob Halprin, K1XA, who developed the local antenna regulation discussion. Edward Mitchell, KF7VY, contributed much on the regulatory issues surrounding emergency communications. ARRL Laboratory Supervisor Ed Hare, W1RFI, contributed much of the material covering EMI/RFI and the RF Exposure Regulations. Thanks to Gary Hendrickson, W3DTN, Chairman of The Middle Atlantic Repeater Council's Open Band Planning Committee, who contributed significantly to Chapter 3. His careful review has made the rules on auxiliary operation, repeater operation, telecommand, cross-band operation and linking easily understandable. Thanks also to Zack Lau, W1VT; Bart Jahnke, W9JJ; Jon Bloom, KE3Z; Jennifer Hagy, N1TDY; Chris Imlay, W3KD; Wayne Irwin, WK1I, Brennan Price, N4QX, Riley Hollingsworth, K4ZDH, and David Sumner, K1ZZ, for reviewing sections of this book, and to Margie Bourgoin, KB1DCO, for her staff support.

Thanks to ARRL Electronic Publications Assistant Tom Hogerty, KC1J, formerly of the Regulatory Information Branch, who completely reorganized the 11th edition. The 12th edition follows the same format. Thanks also go to Rick Palm, K1CE, who reviewed the manuscript for this edition. His name will be familiar to many, as he was the editor of the very first edition of *The FCC Rule Book*, and was ARRL Field Services Manager for many years. Thanks also go to Field and Educational Services Manager Rosalie White, WA1STO, for her guidance throughout the work on the 12th edition.

Special thanks to Associate Technical Editor Joel Kleinman, N1BKE, who guided this book through the publication process from start to finish and helped put on the polish. Thanks to the entire ARRL HQ Production Department and others who never complained about my bad penmanship, especially after I broke my writing hand late in the production process.

And last, but certainly not least, thank *you* for purchasing this book!

John Hennessee, N1KB
Editor

Introduction

Amateur Radio means different things to many different people. That is one of its beauties—diversity. Like a fine-cut gem, it shines in many directions. Steeped in tradition, Amateur Radio means to many old-timers the memory of a past era of racks of black, wrinkle-finished, meter-spattered radio chassis replete with glowing tubes and humming transformers. To many newer amateurs, it equates to "high-tech" and the opportunity to pioneer and develop the latest experimental digital code, data network or satellite technique. To others, it means things perhaps less heady—simply an opportunity to make friends around the world on the long haul high-frequency bands or across town through the local repeater. It means community service—the chance to use radio to help fellow human beings in need, whether by assisting safety services deal with a tornado watch or by organizing a local walkathon. To students, it means a head start on a career path. To most, it's a little of all of the above.

A common thread in Amateur Radio's history has been a dynamic regulatory environment that has nurtured technological growth and the diversity described above. This thread continues to sew together the elements of Amateur Radio today and prepare it for tomorrow's challenges. The license class restructuring rules that went into effect April 15, 2000 went a long way to propel the Amateur Radio Service into the new millennium.

PURPOSE OF THE RULES

It's the Federal Communication Commission's responsibility to see that amateurs are able to operate their stations in a manner consistent with the objectives outlined for the Amateur Radio Service. The FCC must also ensure that hams have the knowledge and ability to operate powerful and potentially dangerous equipment safely without causing interference to other amateurs and to other radio services.

To these ends, before a license is issued, the FCC requires examination of all amateurs in theory, operating, regulations and, except for the Technician license, Morse code. Under the rules effective April 15, 2000, a Technician who has passed the 5 WPM element has the privileges of the "old Technician Plus" class. The Commission fashions its rules in accordance with the Basis and Purpose of Amateur Radio. The rules must be written to create a flexible regulatory environment that encourages, rather than limits, development of Amateur Radio and its ability to use modern technology. The FCC reviews its rules from time to time to remove uncertainty, incorporate existing interpretive policy where necessary, and delete unnecessary or obsolete rules. An example is the Biennial Regulatory

Review of FCC rules to facilitate use of the Universal Licensing System.

Amateur Radio can be compared to our system of public parks: it requires protection from exploitation or conversion to commercial use so the public can use it and benefit from its use. The rules are designed to help protect Amateur Radio from such encroachment.

BASIS FOR THE RULES

The basis for the FCC's regulations is found in treaties, international agreements and statutes that provide for the allocation of frequencies and place conditions on how the frequencies are to be used. For example, Article S25 of the international Radio Regulations limits the types of international communications amateur stations may transmit, and mandates that the technical qualifications of amateur operators be verified.

The Commission's statutory authority to make operational and technical rules, authorize frequencies and license amateurs and stations in the US comes from the Communications Act of 1934, as Amended. For a comprehensive discussion of the Communications Act of 1934, as well as the international Radio Regulations, refer to Chapter 10.

Three other acts of Congress affect FCC rule making. The Administrative Procedure Act allows the public to participate in the rule-making process. You may petition the FCC for rule changes, comment on current proposals, and ask the FCC to reconsider decisions. The FCC must take into consideration your input when making rules. There's more on the Administrative Procedure Act in Chapter 7.

Under the Regulatory Flexibility Act, the Commission certifies that new rules will not have a significant economic impact on a substantial number of small entities, such as businesses.

Finally, the FCC analyzes its rules under the Paperwork Reduction Act to make sure they tend to decrease the information collection burden imposed on the public.

RULE INTERPRETATIONS

The purpose of this book is to provide you with a complete set of the rules and a commentary on them to help amateurs apply the rules in specific situations. The chapters that follow provide time-tested and FCC-approved interpretations, and copies of FCC letters and news releases describe the application of the rules. Graphic depictions of rules are provided where possible to lend clarity—maps, portrayals of antenna structures near airports and glide-slope rules are examples.

There are other parts of the Commission's rules that affect Amateur Radio. In many cases, they are referenced in Part 97. This book discusses these rules and provides the text for reference. It has been updated to reflect all of the FCC rule changes through July 1, 2001.

A FINAL NOTE

Generally, the rules are meant to be inclusive, rather than exclusive. Some hams stay up all night thinking of ways that a certain interpretation will prevent them from doing something with their radio. *Operating flexibility* is the name of the game—the rules provide a framework within which amateurs have wide latitude to do all kinds of constructive things in accordance with the basis and purpose of the service. The rules should be viewed as positive vehicles to promote healthy activity and growth, not as negative constraints that lead to stagnation.

What's New?

In what some consider to be the most important FCC action for amateurs in many years, on December 30, 1999, the FCC issued a Report and Order in WT Docket 98-143. Officially known as the "1998 Biennial Review of the Commission's Amateur Service Rules," and known to amateurs as the "restructuring docket," the FCC made substantial changes to the amateur licensing structure. These changes, effective April 15, 2000, are discussed in this book.

Here are the main points of the FCC Report and Order in the "restructuring docket":

• On and after April 15, 2000, the FCC will issue only three classes of license to those who qualify for a new or upgraded license: Technician, General and Amateur Extra;

• On and after April 15, 2000 only one class of Morse code will exist: 5 WPM,

• On and after April 15, 2000, there are four examination elements: Element 1 (5 WPM CW); Element 2 (35 question examination for Technician); Element 3 (35 question examination for General) and Element 4 (50 question examination for Amateur Extra);

• No new Novice, Technician Plus or Advanced class licenses will be issued on or after April 15, 2000;

• Existing licensees, including Novice, Technician Plus and Advanced, may continue to operate using their assigned privileges and may continue to renew indefinitely;

• There are no changes to the spectrum available to licensees;

• No new RACES licenses will be issued;

• Since the 13 and 20 WPM requirements have been eliminated, so too have the medical exemptions.

Information on the FCC's restructuring changes can be found on *ARRLWeb* at: **http://www.arrl.org/news/restructuring/**. The FCC in a Memorandum Opinion and Order in this docket made minor changes effective July 1, 2001. The updated Part 97 can be found at: **http://www.arrl.org/FandES/field/ regulations/news/part97/**. Other versions of Part 97 exist, but it is important to make sure they have been updated to reflect rule changes through July 1, 2001.

FCC implemented the Universal Licensing System in the Amateur Service on August 16, 1999. ULS has revolutionized the way the FCC processes applications. Under ULS, amateurs must register their stations and give their Social Security Number to the FCC under the Debt Collection Improvement Act of 1996. The ULS docket encourages amateurs to file electronically, but it also gives amateurs the option of filing manually. It also meant the demise of the familiar FCC Form 610, which was replaced by FCC Form 605.

Effective February 16, 1999, the FCC also amended the Amateur Service rules to authorize foreign amateurs to operate their stations while visiting in the US. The FCC eliminated the requirements for foreign amateurs to obtain a reciprocal operating permit provided that the US shares a bilateral or multilateral agreement with the foreign country. The only documentation required is proof of citizenship and an Amateur Radio license issued by the country of citizenship. Foreign amateurs must identify using the letter numeral identifier followed by a slant and their home call. These arrangements are similar to the longstanding arrangement between the US and Canada. This revision affected the following Part 97 rules: §§97.3, 97.5, 97.7, 97.9, 97.13, 97.15, 97.17, 97.19, 97.21, 97.23, 97.25, 97.27, 97.29, 97.107, 97.119, 97.201, 97.203, 97.205, 97.207, 97.301, 97.505, 97.509 and 97.519. Complete details appear in Chapter 1.

Effective June 7, 1999, the FCC implemented the European Conference of Postal and Telecommunications Administrations (CEPT) Recommendation T/R 61-01. This eliminates the need to obtain a special license or permit for US hams wishing to operate during brief visits to most European countries. To operate in a CEPT country, US hams need only a copy of the FCC CEPT Public Notice, their original Amateur Radio document and proof of US citizenship (a US-issued passport or a birth certificate will suffice). They must also identify by using the ITU identifier for the country followed by a stroke and their home call. In addition, the ARRL has begun issuing International Amateur Radio Permits to simplify operation by US hams in certain South American countries. See Chapter 2 for details.

Effective October 5, 1999, the FCC streamlined the authorization procedure for equipment requiring FCC approval. ET Docket 97-94 changed references in §§97.315 and 97.317 from "type acceptance" to "certificated." Amateur external RF power amplifiers must now be certificated rather than type accepted. See Chapter 4.

The FCC also amended overly restrictive Spread Spectrum rules, effective November 1, 1999. The following sections were amended: §§97.3(c)(8) and 97.311. The FCC had already amended its rules to clarify that amateurs are permitted to use the PacTOR, G-TOR and CLOVER digital modes. See §97.309 and Chapter 4.

The FCC amended its guidelines in ET Docket 93-62 for evaluating the environmental effects of RF. See Chapter 1, Appendix 2, §§97.13 and 97.503.

The FCC established a Radio Astronomy Coordination Zone in Puerto Rico in ET Docket 96-2. See §§97.203, 1.924. Details appear in Chapter 3 and 10.

What is the FCC?

The Federal Communications Commission (FCC) is the US government agency charged by Congress with regulating communications involving radio, television, wire, cable and satellites. This includes Amateur Radio. The objective of the FCC is to provide for orderly development and operation of telecommunications services.

The FCC functions like no other Federal agency. Congress created it and it reports directly to Congress. The FCC allocates bands of frequencies to nongovernment communications services and assigns operator privileges (the National Telecommunications and Information Administration allocates government frequencies).

The Amateur's Code

THE RADIO AMATEUR IS:

CONSIDERATE...never knowingly operates in such a way as to lessen the pleasure of others.

LOYAL...offers loyalty, encouragement and support to other amateurs, local clubs, and the American Radio Relay League, through which Amateur Radio in the United States is represented nationally and internationally.

PROGRESSIVE...with knowledge abreast of science, a well-built and efficient station and operation above reproach.

FRIENDLY...slow and patient operating when requested; friendly advice and counsel to the beginner; kindly assistance, cooperation and consideration for the interests of others. These are the hallmarks of the amateur spirit.

BALANCED...radio is an avocation, never interfering with duties owed to family, job, school or community.

PATRIOTIC...station and skill always ready for service to country and community.

—*The original Amateur's Code was written by Paul M. Segal, W9EEA, in 1928.*

General Provisions

Subpart A—General Provisions—covers, as its name suggests, basics that apply to all facets of the Amateur Radio Service. The Basis and Purpose of Amateur Radio is found at the beginning of Part 97 [97.1]. First written in 1951 when Part 97 was called Part 12, these basic principles have withstood the test of time.

Definitions of key terms used throughout Subpart A form the foundation of Part 97. Before heading into the rest of Part 97, make sure you're familiar with these definitions [97.3]. They are fairly self-explanatory. Subpart A is devoted to other issues involving licensing and station location, such as authorization, antenna location and restrictions, control operators, license classes (recently restructured) and call signs, and stations on boats and airplanes. It also includes a useful incorporation of FCC policy on limited preemption of state and local restrictions on amateur antenna installations. The policy has encouraged open cooperation and dialogue between communities seeking to regulate ham towers and antennas, and the amateur community itself [97.15]. This subpart also covers new license grants, vanity calls, renewed or modified licenses and related issues.

SUBPART A RULES SUMMARY: GENERAL PROVISIONS

97.1 Basis and purpose.
97.3 Definitions.
97.5 Station license grant required.
97.7 Control operator required.
97.9 Operator license grant.
97.11 Stations aboard ships or aircraft.
97.13 Restrictions on station location.
97.15 Station antenna structures.
97.17 Application for new license grant.
97.19 Application for a vanity call sign.
97.21 Application for a modified or renewed license grant.

BASIS AND PURPOSE

The very first item in Part 97 is the *Basis and Purpose* of the Amateur Radio Service. All of our amateur operations and activities should be consistent with it. Let's have a look at each of the five basic principles:

Recognition and enhancement of the value of the amateur service to the public as a voluntary noncommercial communication service, particularly with respect to providing emergency communications [97.1(a)].

Probably the best known aspect of Amateur Radio in the public eye is its ability to provide lifesaving emergency communications when normal means of communication are down. In hurricanes, earthquakes, tornadoes, airplane crashes, missing person cases, and other accidents and disasters affecting the general population, Amateur Radio often provides the first means of contact with the outside world. The Red Cross and other civil preparedness agencies rely heavily on the services of volunteer radio amateurs. For example, literally within minutes of the Oklahoma City bombing, amateurs were on the scene providing vital communications.

One of the most important aspects of the service is its *noncommercial* nature. Amateurs are prohibited from receiving any form of payment in exchange for operating their station. This means that hams, whether assisting a search-and-rescue operation in the high Sierra, relaying health-and-welfare messages from a hurricane-ravaged Caribbean island or providing communications assistance at the New York City Marathon, make their services available free of charge. Amateurs operate their stations for the benefit of the public on a volunteer basis, and for their own personal enjoyment.

Continuation and extension of the amateur's proven ability to contribute to the advancement of the radio art [97.1(b)].

For more than 85 years, hams have carried on a tradition of learning by doing, and since the beginning have remained at the forefront of technology. Through experimentation and building, hams have pioneered advances, such as techniques for single-sideband transmission, and are currently engaged in state-of-the-art designs in digital radio and spread-spectrum techniques. Amateurs were among the first to bounce signals off the moon to extend signal range. Amateurs design and build satellites, experimental balloons and rockets at a fraction of the cost of their commercial counterparts. Hams' practical experience has led to technical refinements and cost reductions beneficial to the commercial radio industry.

Encouragement and improvement of the amateur service through rules which provide for advancing skills in both the communication and technical phases of the art [97.1(c)].

The FCC promotes amateur experimentation and the *advancing of communication and technical skills* through a flexible and dynamic rule structure. The Amateur Service rules are constantly changing to meet the changing needs of its users. Amateurs sharpen their *technical* skills by helping others resolve interference problems and by building and troubleshooting equipment and antennas. Amateurs *advance communication skills* by participating in contests, for example, where the goal is to make as many contacts as possible in a given period of time. Amateurs play an important role in the rulemaking process.

Expansion of the existing reservoir within the Amateur Radio Service of trained operators, technicians and electronics experts [97.1(d)].

The greater the number of amateurs proficient in communications techniques and electronics, the greater the resource Amateur Radio is to the public. Amateurs train themselves as *operators, technicians and electronics experts* at no cost to the government. For example, during the Gulf War in 1990, hams were a significant resource to the military. They also provided vital communications to the White House and the Pentagon (see May 1991 *QST*, p 18). Many amateurs cite their early interest in Amateur Radio as a primary motivating factor in a successful business career.

Continuation and extension of the amateur's unique ability to enhance international goodwill [97.1(e)].

In this time when global community initiatives are so important, *amateurs make substantial contributions by representing their respective countries as ambassadors of goodwill*. Amateur-to-amateur communications transcend cultural boundaries between societies.

AMATEUR RADIO DEFINED

Here is the FCC's official definition for the **Amateur Service**:

A radiocommunication service for the purpose of self-training, intercommunication and technical investigations carried out by amateurs, that is, duly authorized persons interested in radio technique solely with a personal aim and without pecuniary interest [97.3(a)(4)].

Note the phrase *without pecuniary interest*. The service is *amateur* because it's strictly noncommercial; you may not earn money or receive any other material compensation for providing amateur communications. Amateur Radio is solely for people interested in the technical and communications aspects of radio out of personal, not commercial, interest.

Amateur Radio began with a few experimenters in the early 1900s and has grown to nearly 700,000 licensed operators in the US alone. Amateur Radio represents principles of radio communications that have endured and

Postscript—90 Years of Licensing

Until 1912, there was no licensing, no regulations and no governing body to oversee "wireless" activities on the airwaves. Before long, however, it became evident to federal authorities that regulation was needed to maintain order: Conflicts between amateur stations and those used by the Navy and commercial services were on the increase. The first regulation came in the form of licensing.

The era of mandatory licensing began when the US Department of Commerce and Labor, under the authority of the Radio Act of 1912, created the Amateur First Grade and Amateur Second Grade operator licenses. The two classes bestowed identical privileges and, at least theoretically, required identical qualifications.

Amateur First Grade applicants took written tests on radio laws, regulations, and the proper adjustment and operation of equipment. The code sending and receiving tests, originally 5 WPM, increased to 10 WPM by 1919. Candidates for Amateur Second Grade, in contrast, certified to Radio Inspectors by mail that they could meet these requirements, but were unable to attend an examination.

Until 1933, station and operator licenses were issued as separate, diploma-sized-certificates. The type of station license held (originally General, Special or Restricted) determined permissible operating wavelengths and power.

In 1923, the Department of Commerce created the Amateur Extra First Grade, a license so special it was printed on pink paper! Only Amateur Extra First Grade licensees thereafter qualified for "Special" station licenses, which had distinctive call signs and conveyed CW privileges on wavelengths longer than 200 meters.

Qualifications for the new class included two years' experience as a licensed operator and a written examination that, among other items, required the applicant to diagram a transmitter and receiver and then explain their principles of operation. The code tests were given at 20 WPM, the speed required of Commercial First Class operators.

As amateur interests shifted to shortwaves, the Amateur Extra First Grade's popularity declined. Only six such licenses were issued in 1926 and the class was discontinued the following year. Reinstated in 1928 with new privileges (described below) added in 1929, the class attracted several hundred licensees most years until its permanent deletion in 1933.

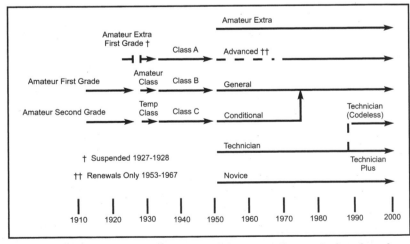

The evolution of Amateur Radio licensing over the past nine decades.

The Radio Act of 1927 transferred the power to issue station licenses to the Federal Radio Commission (FRC) while preserving the authority of the Commerce Department's Radio Division to issue operator licenses. Months later, the Radio Division redesignated the Amateur First and Second Grade classes as Amateur Class and Temporary Amateur, respectively. To First Grade licensees, the change meant little more than a new name. Temporary Amateur differed from the previous Second Grade, however, in that the former expired in one year and (after 1932) could not be renewed. Hams could no longer indefinitely avoid taking an examination.

In late 1929, the Radio Division began endorsing Amateur Extra First Grade licenses for "unlimited radiotelephone privileges." Initially, the endorsement authorized voice privileges on the 20-meter band. In 1932, the endorsement became available to other amateurs having at least one year of experience, upon passing a special test on radiotelephone subjects. At the same time, phone use of 75 meters was also reserved to holders of endorsed licenses.

The Radio Division merged with the FRC in 1932. A year later, the FRC completely revised the amateur regulations. Station and operator licenses were thereafter combined on a single, wallet-sized card.

The amateur's basic license was endorsed as Class A, B or C. All three classes required code tests at 10 WPM (13 WPM after 1936). Class A conveyed exclusive phone use on 20 and 75 meters. It required one year of prior experience and a written examination on radiotelephone and radiotelegraph theory and amateur regulations.

Classes B and C conveyed all privileges other than those reserved to Class A. The written test for those classes was less comprehensive than that for Class A with regard to radiotelephone theory. The two classes differed in that Class C written examinations were furnished by mail to applicants residing at least 125 miles from the nearest FRC quarterly examining point. Class C code tests were administered by Class A and B licensees acting as volunteer examiners.

Amateur Extra First Grade licensees qualified for Class A privileges upon renewal. Amateur Class licensees were grandfathered into Class B. Temporary Amateur licenses could not be renewed, however, so holders of this class had to qualify anew in Class B or C upon expiration of their licenses.

The Federal Communications Commission (FCC) succeeded the FRC with the passage of the Communications Act of 1934. It revised the regulations in 1951 to create the license-class names that are familiar today. Advanced, General and Conditional licenses replaced Classes A, B and C, respectively. The Advanced class was closed to new applicants in January 1953, although renewal of existing licenses continued. A month later, the 20 and 75-meter "Class A Phone Bands" were opened to General and Conditional licensees.

The same rule-making action created the Amateur Extra, Novice and Technician classes. The Extra Class originally required two years' experience as a Conditional (or Class C) licensee or higher, code tests at 20 WPM and a theory examination more comprehensive than that previously given for Class A. No exclusive privileges were reserved for the new class.

The Technician ticket originally conveyed all amateur privileges above 220 MHz. Novices were initially restricted to CW operation on portions of the 11 and 80-meter bands, and voice at 145-147 MHz, at 75-W input, using only crystal-controlled transmitters. The first Novice licenses expired after one year and could not be renewed. After 1954, Novice and Technician exams were obtained from the FCC by mail and administered through volunteer examiners. In 1976, the system changed again: Potential Technician licensees were required to appear before an FCC examiner, although existing

Technician licenses were grandfathered.

A glimpse at our current regulations reveals that the licensing system has undergone many changes since 1951. Although it is beyond the scope here to examine them all, some of the most important have been the establishment of license upgrading incentives and the reopening of the Advanced class to new licensees in 1967; elimination of activity and code speed requirements for renewal; the expansion and realignment of Novice and Technician frequency privileges, notably in 1976; the increase of the Novice power level, the removal of the crystal-control requirement and the merger of Conditional licenses into the General class in 1976; the extension of license terms to 10 years in 1983; and Novice Enhancement in 1987.

On February 14, 1991, the FCC removed the code requirement from the Technician license, creating the first codeless license class in the US.

On April 15, 2000, the FCC effected sweeping changes to the US Amateur Radio licensing structure: the number of operator license classes (for new licenses) was reduced from six to three; the number of code test elements was reduced from three to one; and the number of theory test elements was reduced from five to three.

Ever since the early days, the amateur service has been in a constant state of evolution, and there is every reason to believe that Amateur Radio of the future will look quite different.—*Neil D. Friedman, N3DF*

advanced since the days of the earliest radio pioneers. Amateur Radio was one of the first non-government communication services.

STATION LICENSE REQUIRED

We all know that a license is required before operation can commence on the amateur bands. Since most amateurs are familiar only with what Part 97 says about rules and regulations affecting the Amateur Radio Service, let's look a bit further. An amateur license gives an amateur authority to operate from *most* locations regulated by the FCC. The basis for all FCC rules is the Communications Act of 1934, as amended. Sections 302 and 303 of the Act give the FCC the authority to require a license for radio transmitters. The Communications Act is part of a much larger body of rules called the United States Code and the legal cite for these two sections is 47 USC 302 and 303 (Title 47 of the United States Code, Sections 302 and 303).

Because radio signals cross the borders of countries, Amateur Radio is also governed by international Radio Regulations as administered by the International Telecommunication Union. Under international agreements, the FCC is obligated to ensure that you have a license before you operate on amateur frequencies [international Radio Regulations (RR) Article S25] and that you can operate your station safely while limiting interference to others. It must also make sure you can copy Morse code if you want to operate on the HF bands [RR, Article S25]. Thus, the Morse code examination for FCC licenses that permit HF operation is an *international* requirement.

The United States Code and the international Radio Regulations are incorporated into the Code of Federal Regulations, which is much more specialized than the bodies of rules mentioned above. Title 47 of the Code of Federal Regulations governs telecommunications. It covers Parts 0-300 and this, of course, includes our own Part 97.

Before an individual may begin operating in the amateur bands, the person in physical control of the station must hold an unexpired amateur authorization when operating:

(1) Within 50 km of the Earth's surface and at a place where the amateur service is regulated by the FCC;

(2) Within 50 km of the Earth's surface and aboard any vessel or craft that is documented or registered in the United States; or

(3) More than 50 km above the Earth's surface aboard any craft that is documented or registered in the United States [97.5(a)].

FOUR TYPES OF STATION LICENSES

There are four types of station licenses. All of the stations mentioned below must be under the control of an amateur named in a Universal Licensing System database. ULS is the FCC's database for all FCC services. One of the following must be held by the person in physical control of the transmitter [97.5(b)]:

(1) An operator/primary station license;

(2) A club station license;

(3) A military recreation station license; or

(4) A RACES station license.

OPERATOR/PRIMARY STATION LICENSE

Most stations hold an **operator/primary station license**. *One, and only one*, operator/primary station license is granted to each amateur operator. The primary station license is granted together with the amateur operator license. In fact, it's on the same sheet of paper. Except for a representative of a foreign government, any person who qualifies by examination is eligible to apply for an operator/primary station license [97.5(b)(1)]. Individuals are issued licenses from the Sequential Call Sign Assignment System according to license class. You don't have to be a US citizen to hold a US amateur license, but you must have a US mailing address.

A person's amateur operator/primary license is actually two licenses in one: The **operator license** specifies your license class and privileges and allows you to be a control operator of a station. The **primary station license** permits operation of all transmitter equipment under the physical control of the licensee at locations where Amateur Radio is regulated by the FCC [97.5(b)]. The license form lists your mailing address and call sign of your station. The FCC requires that you notify them when your mailing address changes by filing for a modification of your license on FCC Form 605, or on-line at **www.fcc.gov/wtb/uls**. As a free membership service, ARRL members may submit the

NCVEC Form 605 to the ARRL VEC for processing. See **www.arrl.org/fcc/ forms.html**. The FCC can suspend or revoke your license if their mail to you is returned as undeliverable [97.23].

CLUB STATION LICENSE

A **club station license** is granted only to the person who is the license trustee designated by the club. The Club Station License Trustee must hold a Technician or higher operator license. For licensing purposes, a club must be composed of at least four persons and must have a name, a document of organization, management and a primary purpose devoted to amateur service activities consistent with Part 97 [97.5(b)(2)]. Effective March 24, 1995, for the first time since 1978, the FCC began once again to issue new club station licenses. The trustee and an officer in the club (they must be two separate people) must complete an NCVEC Form 605 and send it to the ARRL VEC for processing. The FCC privatized the club call sign assignment program January 22, 2001 and no longer accepts FCC Form 610-B. There is no fee and a call will be issued from the Group D (2×3) of the Sequential Call Sign Assignment System. FCC has eliminated all of the various types of Form 610 with the implementation of the Universal Licensing System. The only means to amend or renew a club station license with the privatization of the club call sign assignment program is to send an NCVEC to a Club Station Call Sign Administrator. ARRL is a CSCSA.

MILITARY RECREATION STATION LICENSE

A **military recreation station license** is granted only to the person who is the *license custodian*. This is the person in charge of the *station* designated by the official in charge of the United States military base for recreational use where the station is located. The person must not be a representative of a foreign government. The person doesn't even need to be an amateur [97.5(b)(3)]. The application must also be signed by the official in *charge of the physical location* where the station is located (they must be two separate people): The person, typically someone the Base Commander appoints, must give permission before a station can be set up; another person has authority over the building where the station is located. These persons aren't always amateurs themselves, but a control operator *must* be at the control point at all times the station is in operation to ensure that all FCC rules are followed. As with club licenses, effective March 24, 1995, the FCC began once again to issue new military recreation station licenses. As with club stations, military-recreation stations are also governed by Club Station Call Sign Administrators. The applicant must complete an NCVEC Form 605 and send it to a CSCSA. The NCVEC Form 605 can be found on *ARRLWeb* at **http:// www.arrl.org/fcc/forms.html**. Calls are issued from the Group D (2×3) of the FCC Sequential Call Sign Assignment System. Military recreation stations are not eligible for vanity calls [97.19(a)].

RACES STATION LICENSE

RACES station licenses are no longer granted or renewed by the FCC. In an action at the end of 1999, the FCC said by eliminating RACES station licenses, it would eliminate licensing duplication because emergency communications that are now transmitted by RACES stations also may be transmitted by primary, club or military recreation stations. The FCC said it did away with the RACES station license to "conserve our financial resources."

Remaining RACES licenses are held only by the person who is the *license custodian* designated by the official responsible for the governmental agency served by that civil defense organization. The custodian must be the civil defense official responsible for coordination of all civil defense activities in the area concerned. The custodian must not be a representative of a foreign government. The custodian need not have been granted an amateur operator license but the control operator must [97.5(b)(4)].

THE UNIVERSAL LICENSING SYSTEM

Implementation of the Universal Licensing System in the Amateur Radio Service ushers in a new era of electronic, interactive filing and handling of Amateur Radio applications. It promises users fast and easy electronic filing, improved data accuracy through automated checking of applications filed on-line, and enhanced electronic access to licensing information. With ULS, you can renew or modify your ticket or apply for a vanity call sign on-line from a dial-up network and, eventually, on the Web. The ULS also meant the demise of the FCC Form 610 series long familiar to amateurs in favor of the "universal" Form 605. Although this Form is primarily an electronic document, it is also available on paper from the FCC. ULS also gives Volunteer Examiner Coordinators (VECs) the authority to design their own forms. As of early 2001, many hams had already registered in the ULS. Amateurs may file applications using the new FCC Form 605 electronically at any time of day, seven days a week. FCC Form 605 is used for license renewals, modifications, cancellations, application withdrawals and amendments, as well as requests for a vanity call sign, duplicate license, change of address or other clerical license modification. Visit the Wireless Telecommunications Bureau ULS page, **http://www.fcc.gov/wtb/uls** and click "Connecting to ULS" for information on accessing the ULS system. Changing your FCC license data on the ULS database requires a telephone modem. A toll-free number, 800-844-2784, connects users to the FCC's Wide Area Network. Amateurs experiencing problems with ULS should contact the FCC License Support staff at 202-414-1250 or at **ulscomm@fcc.gov**.

One feature of the new ULS is a renewal reminder sent 90 days prior to a license's expiration date. Renewal sooner than 90 days before expiration is not permitted under the ULS and any such application will be returned without action.

Q & A—The Universal Licensing System

Q. What applications must I use?

A. Amateurs can register under ULS electronically through the Web or manually by using the proper form.

All of the Forms mentioned can be found on *ARRLWeb*. See **http://www.arrl.org/fcc/forms.html**. Here is a brief synopsis of the forms (electronic or manual) needed for various purposes in the Amateur Radio Service. To make modifications to a license or any other FCC change electronically, see **http://www.fcc.gov/wtb/uls/**.

Amateur Purpose:	*Form:*	*Plus:*
Pay Vanity Fee	FCC 159	605-main form, Schedule D
Renew or modify an amateur license	**FCC 605**	—
Renew or modify an amateur license	**NCVEC 605****	
Apply for a Systematic Call Sign Change	FCC 605	Schedule D, Part 1
Apply for a Vanity Call	FCC 605	Schedule D, Part 1; Form 159
Obtain a duplicate license	FCC 605	—
Register under ULS	**FCC 606**	—
Register under ULS (non-US citizen)*	FCC 606	—

*Must contact the FCC and ask for an Assigned Taxpayer Identification Number (ATIN) in order to register under ULS. See contact for the FCC Support Staff in this sidebar.

**The NCVEC Form 605, different from the FCC Form 605, is much more "user-friendly", but must be sent to a VEC for processing, not to the FCC. As a free service to ARRL members, the ARRL will process NCVEC Forms 605 at no charge for members.

Note: Licenses may be renewed no sooner than 90 days before expiration or FCC will return them without action.

Q. If applying manually, where do I send the form(s)?

A. The various forms mandated by ULS can be sent to one of the following addresses (where applicable):

The FCC Gettysburg address: All forms mentioned above, with the exception of vanity call applications and FCC Forms 159, must be sent to:

> FCC
> 1270 Fairfield Road
> Gettysburg, PA 17325-7245

There is no fee. Allow 2 to 4 weeks for processing. Only applications not requiring a fee may be sent to the FCC Gettysburg address.

The FCC Bank Contractor Pittsburgh address: The manually filed vanity applications using an FCC Form 605 and the Schedule D, Part 1, and also the Form 159 with the $14 fee must be sent to:

> FCC
> Wireless Bureau Applications
> PO Box 358130
> Pittsburgh, PA 15251-5130

FCC 605
Approved by OMB
Main Form

Quick-Form Application for Authorization in the Ship, Aircraft,
Amateur, Restricted and Commercial Operator, and the
General Mobile Radio Services

3060 - 0850
See instructions for
public burden estimate

---

1) Radio Service Code:

Application Purpose (Select only one) ( )

2)	NE - New	RO - Renewal Only	WD - Withdrawal of Application
	MD - Modification	RM - Renewal/Modification	DU - Duplicate License
	AM - Amendment	CA - Cancellation of License	AU - Administrative Update

3)	If this request is for a Developmental License or STA (Special Temporary Authorization) enter the appropriate code and attach the required exhibit as described in the instructions. Otherwise enter N (Not Applicable).	( )D S N/A
4)	If this request is for an Amendment or Withdrawal of Application, enter the file number of the pending application currently on file with the FCC.	File Number
5)	If this request is for a Modification, Renewal Only, Renewal/Modification, Cancellation of License, Duplicate License, or Administrative Update, enter the call sign of the existing FCC license.	Call Sign
6)	If this request is for a New, Amendment, Renewal Only, or Renewal/Modification, enter the requested authorization expiration date (this item is optional).	MM DD
7)	Does this filing request a Waiver of the Commission's rules? If 'Y', attach the required showing as described in the instructions.	( )Yes No
8)	Are attachments (other than associated schedules) being filed with this application?	( )Yes No

---

Applicant Information

9a) Taxpayer Identification Number:	9b) SGIN:

10) Applicant/Licensee is a(n): ( )   Individual   Unincorporated Association   Trust   Government Entity   Joint Venture
Corporation   Limited Liability Corporation   Partnership   Consortium

11) First Name (if individual):	MI:	Last Name:	Suffix:

12) Entity Name (if other than individual):

13) Attention To:

14) P.O. Box:	And/Or	15) Street Address:

16) City:	17) State:	18) Zip:	19) Country:

20) Telephone Number:	21) FAX:

22) E-Mail Address:

FCC 605- Main Form
July 1999 - Page 1

The all-purpose FCC Form 605 is used to renew or modify a license, obtain a duplicate license and apply for a vanity or systematic call sign. Non-ARRL members must use this form.

Note: The payment-type code for vanity applications for the Form 159 is **WAVR**. The Form 159 Lockbox Number is the PO Box you are mailing the forms (for example, for non-electronically filed applications, the Lockbox is "358130"; for electronically filed applications, the Lockbox is "358994").

When submitting a vanity application electronically and when the fee is paid by check or money order, ULS will assign a file number and show the correct fee amount due as well as the payment type code on a confirmation screen. Click the "Form 159" button to put this information onto the Form

23) Is the applicant exempt from FCC application fees?	( )Yes No
24) Is the applicant exempt from FCC regulatory fees?	( )Yes No

General Certification Statements

1) The Applicant waives any claim to the use of any particular frequency or of the electromagnetic spectrum as against the regulatory power of the United States because of the previous use of the same, whether by license or otherwise, and requests an authorization in accordance with this application.

2) The applicant certifies that all statements made in this application and in the exhibits, attachments, or documents incorporated by reference are material, are part of this application, and are true, complete, correct, and made in good faith.

3) Neither the Applicant nor any member thereof is a foreign government or a representative thereof.

4) The applicant certifies that neither the applicant nor any other party to the application is subject to a denial of Federal benefits pursuant to Section 5301 of the Anti-Drug Abuse Act of 1988, 21 U.S.C. § 862, because of a conviction for possession or distribution of a controlled substance. **This certification does not apply to applications filed in services exempted under Section 1.2002(c) of the rules, 47 CFR § 1.2002(c).** See Section 1.2002(b) of the rules, 47 CFR § 1.2002(b), for the definition of "party to the application" as used in this certification.

5) Amateur or GMRS Applicant certifies that the construction of the station would NOT be an action which is likely to have a significant environmental effect (see the Commission's Rules 47 CFR Sections 1.1301-1.1319 and Section 97.13(a).

6) Amateur Applicant certifies that they have READ and WILL COMPLY WITH Section 97.13(c) of the Commission's Rules regarding RADIOFREQUENCY (RF) RADIATION SAFETY and the amateur service section of OST/OET Bulletin Number 65.

Certification Statements For GMRS Applicants

1) Applicant certifies that he or she is claiming eligibility under Rule Section 95.5 of the Commission's Rules.

2) Applicant certifies that he or she is at least 18 years of age.

3) Applicant certifies that he or she will comply with the requirement that use of frequencies 462.650, 467.650, 462.700 and 467.700 MHz is not permitted near the Canadian border North of Line A and East of Line C. These frequencies are used throughout Canada and harmful interference is anticipated.

Signature

25) Typed or Printed Name of Party Authorized to Sign

First Name:	MI:	Last Name:	Suffix:

26) Title:	
Signature:	27) Date:

Failure To Sign This Application May Result In Dismissal Of The Application And Forfeiture Of Any Fees Paid

WILLFUL FALSE STATEMENTS MADE ON THIS FORM OR ANY ATTACHMENTS ARE PUNISHABLE BY FINE AND/OR IMPRISONMENT (U.S. Code, Title 18, Section 1001) AND/OR REVOCATION OF ANY STATION LICENSE OR CONSTRUCTION PERMIT (U.S. Code, Title 47, Section 312(a)(1)), AND/OR FORFEITURE (U.S. Code, Title 47, Section 503).

FCC 605 - Main Form
July 1999 - Page 2

The back of FCC Form 605.

159 Print the completed form and mail it with the proper fee. Payments made for electronic filed applications (except credit card payments), go to a different PO Box. All payments for *electronically filed applications* will go to:

FCC
ULS Electronic Filings
PO Box 358994
Pittsburgh, PA 15251-5994.

Non-Vanity Applications

The Newington address: The ARRL will check and forward to the FCC

NCVEC QUICK-FORM 605 APPLICATION FOR
AMATEUR OPERATOR/PRIMARY STATION LICENSE

SECTION 1 - TO BE COMPLETED BY APPLICANT

PRINT LAST NAME	SUFFIX	FIRST NAME	INITIAL	STATION CALL SIGN (IF ANY)

MAILING ADDRESS (Number and Street or P.O. Box)	SOCIAL SECURITY NUMBER (OR LICENSEE ID)

CITY	STATE CODE	ZIP CODE (5 or 9 Numbers)	E-MAIL ADDRESS (OPTIONAL)

DAYTIME TELEPHONE NUMBER (Include Area Code) OPTIONAL	FAX NUMBER (Include Area Code) OPTIONAL	ENTITY NAME (IF CLUB, MILITARY RECREATION, RACES)

Type of Applicant: ☐ Individual ☐ Amateur Club ☐ Military Recreation ☐ RACES (Renewal Only)

TRUSTEE OR CUSTODIAN CALL SIGN

SIGNATURE OF RESPONSIBLE CLUB OFFICIAL

I HEREBY APPLY FOR (Make an X in the appropriate box(es))

☐ **EXAMINATION** for a **new** license grant

☐ **EXAMINATION** for **upgrade** of my license class

☐ **CHANGE** my **name** on my license to my new name

Former Name: _____
(Last name) (Suffix) (First name) (MI)

☐ **CHANGE** my mailing address to **above** address

☐ **CHANGE** my station **call sign** systematically

Applicant's Initials: _____

☐ **RENEWAL** of my license grant.

Do you have another license application on file with the FCC which has not been acted upon?	PURPOSE OF OTHER APPLICATION	PENDING FILE NUMBER (FOR VEC USE ONLY)

I certify that:
* I waive any claim to the use of any particular frequency regardless of prior use by license or otherwise;
* All statements and attachments are true, complete and correct to the best of my knowledge and belief and are made in good faith;
* I am not a representative of a foreign government;
* I am not subject to a denial of Federal benefits pursuant to Section 5301of the Anti-Drug Abuse Act of 1988, 21 U.S.C. § 862;
* The construction of my station will NOT be an action which is likely to have a significant environmental effect (See 47 CFR Sections 1.301-1.319 and Section 97.13(a));
* I have read and WILL COMPLY with Section 97.13(c) of the Commission's Rules regarding RADIOFREQUENCY (RF) RADIATION SAFETY and the amateur service section of OST/OET Bulletin Number 65.

Signature of applicant (Do not print, type, or stamp. Must match applicant's name above.)

X _____ Date Signed: _____

SECTION 2 - TO BE COMPLETED BY ALL ADMINISTERING VEs

Applicant is qualified for operator license class:

☐ **NOVICE** — Elements 1(A), 1(B), 1(C) and 2

☐ **TECHNICIAN** — Elements 2 and 3(A)

☐ **TECHNICIAN PLUS** — Elements 1(A), 1(B), or 1(C), 2 and 3(A)

☐ **GENERAL** — Elements 1(B), or 1(C), 2, 3(A) and 3(B)

☐ **ADVANCED** — Elements 1(B), or 1(C) and 2, 3(A), 3(B) and 4(A)

☐ **AMATEUR EXTRA** — Elements 1(C) and 2, 3(A), 3(B), 4(A) and 4(B)

DATE OF EXAMINATION SESSION

EXAMINATION SESSION LOCATION

VEC ORGANIZATION

VEC RECEIPT DATE

I CERTIFY THAT I HAVE COMPLIED WITH THE ADMINISTERING VE REQUIRMENTS IN PART 97 OF THE COMMISSION'S RULES AND WITH THE INSTRUCTIONS PROVIDED BY THE COORDINATING VEC AND THE FCC.

1st VEs NAME (Print First, MI, Last, Suffix)	VEs STATION CALL SIGN	VEs SIGNATURE (Must match name)	DATE SIGNED
2nd VEs NAME (Print First, MI, Last, Suffix)	VEs STATION CALL SIGN	VEs SIGNATURE (Must match name)	DATE SIGNED
3rd VEs NAME (Print First, MI, Last, Suffix)	VEs STATION CALL SIGN	VEs SIGNATURE (Must match name)	DATE SIGNED

NCVEC FORM 605 - AUGUST 1999
FOR VE/VEC USE ONLY - Page 1

NCVEC Form 605 is a shortened version of the FCC Form 605 that can be processed only by a VEC. ARRL members may use this form, and it will be processed as a free membership service.

non-Vanity FCC Forms 605 and NCVEC Forms 605 for *ARRL Members Only* as a *free* service. The NCVEC Form 605 can only be processed by a VEC, *not by the FCC*. Processing time is 2 to 3 business days for an ARRL-VEC electronically processed application. The NCVEC Form 605, a quick and easy form, can *not* be sent directly to the FCC. ARRL members can send forms to:

ARRL VEC
225 Main St.
Newington, CT 06111

Q. What is ULS registration? If you are a ham, aren't you already in the FCC's database?

A. Registration in ULS is the process of identifying your Taxpayer Information Number (typically your Social Security Number), your name and your call sign (or call signs if you hold any in other FCC Wireless Tele-communications Bureau-administered services) into the ULS. Registration enables quick license data retrieval each time you file an application with the FCC. Existing Amateur Radio licensing data has been transferred into the ULS database, and the pre-ULS database no longer is available.

You can register at any time. ULS registration has been available to amateurs for many months now. In order to avail themselves of FCC services, all amateur applicants and licensees must be registered in the ULS. This is not an option. If you are not registered at the time you seek FCC services, the application will be returned without action. You do not *need* to register until the first time you intend to file an application, however. For most Amateur Radio operators, this will be when you renew or modify your license (that is, change your address, name or call sign, upgrade your class of operator license, or apply for a vanity call sign).

Q: How do I register?

A: You need to register only once. It can be done manually or electronically using FCC Form 606 (not to be confused with the new, multipurpose Form 605; more on that later). While Form 606 is primarily a "virtual" form, it is available in hard-copy form from the FCC. Not having a computer or electronic access is no excuse for not being registered.

To file on the Internet, point your Web browser to **http://www.fcc.gov/wtb/uls** and click on "TIN/Call Sign Registration."

To file via the FCC's Wide Area Network, establish a direct connection to the FCC's WAN by using the "Dial-up Networking" utility of *Windows 95/98* and call 800-844-2784. Once connected, point your Web browser to **http://wtbwww05.fcc.gov/wtb/uls**, and click on the "TIN/Call Sign Registration" button.

Automatic TIN registration is available for those filing an application through a VEC and who have not previously registered. Submit your TIN to the VEC with your application, and when the VEC files the application with the FCC, your TIN will be automatically registered in ULS.

You can file a paper application using FCC Form 606 (TIN Registration Form). Obtain this form from the Web at **http://www.fcc.gov/formpage.html** or from the FCC's Forms Distribution Center, 800-418-FORM (3676). The hard-copy FCC Form 606 can be faxed (717-338-2693) or mailed to Federal Communications Commission, 1270 Fairfield Rd, Gettysburg, PA 17325-7245. For a step-by-step primer on registering on-line, see **http://www.arrl.org/fcc/uls101.html#Universal**.

Q: What happens when I register electronically?

A: When you register electronically with the ULS and provide your TIN/SSN, you'll be asked to select a password to identify yourself in the future. This is like setting a PIN when your bank gives you a new ATM card. Your password can be 5 to 30 characters (letters and/or numbers) long and is case-sensitive. For additional security, you must also specify a personal

FEDERAL COMMUNICATIONS COMMISSION

REMITTANCE ADVICE

APPROVED BY OMB   3060-0589

SPECIAL USE

FCC USE ONLY

PAGE NO._____ OF _____

(1) LOCKBOX #

SECTION A - PAYER INFORMATION

(2) PAYER NAME (if paying by credit card, enter name exactly as it appears on your card)

(3) TOTAL AMOUNT PAID (dollars and cents)
$

(4) STREET ADDRESS LINE NO. 1

(5) STREET ADDRESS LINE NO. 2

(6) CITY	(7) STATE	(8) ZIP CODE

(9) DAYTIME TELEPHONE NUMBER (include area code)	(10) COUNTRY CODE (if not in U.S.A.)

IF PAYER NAME AND THE APPLICANT NAME ARE DIFFERENT, COMPLETE SECTION B
IF MORE THAN ONE APPLICANT, USE CONTINUATION SHEETS (FORM 159-C)

SECTION B - APPLICANT INFORMATION

(11) APPLICANT NAME (if paying by credit card, enter name exactly as it appears on your card)

(12) STREET ADDRESS LINE NO. 1

(13) STREET ADDRESS LINE NO. 2

(14) CITY	(15) STATE	(16) ZIP CODE

(17) DAYTIME TELEPHONE NUMBER (include area code)	(18) COUNTRY CODE (if not in U.S.A.)

COMPLETE SECTION C FOR EACH SERVICE. IF MORE BOXES ARE NEEDED, USE CONTINUATION SHEETS (FORM 159-C)

SECTION C - PAYMENT INFORMATION

(19A) FCC CALL SIGN/OTHER ID	(20A) PAYMENT TYPE CODE (PTC)	(21A) QUANTITY	(22A) FEE DUE FOR (PTC) IN BLOCK 20A	FCC USE ONLY
(23A) FCC CODE 1			(24A) FCC CODE 2	
(19B) FCC CALL SIGN/OTHER ID	(20B) PAYMENT TYPE CODE (PTC)	(21B) QUANTITY	(22B) FEE DUE FOR (PTC) IN BLOCK 20B	FCC USE ONLY
(23B) FCC CODE 1			(24B) FCC CODE 2	
(19C) FCC CALL SIGN/OTHER ID	(20C) PAYMENT TYPE CODE (PTC)	(21C) QUANTITY	(22C) FEE DUE FOR (PTC) IN BLOCK 20C	FCC USE ONLY
(23C) FCC CODE 1			(24C) FCC CODE 2	
(19D) FCC CALL SIGN/OTHER ID	(20D) PAYMENT TYPE CODE (PTC)	(21D) QUANTITY	(22D) FEE DUE FOR (PTC) IN BLOCK 20D	FCC USE ONLY
(23D) FCC CODE 1			(24D) FCC CODE 2	

SECTION D - TAXPAYER INFORMATION (REQUIRED)

(25)
PAYER TIN

(26) COMPLETE THIS BLOCK ONLY IF APPLICANT NAME IN B-11 IS DIFFERENT FROM PAYER NAME IN A-2
APPLICANT TIN

SECTION E - CERTIFICATION

(27) CERTIFICATION STATEMENT
I,_____ , Certify under penalty of perjury that the foregoing and supporting information
                (PRINT NAME)
are true and correct to the best of my knowledge, information and belief. SIGNATURE_____

SECTION F - CREDIT CARD PAYMENT INFORMATION

(28)
MASTERCARD/VISA ACCOUNT NUMBER:

EXPIRATION DATE:

MONTH   YEAR

MASTERCARD

VISA   I hereby authorize the FCC to charge my VISA or MASTERCARD
        for the service(s)/authorization(s) herein described.

AUTHORIZED SIGNATURE

DATE

SEE PUBLIC BURDEN ESTIMATE ON REVERSE

FCC FORM 159 JULY 1997 (REVISE)

Along with Form 605, Form 159 is the one to use for paying the fee for a manually filed vanity call sign.

identifier. We recommend *not* using your Amateur Radio call sign or any other call sign that might be associated with you as a password or identifier.

After registering your TIN, you will be asked to enter your call sign(s). Associating your call sign with your TIN in ULS will enable you to file renewals, modifications, notifications, and other filings with respect to the call sign(s) identified.

When you register, you'll receive a nine-character Licensee Identification Number beginning with the letter "L" and followed by eight digits. You may use this number in place of your TIN/SSN in future dealings with the FCC.

One big advantage to on-line registration is that the ULS application system checks for errors before you submit your data. This advantage is not available to manual filers. See **http://www.fcc.gov/wtb/uls/**. The Commission Registration System (CORES) will eventually replace ULS, but it has not been fully implemented as of this writing.

Q: I registered manually under ULS. How do I get my Licensee ID Number?

A: If you registered manually or via a VEC, you will need to call the ULS Technical Support Staff (202-414-1250; e-mail **ulscomm@fcc.gov**) to obtain a password. After that, you can only change your password online using the TIN/Call Sign Registration utility.

To get your Licensee ID Number, use the ULS license search tool to search for your database record. The search result will display your Licensee ID Number.

Q: Why do I have to give the FCC my Social Security Number? Why does the FCC ask for phone and fax numbers and e-mail addresses?

A: The Debt Collection Improvement Act of 1996 requires all federal agencies to collect Taxpayer Identification Numbers from all persons doing business with the agency. For the actual Act, see **http://frwebgate.access. gpo.gov/cgi-bin/getdoc.cgi?dbname=104_cong_public_laws& docid=f:publ134.104.pdf**. This includes all applicants and holders of FCC licenses. The ULS uses your SSN as a unique identifier. Your SSN and your password will provide access to the electronic filing features of the ULS.

Supplying a telephone and fax number is optional as is supplying an e-mail address. Although the FCC still asks for the telephone number on the form, there are ways to "trick" the system—filling in the field with all zeros, for example.

Q: What security measures is the FCC taking to keep my Social Security Number private?

A: Once registered, your SSN will not be disclosed to the public. The Commission has taken several steps to ensure the privacy of your SSN. Electronic registration on the Internet is accomplished using the FCC's secure Web server. For an additional measure of security, you can register by connecting directly to the FCC's Wide Area Network.

Q. How do I complete an FCC Form 605?

A. The FCC Form 605 is long, but many of the questions do not apply to the amateur service because this form is used with many services in addition to the Amateur Service. It is critical that amateurs use the correct application codes on the Form 605. For example, if an application for renewal indicates an application code of "RM" (to renew *and* modify a license), the entire application will be rejected if the license is not within 90 days of expiration.

Here are quick instructions on completing the form:

For Address Changes and Name Changes:
Complete Items 1-27
Under "Radio Service Code (#1), write **HA**
Under "Application Purpose Code," (#2), write **AU**
If filing manually, remember to date and sign the back of the form

Systematic Call Sign Changes
A systematic call sign change is the same as a call issued under the FCC's Sequential Call Sign Assignment System. It is a call assigned at random by the FCC according to your FCC call sign region and license class. If you would like a call to reflect your license class and mailing address:
Complete items 1-27
Under "Radio Service Code," (#1) write **HA**
Under "Application Purpose Code," (#2) write **MD**
Under Schedule D, Part 1, Item 1 "Is this a request to change a station call sign systematically?" check "Yes."
If filing manually, remember to date and sign the back of the form.

License Renewal and Reinstatement (if expired less than 2 years):
Complete FCC Form 605 by completing Items 1-27;
Under "Radio Service Code (#1), enter **HA**;
Under "Application Purpose Code" (#2), enter **RO** to Renew Only;
Under "Application Purpose"(#2) code enter **RM** for Renewal *and* Modification of the license;
If filing manually, remember to sign and date the back of the form.
Amateurs may renew their license no more than 90 days before expiration. Licenses submitted prematurely will be returned without action. If an amateur needs to change only the address, is outside the 90 day renewal window before expiration of the license and uses the code "RM," the application will be rejected. The amateur will then need to submit a new application. If the license has been expired more than 2 years, the individual must be retested.

License Lost or Destroyed:
Complete the FCC Form 605 by completing Items 1-27;
Under "Radio Service Code (#1), write **HA**;
Under "Application Purpose Code," (#2), write **DU**;
If filing manually, remember to sign and date the back of the form.
Unlike the pre-ULS system, you must now complete an FCC Form 605 in order to receive a duplicate license. Amateurs are not required to carry a copy of their license at all times as they were at one time; as long as your license data appears in the FCC database, that's sufficient. There are other times when you need to carry a copy of your FCC license, at a testing session or during foreign travel, for example.

Q: I need to change the address on our club station license. Can I do this via the ULS?

A: In the future, the ULS will accommodate the processing of club and military recreation license applications on Form 605 through call sign administrators, but until this program is in place, applicants should continue to use FCC Form 610-B.

The FCC says that trustees and custodians of club and military-recreation licenses should not use their personal Social Security Number as the TIN for these licenses. Club station trustees and applicants should contact ULS Technical Support (202-414-1250 or **ulscomm@fcc.gov**) to obtain an FCC-generated identification number. You must provide this FCC-generated ID number on each FCC Form 610-B you submit. Applications that do not include this number are subject to dismissal.

Q: What if I don't have a Social Security Number?

A: If you are eligible for an SSN, you must obtain one before using ULS. In general, all US citizens and individuals admitted for permanent residence in the US are eligible for an SSN. Most younger US amateurs who are US citizens will eventually need a SSN. For more information, contact the Social Security Administration at **http://www.ssa.gov** or by calling 800-772-1213 (TTY 800-325-0778).

Q: I hold a US ham ticket, but I'm a citizen of another country and not eligible for a SSN. How can I register in the ULS?

A: Everyone using ULS needs a Taxpayer Information Number, including amateurs who are not US citizens. TINs come in several forms:

1) Individual US citizens and nationals can get a TIN/Social Security Number; 2) aliens who meet certain criteria must get an Individual Taxpayer Identification Number (ITIN) from the IRS; 3) all others can get an Assigned TIN (ATIN) from the FCC. A nonresident alien who must file a US tax return or can be named on someone else's US tax return, is eligible for an Individual TIN (ITIN) from the Internal Revenue Service. For more information, contact the IRS at **http://www.irs.ustreas.gov** or call 800-829-1040 inside the US or 215-516-ITIN outside the US.

The FCC has said that ATINs will be available to those doing business with the FCC who are ineligible to obtain an SSN. You may not obtain an ATIN if you already have an SSN or are eligible to have one, nor can you substitute an ATIN for an SSN. An ATIN will consist of the letter "A" followed by eight digits. Alien licensees needing an assigned TIN should contact FCC Technical Support (202-414-1250; **ulscomm@fcc.gov**). FCC personnel will ask a series of questions to establish eligibility to obtain an ATIN. Those seeking an ATIN must supply a reason for having one.

Q: Where can I find information about the ULS?

A: For general information about ULS, including answers to frequently asked questions regarding submitting applications, finding the status of pending applications, and searching the ULS database, consult the ULS Web site, **http://www.fcc.gov/wtb/uls**. Individuals with specific questions not addressed on this page may contact FCC Technical Support via telephone or e-mail (202-414-1250; e-mail **ulscomm@fcc.gov**) with questions concerning computer access to ULS, TIN registration, uploading files, or submitting attachments in ULS. The hotline is available Monday through Friday, 8 AM-6 PM Eastern Time.

For all other application/licensing questions, contact FCC Consumer Center (toll-free, 888-CALL-FCC or 888 225-5322; e-mail **ulshelp@fcc.gov**). ULS Licensing Support is available Monday through Friday 8 AM-5:30 PM Eastern Time. Comments on the ULS go to **ulscomm@fcc.gov**.

Before you can take advantage of all of these new features, *first* you must *register*! For a step-by-step primer for registering on-line, see **http://www.arrl.org/fcc/uls101.html**. Registration involves simply entering your Taxpayer Information Number (typically your Social Security Number), your name and your call sign (or call signs if you hold any in other FCC Wireless Telecommunications Bureau-administered services) into the ULS. Those without Internet access may register manually using FCC Form 606.

Amateurs may now file electronically over the Web at **http://www.fcc.gov/wtb/uls**. Manual filing using the paper form will not go away, but people are encouraged to file electronically.

The ULS also simplified the process of submitting fees to the FCC. See the sidebar entitled, "The Universal Licensing System Q & A" elsewhere in this chapter. For more information, visit the FCC's ULS page, **http://www.fcc.gov/wtb/uls**.

Other License Authorizations

In two cases, a person need not hold one of the four licenses mentioned earlier. They both involve operation by a licensee of another country who is a citizen of that country where:

1) A **Canadian amateur licensee** who is a Canadian citizen may operate under the auspices of the automatic reciprocal agreement the US shares with Canada [97.107(a].

2) **An amateur license issued by any country that shares a bilateral or multilateral agreement with the US**. A reciprocal operating permit used to be issued by the FCC to an amateur who was licensed in his or her home country. This was commonly called a "reciprocal permit." The foreign amateur must have completed and had processed the application before operation could begin. Effective February 12, 1999, alien visitors to the US holding an amateur license issued by the home country may operate in the US without submitting any FCC paperwork—provided that a bilateral or multilateral agreement is in effect between the two countries. The only documentation required is proof of citizenship and an Amateur Radio license issued by the country of citizenship. The foreign amateur may not be a US citizen. Amateurs from countries that do not share a bilateral or multilateral reciprocal agreement may not operate in the US [97.5(c) and 97.107(b)]. See **Table 1** for the complete list of countries that share a bilateral agreement with the US. Amateurs from countries that do not share a reciprocal agreement with the US may not operate in the US, but may obtain a US license after passing the required examinations. More information on multilateral agreements appears in Chapter 2.

Control Operator Required

A control operator is *required* any time an amateur transmitter is in operation. The FCC defines a **control operator** as "An amateur designated by the licensee of a station to be responsible for the transmissions from that

Table 1

Countries that Share Bilateral Reciprocal Licensing Agreements with the United States

V2	Antigua/Barbuda	3A	Monaco
LU	Argentina	PA	Netherlands
VK	Australia	PJ	Netherlands Antilles
OE	Austria	ZL	New Zealand
C6	Bahamas	YN	Nicaragua
8P	Barbados	LA	Norway
ON	Belgium	HP	Panama
V3	Belize	P2	Papua-New Guinea
CP	Bolivia	ZP	Paraguay
T9	Bosnia-Herzegovina	OA	Peru
A2	Botswana	DU	Philippines
PY	Brazil	CT	Portugal
VE	Canada	J6	St. Lucia
CE	Chile	J8	St. Vincent/Grenadines
HK	Colombia	S7	Seychelles
TI	Costa Rica	9L	Sierra Leone
9A	Croatia	H4	Solomon Islands
5B	Cyprus	ZS	South Africa
OZ	Denmark (incl. Greenland)	EA	Spain
HI	Dominican Republic	PZ	Suriname
J7	Dominica	SM	Sweden
HC	Ecuador	HB	Switzerland
YS	El Salvador	HS	Thailand
V6	Federated States of Micronesia	9Y	Trinidad/Tobago
		TA	Turkey
3D	Fiji	T2	Tuvalu
OH	Finland	G	United Kingdom**
F	France*	CX	Uruguay
DL	Germany	YV	Venezuela
SV	Greece		
J3	Grenada		
TG	Guatemala		
8R	Guyana		
HH	Haiti		
HR	Honduras		
TF	Iceland		
VU	India		
YB	Indonesia		
EI	Ireland		
4X	Israel		
I	Italy		
6Y	Jamaica		
JA	Japan		
JY	Jordan		
T3	Kiribati		
9K	Kuwait		
EL	Liberia		
LX	Luxembourg		
Z3	Macedonia		
V7	Marshall Islands		
XE	Mexico		

Notes: Because of the longstanding agreement between the US and Canada, US amateurs need only sign their US call sign followed by a slant bar and the Canadian prefix/numeral combination to identify the province where they are located.

*Including French Guyana, French Polynesia, Guadeloupe, Amsterdam Island, Saint Paul Island, Crozet Island, Kerguelen Island, Martinique, New Caledonia, Reunion, St. Pierre and Miquelon, and Wallis and Futuna Islands.

**Including Ascension Island, Bermuda, British Virgin Islands, Cayman Islands, Channel Islands (including Guernsey and Jersey), Falkland Islands (including South Georgia Islands and South Sandwich Islands), Gibraltar, Isle of Man, Montserrat, St. Helena, Gough Island, Tristan da Cunha Island, Northern Ireland, and the Turks and Caicos Islands.

station to assure compliance with FCC rules [97.3(a)(12)]." This will be discussed later in this book, but first, which stations are eligible to be control operators? The control operator must be:

1) A person who has been granted an amateur operator/primary station license (that's the license the FCC sends you when you successfully pass an amateur examination); or

2) A non-US amateur who is a citizen of a country that holds a bilateral or multilateral agreement with the US; or

3) An amateur who holds an unexpired license issued by the government of Canada and who is a citizen of that country [97.7].

THE CLASSES OF OPERATOR LICENSE
Major Changes in Licensing Structure

As 1999 ended, the FCC announced a sweeping reform of the amateur licensing structure. Effective April 15, 2000, the number of new license classes was reduced from five to three; the number of written exam elements was reduced from five to three; and the number of code exam elements for all classes became five words per minute. The three license classes for new licenses are Technician, General and Amateur Extra [97.17; 97.501; 97.503].

No existing licensee lost any privileges. All pre-restructuring licensees retain their privileges and licenses—including the Novice, Technician Plus and Advanced. All licensees will be able to renew their licenses indefinitely. The main difference is that effective April 15, 2000, the FCC does not issue new Novice, Technician Plus and Advanced class licenses [97.17(a)].

The FCC will not upgrade any existing license privileges automatically. An upgrade opportunity exists, however, for pre-1987 Technician licensees to General class on or after April 15, 2000. Holders of a pre-March 21, 1987, Technician class license (or a CSCE) may claim credit for a new General class license [97.505(a)(8)]. (Before that date, the written examination for Technician and General class was identical; the only difference was that Technicians had to pass a 5 WPM Morse code test, while Generals had to pass a 13 WPM test.) The upgrade is not automatic, however. You will have to apply through a Volunteer Examiner test session, complete Form 605, attach documentary proof of having completed the requirements for a Technician license prior to March 21, 1987, and pay a processing fee, if any, to the VEC involved. In turn, the VE Team will process the application Form 605 and issue a CSCE granting temporary operating authority at the new higher class earned.

An original or a copy of your Technician license issued anytime prior to March 21, 1987, would suffice as proof. Other evidence might include an original CSCE for Element 3 issued prior to that date; an FCC verification letter of having held a Technician license prior to March 21, 1987; a document from the FCC's contractor, ITS Inc; or possibly a *Callbook* listing dated prior to March 21, 1987. Licensees also may contact ITS Inc on the Web at

www.itsdocs.com/ or by phone at 717-337-1433. For a fee, ITS will research prior FCC records and should be able to provide you with the necessary proof.

The FCC's action establishes the Technician license (with or without Morse code credit) as the sole entry-level ticket to Amateur Radio. After April 15, 2000, Technician and Technician Plus licensees were placed in a single Technician licensee database. When renewed, current Tech Plus licenses will be stamped simply "Technician." Despite the name change, Tech Plus licensees who can show proof that they passed a code exam through an Element 1 CSCE or a copy of an old license which says "Technician Plus", will keep their HF privileges. Amateurs are encouraged to retain a copy of a license which says "Technician Plus." No privileges are lost, however.

The FCC said by reducing the Morse code requirements, it eliminates "unnecessary requirements that may discourage or limit individuals from becoming trained operators, technicians, and electronic experts."

Written Test Changes

The new licensing regime has four examination elements:
• Element 1: 5 WPM Morse code test
• Element 2: 35 question Technician exam
• Element 3: 35 question General exam
• Element 4: 50 question Amateur Extra exam

The new Amateur Extra class exam combines the important elements of the old Advanced and Extra class exams. There are only minor changes to the new General class exam. The new Technician exam incorporates some questions from the retired Novice question pool. The FCC has left it in the hands of the National Conference of VECs Question Pool Committee to determine the specific mix and makeup of exam questions for each written exam element.

End of Handicapped Waivers

Elimination of the 13 and 20 WPM Morse requirements also means an end to physician certification exemption for applicants claiming an inability to pass the higher speed Morse code exam due to a severe handicap or disability. The FCC has never offered a waiver for the 5 WPM code test. However, provisions must remain in place for accommodating individuals with severe disabilities. VEs may require a physician's certification before determining which, if any, special accommodations are needed [97.509(k)].

Each of the licenses builds on the material from the previous license examinations and the examinations become progressively more difficult as more operating privileges are sought. If, for example, a person who holds no amateur license wants to obtain his Amateur Extra license, he or she must successfully pass all three of the license class examinations plus the 5-WPM Morse code element. Remember that an amateur may only be a control operator up to the privileges outlined on his or her license [97.9(a)]. For a detailed look at the classes of license, see **Table 2**.

An amateur who passes an amateur examination doesn't need to wait for the FCC to issue the license; the Certificate of Successful Completion of Examination (CSCE) is proof enough. CSCEs are issued for 365 days or until the license arrives in the mail [97.9(b)]. The only amateurs who can't operate immediately are those who hold no call sign since they must wait for the paperwork to catch up; after all, you can't operate if you don't have a call sign!

Because the FCC now considers its database to be the final authority for its license grants, it *no longer requires that the original written authorization or a photocopy be retained at the station*—but it's still a good idea! [FCC Order, October 17, 1994]. An examination is always required for a new amateur license and for each change in license class. The FCC makes no exception [97.501]. Amateurs with pending applications may contact the administering VEC or the FCC at 1-888 CALL FCC to find out whether the license has been issued. Amateurs with Internet access may check the FCC License Search Database at **http://www.arrl.org/fcc/fccld.html**. Additional information covering the licensing process is covered in the Rules under Subpart F Qualifying Examination Systems.

STATIONS ABOARD SHIPS OR AIRCRAFT

Most amateurs operate almost exclusively on land, whether it is from one's home station, from the home of another amateur, from a club station, or from a mobile or portable station. Occasionally, amateurs will operate stations maritime mobile from water or aeronautical mobile from air. When you are operating aboard a ship or an aircraft, three additional rule sections apply:

- The installation and operation of an amateur station on a ship or aircraft must be approved by the master of the ship or pilot in command of the aircraft [97.11(a)].
- The station must be separate from and independent of all other radio apparatus installed on the ship or aircraft, except a common antenna may be shared with a voluntary ship radio installation. The station's transmissions must not cause interference to any other apparatus installed on the ship or aircraft [97.11(b)].
- The station must not constitute a hazard to the safety of life or property. For a station aboard an aircraft, the apparatus shall not be operated while the aircraft is operating under Instrument Flight Rules, as defined by the FAA, unless the station has been found to comply with all applicable FAA Rules [97.11(c)].

It is important to note that amateurs are *not required* to append a special designator after their calls when operating maritime mobile or aeronautical mobile, provided that they are in an area regulated by the FCC. See Appendix 1 of Part 97 for a list of places where the amateur service is regulated by the FCC. When in international waters or in international air space, FCC-licensed amateurs are authorized to transmit since a vessel or

Table 2

Amateur Operator License Requirements† and Privileges for Amateurs Licensed Prior to April 15, 2000

Class	Code Test	Written Examination	Privileges
Novice	5 WPM (Element 1A)	Novice theory and regulations (Element 2)	CW: 3675-3725, 7100-7150$^\Diamond$ and 21,100-21,200 kHz with 200 W PEP output maximum; telegraphy, RTTY and data on 28.100-28,300 kHz and telegraphy and SSB voice on 28,300-28,500 kHz with 200 W PEP max; all amateur modes authorized on 222-225 MHz, 25 W PEP max; all amateur modes authorized on 1270-1295 MHz, 5 W PEP max.
Technician	None	Novice theory and regulations; Technician-level theory and regulations. (Elements 2, 3A)*	All amateur privileges 50.0 MHz and above.
Technician Plus	5 WPM (Element 1A)	Novice theory and regulations; Technician-level theory and regulations. (Elements 2, 3A)*	All Novice HF privileges in addition to all Technician privileges.
General	13 WPM (Element 1B)	Novice theory and regulations; Technician and General theory and regulations. (Elements 2, 3A and 3B)	All amateur privileges except those reserved for Advanced and Amateur Extra class.
Advanced	13 WPM (Element 1B)	All lower exam elements, plus Advanced theory. (Elements 2, 3A, 3B and 4A)	All amateur privileges except those reserved for Amateur Extra class.
Amateur Extra	20 WPM (Element 1C)	All lower exam elements plus Amateur Extra theory. (Elements 2, 3A, 3B, 4A and 4B)	All amateur privileges.

Note: See footnotes on next page.

Amateur Operator License Requirements† and Privileges for New Amateurs Licensed on or after April 15, 2000

Class	Code Test	Written Examination	Privileges
Technician	None	Technician level theory and regulations (Element 2)	All amateur privileges 50 MHz and above.
Technician	5 WPM** (Element 1)	Technician level privileges and regulations (Element 2)	All Novice HF privileges in addition to all Technician level privileges.
General	5 WPM (Element 1)	Technician and General theory (Elements 2 and 3)	All amateur privileges except those reserved for Advanced and Amateur Extra class
Amateur Extra	5 WPM (Element 1)	Technician and General plus Amateur Extra theory (Elements 2, 3 and 4)	All amateur privileges.

†A licensed radio amateur will be required to pass only those elements that are not included in the examination for the amateur license currently held.

*If you hold a valid Technician license issued before March 21, 1987, you also have credit for Element 3 (formerly Element 3B). You must be able to prove your Technician license was issued before March 21, 1987 to claim this credit.

**The operating privileges of Technicians with a Element 1 credit are valid indefinitely. If the Element 1 credit is a CSCE, exam credit is valid for only 1 year.

◊Varies according to region; see Chapter 4.

aircraft is considered to be a "piece" of the country of its registry. FCC rules apply until an amateur enters the territorial waters of another country or until an amateur enters the air space of another country. An amateur transceiver is *never* a substitute for the appropriate and required emergency communications systems for a vessel or aircraft.

FEDERAL RESTRICTIONS ON STATION LOCATIONS

We mentioned earlier that an amateur license gives amateurs the authority to set up an amateur station from most locations regulated by the FCC. There are three types of Federal restrictions on amateur station locations mentioned in §97.13:

The first type of Federal restriction on station locations states that "Before placing an amateur station on land of environmental importance or that is significant in American history, architecture or culture, the licensee may be required to take certain actions prescribed by §§1.1305-1.1319 of this Chapter [97.13(a)]." Amateurs must also sign a statement on FCC

Form 605 stating that "construction of the station would *not* be an action which is likely to have a significant environmental impact." The only amateurs required to file an environmental impact statement along with the FCC Form 605 are those who build stations on an officially designated wilderness area, or on land that is significant in American history, architecture or culture, or where extensive changes in surface features are required, or where the tower must be lighted and is located in a residential area. For 99.9% of amateurs, this isn't a problem. For the 0.1% of amateurs who must file an environ-mental impact statement along with their Form 605, the applicable rules from Part 1 can be found in Chapter 10 of this book. Amateurs with access to the Web may download Part 1 from **http://www.fcc.gov/wtb/rules.html**.

The second type of Federal restriction on station locations states that a station within 1600 meters (1 mile) of an FCC monitoring facility must protect that facility from harmful interference. Failure to do so could result in imposition of operating restrictions upon the amateur station by an FCC District Director pursuant to §97.121 of this Part. Geographical coordinates of the facilities that require protection are listed in §0.121 of the FCC Rules [§97.13(b)]. The FCC monitoring site in Columbia, Maryland is protected from harmful interference as are the other remotely controlled sites controlled through the FCC National Automated Monitoring Network. FCC sites in the following locations are protected from harmful interference: Allegan, Michigan; Anchorage, Alaska; Belfast, Maine; Canandaigua, New York; Douglas, Arizona; Ferndale, Washington; Grand Island, Nebraska; Kingsville, Texas; Laurel, Maryland; Livermore, California; Powder Springs, Georgia; Sabana Seca, Puerto Rico; Santa Isabel, Puerto Rico; Vero Beach, Florida; and Waipahu, Hawaii [§0.121].

The third type of Federal restriction sets limits on the maximum permissible exposure (MPE) allowed from operation of transmitters in all radio services. They also require that certain types of stations be evaluated to determine if they are in compliance with the MPEs specified in the rules. Specifically, the rules state "Before causing or allowing an amateur station to transmit from any place where the operation of the station could cause human exposure to RF electromagnetic field levels in excess of those allowed under §1.1310 of this chapter, the licensee is required to take certain actions [§97.13(c)]." *The rules do not set limits on transmitter output, only on exposure to RF beyond the MPEs.*

A station is presumed to be in compliance with the MPE levels if the transmitter power is at or below a certain level. A station must perform the routine RF environmental evaluation prescribed by §1.1307(b) if the power of the licensee's station exceeds the limits given in **Table 3**.

FCC RF-EXPOSURE REGULATIONS

FCC regulations control the amount of RF exposure to humans that is permitted from your station's operation [§§97.13, 97.503, 1.1307(b)(c)(d), 1.1310 and 2.1093]. These rules can be found in Chapters 9 and 10. The regulations set limits on the maximum permissible exposure (MPE) allowed from operation of transmitters in all radio services regulated by the FCC.

These regulations are not new. They have been on the books since the mid-1980s. Now, as was true then, they apply to all radio services. Under the old rules, although the exposure levels generally applied to the Amateur Radio Service, there were no specific requirements for hams. Amateur Radio stations were categorically exempt from the requirement to evaluate their stations.

The FCC announced a change to the rules in 1996. The rules change lowered the permitted exposure levels, and, more important to hams, removed the categorical exemption for Amateur Radio. Although some

Table 3
Power Thresholds for Routine Evaluation of Amateur Radio Stations

Wavelength Band	Evaluation Required if Power* (watts) Exceeds:
MF	
160 m	500
HF	
80 m	500
75 m	500
40 m	500
30 m	425
20 m	225
17 m	125
15 m	100
12 m	75
10 m	50
VHF (all bands)	50
UHF	
70 cm	70
33 cm	150
23 cm	200
13 cm	250
SHF (all bands)	250
EHF (all bands)	250
Repeater stations (all bands)	*Non-building-mounted antennas*: height above ground level to lowest point of antenna < 10 m *and* power > 500 W ERP
	Building-mounted antennas: power > 500 W ERP

*Transmitter power = Peak-envelope power input to antenna. For repeater stations *only,* power exclusion based on ERP (effective radiated power).

categorical exemptions for certain amateur stations were written into the rules changes, some hams now needed to evaluate their stations.

This section offers an overview of the requirements of the RF-exposure rules. The ARRL book *RF Exposure and You* explains the fine points of the rules and tells hams how they can complete their station evaluations. *RF Exposure and You* is available from many Amateur Radio dealers or directly from ARRL HQ. The toll free order line is 888-277-5298 (voice) or 860-594-0303 (fax). The ARRL HQ Publication Sales staff can be contacted by e-mail at **pubsales@arrl.org**. Amateurs can view the ARRL publications catalog at **http://www.arrl.org/catalog**.

The FCC has also prepared a bulletin, OET Bulletin 65: *Evaluating Compliance with FCC Guidelines for Human Exposure to Radiofrequency Electromagnetic Fields*. They have also prepared OET Bulletin 65, Supplement B: *Additional Information for Amateur Radio Operators*. Both of these bulletins have been reprinted in *RF Exposure and You*. They are also available from the FCC on the Web at: **http://www.fcc.gov/oet/info/documents/bulletins/#65**.

The Rules: Maximum Permissible Exposure (MPE)

The regulations control human exposure to RF fields, not the strength of RF fields. There is no limit to how strong a field can be as long as no one is being exposed to it, although FCC regulations require that amateurs use the minimum necessary power at all times [97.313(a)]. All radio stations must comply with the requirements for MPEs, even QRP stations running only a few watts or less. The MPEs vary with frequency, as shown in **Table 4**. These limits are based on the way humans absorb energy at different frequencies.

MPE limits are specified in maximum electric and magnetic fields for frequencies below 30 MHz, in power density for frequencies above 300 MHz and all three ways for frequencies from 30 to 300 MHz. For compliance purposes, all of these limits must be considered separately—if any one is exceeded, the station is not in compliance. For example, your 2-meter (146 MHz) station radiated electric field strength and power density may be less than the maximum allowed. If the radiated magnetic field strength exceeds that limit, however, your station does not meet the requirements.

Environments

The FCC has defined two exposure environments—*controlled* and *uncontrolled*. A controlled environment is one in which the people who are being exposed are aware of that exposure and can take steps to minimize that exposure, if appropriate. In an uncontrolled environment, the people being exposed are not normally aware of the exposure. The uncontrolled environment limits are more stringent than the controlled environment limits.

Although the controlled environment is usually intended as an occupational environment, the FCC has determined that it generally applies to amateur operators and members and guests in their immediate households, provided that they are made aware that RF is being used on the premises. With this stipulation, in most cases, controlled-environment limits can be applied to your home and property to which you can control physical access. You may, if you wish, apply the more stringent uncontrolled limits to your station and other areas that would normally be considered as a controlled environment.

The uncontrolled environment is intended for areas that are accessible by the general public, normally your neighbors' properties and the public sidewalk areas around your home.

As shown in Table 4, the permitted MPE levels are greater for controlled environments than they are for uncontrolled environments. "The MPE levels are based on generally accepted standards which are, in turn, based on a scientific data base of reported biological effects from exposure to RF energy. Though the data base included both athermal and thermal effects, the only demonstrated health hazards were found to occur at exposure levels that cause harmful increases in tissue or body temperature."

Table 4
(From §1.1310) Limits for Maximum Permissible Exposure (MPE)

(A) Limits for Occupational/Controlled Exposure

Frequency Range (MHz)	Electric Field Strength (V/m)	Magnetic Field Strength (A/m)	Power Density (mW/cm²)	Averaging Time (minutes)
0.3-3.0	614	1.63	(100)*	6
3.0-30	1842/f	4.89/f	(900/f²)*	6
30-300	61.4	0.163	1.0	6
300-1500	—	—	f/300	6
1500-100,000	—	—	5	6

f = frequency in MHz
* = Plane-wave equivalent power density (see Note 1).

(B) Limits for General Population/Uncontrolled Exposure

Frequency Range (MHz)	Electric Field Strength (V/m)	Magnetic Field Strength (A/m)	Power Density (mW/cm²)	Averaging Time (minutes)
0.3-1.34	614	1.63	(100)*	30
1.34-30	824/f	2.19/f	(180/f²)*	30
30-300	27.5	0.073	0.2	30
300-1500	—	—	f/1500	30
1500-100,000	—	—	1.0	30

f = frequency in MHz
* = Plane-wave equivalent power density (See Note 1.)

Note 1: This means the equivalent far-field strength that would have the E or H-field component calculated or measured. It does not apply well in the near field of an antenna.

This means that the MPE limits are not peak exposure levels, but are average exposure levels. The averaging time is defined in the rules—6 minutes for controlled exposure and 30 minutes for uncontrolled exposure. You can take an average of the exposure over the appropriate averaging period and apply that to the permitted MPE levels. It is, for example, possible for someone to be exposed to twice the permitted MPE limit for half the time, within the averaging period.

This factor is generally considered in doing a station evaluation by determining the average power over the appropriate time period, considering both the duty factor of the mode being used and the operating on and off times. For example, a voice single-sideband station with no speech processing typically has a duty factor of about 20%. If this station were transmitting using 1500 watts for 15 minutes out of every 30 (50%), in an uncontrolled environment, the average power would be: 1500 W×20%×40% = 120 W. In a controlled environment, you should determine the percentage of time the station is transmitting in any 6 minute period. Any feed-line losses may also be considered when making these calculations.

Station Evaluations

The FCC requires that certain amateur stations be evaluated for compliance with the MPEs. This will help ensure a safe operating environment for amateurs, their families and neighbors.

Although an amateur can have someone else do the evaluation, it is not difficult for hams to evaluate their own stations. *RF Exposure and You* and the FCC's *Bulletin 65* contain basic information about the regulations and a number of tables that show compliance distances for specific antennas and power levels. Generally, hams will use these tables to evaluate their stations. If they choose, however, they can do more extensive calculations, use a computer to model their antenna and exposure, or make actual measurements.

In most cases, hams will be able to use a simple table from the book that best describes their station's operation to determine the minimum compliance distance that people must be from their antenna for their specific operation. There are several sets of tables to choose from, either based on frequency, power and antenna gain, or on specific antennas modeled at specific heights above ground. In these tables, the power levels shown in a table would be average power levels, adjusted for the duty cycle of the operating mode being used, and operating on and off time. An example of such a table is shown in **Table 5**.

Categorical Exemptions

The good news is that most amateur stations do not need to be evaluated! The FCC has exempted many types of station operation from the evaluation requirement because their output power, operating mode and frequency are such that they are presumed to be in compliance with the rules. One

Table 5

Estimated distances from transmitting antennas necessary to meet FCC power-density limits for Maximum Permissible Exposure (MPE) for either occupational/controlled exposures ("Con") or general-population/uncontrolled exposures ("Unc"). The estimates are based on typical amateur antennas and assuming a 100% duty cycle and typical ground reflection. (The figures shown in this table generally represent worst-case values, primarily in the main beam of the antenna.) The compliance distances apply to average exposure and average power, but can be used with PEP for a conservative estimate.

Distance from antenna (feet)

Frequency (MHz)	Gain (dBi)	100 W Con	100 W Unc	500 W Con	500 W Unc	1,000 W Con	1,000 W Unc	1,500 W Con	1,500 W Unc
2	0	0.5	0.7	1.0	1.6	1.5	2.2	1.8	2.7
	3	0.7	1.0	1.5	2.2	2.1	3.1	2.6	3.8
4	0	0.6	1.4	1.4	3.1	2.0	4.4	2.4	5.4
	3	0.9	2.0	2.0	4.4	2.8	6.2	3.4	7.6
7.3	0	1.1	2.5	2.5	5.7	3.6	8.1	4.4	9.9
	3	1.6	3.6	3.6	8.0	5.1	11.4	6.2	13.9
	6	2.3	5.1	5.1	11.4	7.2	16.1	8.8	19.7
10.15	0	1.6	3.5	3.5	7.9	5.0	11.2	6.1	13.7
	3	2.2	5.0	5.0	11.2	7.1	15.8	8.7	19.4
	6	3.2	7.1	7.1	15.8	10.0	22.4	12.2	27.4
14.35	0	2.2	5.0	5.0	11.2	7.1	15.8	8.7	19.4
	3	3.2	7.1	7.1	15.8	10.0	22.4	12.3	27.4
	6	4.5	10.0	10.0	22.3	14.1	31.6	17.3	38.7
	9	6.3	14.1	14.1	31.6	20.0	44.6	24.4	54.7
18.168	0	2.8	6.3	6.3	14.2	9.0	20.1	11.0	24.6
	3	4.0	9.0	9.0	20.0	12.7	28.3	15.5	34.7
	6	5.7	12.7	12.7	28.3	17.9	40.0	21.9	49.0
	9	8.0	17.9	17.9	40.0	25.3	56.5	31.0	69.2
21.45	0	3.3	7.5	7.5	16.7	10.6	23.7	13.0	29.0
	3	4.7	10.6	10.6	23.6	15.0	33.4	18.3	41.0
	6	6.7	14.9	14.9	33.4	21.1	47.2	25.9	57.9
	9	9.4	21.1	21.1	47.2	29.8	66.7	36.5	81.7
24.99	0	3.9	8.7	8.7	19.5	12.3	27.6	15.1	33.8
	3	5.5	12.3	12.3	27.5	17.4	39.0	21.3	47.7
	6	7.8	17.4	17.4	38.9	24.6	55.0	30.1	67.4
	9	11.0	24.6	24.6	55.0	34.8	77.7	42.6	95.2
29.7	0	4.6	10.4	10.4	23.2	14.7	32.8	18.0	40.1
	3	6.5	14.6	14.6	32.7	20.7	46.3	25.4	56.7
	6	9.2	20.7	20.7	46.2	29.3	65.4	35.8	80.1
	9	13.1	29.2	29.2	65.3	41.3	92.4	50.6	113.2

Frequency (MHz)	Gain (dBi)	50 W Con	50 W Unc	100 W Con	100 W Unc	500 W Con	500 W Unc	1,000 W Con	1,000 W Unc
50, 144, 222	0	3.3	7.4	4.7	10.5	10.5	23.4	14.8	33.1
	3	4.7	10.5	6.6	14.8	14.8	33.1	20.9	46.8
	6	6.6	14.8	9.3	20.9	20.9	46.7	29.5	66.1
	9	9.3	20.9	13.2	29.5	29.5	66.0	41.7	93.3
	12	13.2	29.5	18.6	41.7	41.7	93.2	59.0	131.8
	15	18.6	41.6	26.3	58.9	58.9	131.7	83.3	186.2
	20	33.1	74.0	46.8	104.7	104.7	234.1	148.1	331.1
420	0	2.8	6.3	4.0	8.8	8.8	19.8	12.5	28.0
	3	4.0	8.8	5.6	12.5	12.5	28.0	17.7	39.5
	6	5.6	12.5	7.9	17.7	17.7	39.5	25.0	55.8
	9	7.9	17.6	11.2	24.9	24.9	55.8	35.3	78.9
	12	11.1	24.9	15.8	35.2	35.2	78.8	49.8	111.4
	15	15.7	35.2	22.3	49.8	49.8	111.3	70.4	157.4
1240	0	1.6	3.6	2.3	5.2	5.2	11.5	7.3	16.3
	3	2.3	5.1	3.3	7.3	7.3	16.3	10.3	23.0
	6	3.2	7.3	4.6	10.3	10.3	23.0	14.5	32.5
	9	4.6	10.3	6.5	14.5	14.5	32.5	20.5	45.9
	12	6.5	14.5	9.2	20.5	20.5	45.8	29.0	64.8
	15	9.2	20.5	13.0	29.0	29.0	64.8	41.0	91.6

exemption is based on power level and frequency. Those stations using the power levels shown in Table 3 are categorically exempt from the requirement to do a station evaluation. The power levels in Table 3 are in peak-envelope power (PEP) to the antenna.

Hand-held radios and vehicle-mounted mobile radios that operate using a push-to-talk (PTT) button are also categorically exempt from performing the routine evaluation. They are not, however, exempt from meeting the maximum permissible exposure (MPE) limits established by the rules. All amateur stations are required to comply with the MPE limits. The station licensee is responsible for ensuring that the station meets these requirements.

Repeaters used in the Amateur Radio Service are exempt from the requirement to perform a routine station evaluation if they use 500 W effective radiated power (ERP) or less, or if they have antennas not mounted on buildings, if those antennas are greater than 30 meters above ground.

Correcting Problems

Most hams are already in compliance with the MPE requirements. Some amateurs, especially those using indoor antennas or high-power, high-duty-cycle modes such as an RTTY bulletin station and specialized stations for moonbounce operations and the like may need to make adjustments to their station or operation to be in compliance.

The FCC permits amateurs considerable flexibility in complying with these regulations. Hams can adjust their operating frequency, mode or power to comply with the MPE limits. They can also adjust their operating habits or control the direction their antenna is pointing. For example, if an amateur were to discover that the MPE limits had been exceeded for uncontrolled exposure after 28 minutes of transmitting, the FCC would consider it perfectly acceptable to take a 2-minute break after 28 minutes.

Multiple Transmitter Environments

All stations in a multitransmitter site are jointly responsible for the total RF exposure that results from the operation of the transmitters on the site in all areas where the actual exposure level from the station is greater than 5% of the MPE level permitted to that station. This requirement applies to multitransmitter amateur stations, such as are used in some contests, and to commercial sites, such as the mountaintop location of some amateur repeaters. In most cases, the amateur operator will need to cooperate with other site users to determine the overall exposure of all the transmitters on the site. In some cases, the overall evaluation will be done by professionals hired by the site operators. Multitransmitter sites are discussed in detail in FCC *Bulletin 65*.

Paperwork

Other than a short certification on Form 605 station applications, the regulations do not normally require hams to file proof of evaluation with the FCC. The Commission recommends, however, that each amateur keep a record of the station evaluation procedure and its results, in case questions arise.

OTHER FEDERAL RESTRICTIONS ON STATION LOCATIONS

Section 97.15(a) concerns antennas taller than 200 feet and near airports. There are many regulations in Part 97 which tell amateurs what communications can and can't be transmitted from our amateur stations. In addition to the three restrictions on antenna locations mentioned earlier in this chapter, amateurs should note that there are additional Federal restrictions on physical station locations. These must be complied with before a station can transmit. Fortunately, there are few restrictions on antennas in Part 97. These apply only in unusual circumstances. The Federal restrictions that do apply are to:

• Antennas over 200 feet in height and antennas near airports;

• Notification to the National Radio Astronomy Observatory in Green Bank, WV, and the Naval Radio Research Observatory in Sugar Grove, WV, of new stations or changes to existing nearby amateur stations in the National Radio Quiet Zone.

• Regional prohibitions on interference to higher status services.

• Protection of FCC Field Office sites from amateur stations within 1.5 miles.

• Notification to the Arecibo Observatory in Puerto Rico from amateurs planning to operate a new or modified amateur station within 10 miles of the facility.

Tall Towers and Antennas Near Airports

In November 1995, the FCC adopted rules requiring tower owners to register with the FCC each antenna structure for which Federal Aviation Administration (FAA) notification is required. Generally, this includes all structures *more than 200 feet above ground* or *certain towers located near or on a public use airport*. The FCC has long required registration and FAA notification, but they now have specific rules that appear in Part 17 of FCC rules. FCC may assess stiff fines to tower owners who do not comply and the fines, which can range up to $10,000, appear in §1.80 of FCC rules. *If required, all tower owners, including amateurs, must register their towers with the FCC and they are required to do so immediately*. Part 17 mandates marking and lighting of non-exempt antenna structures to help protect the safety of air navigation. A copy of Part 17 is available from ARRL for an SASE with two units of postage or from the FCC Web page at **http://www.fcc.gov/wtb/rules.html**.

Fortunately, the vast majority of amateurs are *exempt* from the *federal* tower registration process, but amateurs must still abide by local *government zoning ordinance*.

Am I Required to Register My Tower?

Most antenna structures that are higher than 200 feet above ground level or that may interfere with the flight path of a nearby airport must be cleared by the Federal Aviation Administration (FAA) and registered with the FCC. Unless specifically exempted, FAA notification and FCC registration are required:

1) For any construction or alteration of more than 200 feet in height above ground level at its site.

2) When requested by the FAA if it is determined that the antenna structure might exceed an obstruction standard of the FAA.

3) For any construction or alteration of greater height than an imaginary surface extending outward and upward at one of the following slopes which represent the ratio of distance from the longest runway to the feet in height an antenna may be:

- 100 to 1 for a horizontal distance of 20,000 feet from the nearest point of the nearest runway of each Specified Airport with at least one runway *longer than* 3280 feet in actual length. If the runway is *longer* than 1 km (3280 feet) and the airport is within 6.1 km (3.79 miles) of your proposed installation, your antenna may be *no higher than 1 meter (3.28 feet) above the airport elevation for every 100 meters (328 feet) from the nearest runway*. This is a slope of 100 to 1. See **Fig 1**.

- 50 to 1 for a horizontal distance of 10,000 feet from the nearest point of the nearest runway of each Specified Airport with its longest runway *shorter than* 3,200 feet (6.1 km or 3.79 miles) in actual length. If the runway is *shorter* than 1 km (3280 feet) and the airport is within 6.1 km (3.79 miles) of your proposed installation, *your antenna may be no higher than 2 meters (6.56 feet) above the airport elevation for every 100 meters (328 feet) from the nearest runway*. This is a slope of 50 to 1. See **Fig 2**.

- 25 to 1 for a horizontal distance of 5,000 feet from the nearest point of the nearest landing and takeoff area of each heliport at a Specified Airport. If the installation is *within 1.5 km* (4920 feet) of a helipad, your antenna may be *no higher than 4 meters (13.1 feet) above the airport elevation for every 100 meters (328 feet) from the nearest landing pad*. That's a slope of 25 to 1. See **Fig 3**.

"Specified Airports"

A Specified Airport refers to:

- A public use airport listed in the *Airport Directory* of the current *Aeronautical Information Manual* or in either the *Alaska* or *Pacific Airman's Guide and Chart Supplement*;

- An airport under construction, that is the subject of a notice or proposal on file with the FAA, and except for military airports, it is clearly indicated that the airport will be available for public use; or

- An airport that is operated by an armed force of the United States.

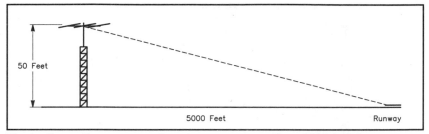

Fig 1—If you live near an airport runway more than 3280 feet long, you must notify the FAA and FCC if your antenna will exceed heights limited by a slope of 100 to 1.

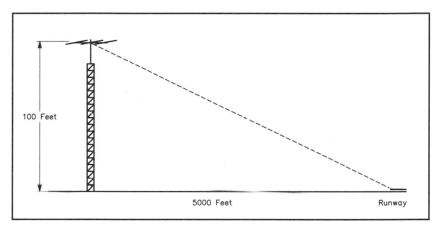

Fig 2—Where airport runways are less than 3280 feet long, you must notify the FAA and FCC if your antenna will exceed heights limited by a slope of 50 to 1.

Which Towers are Exempt?

The following types of antenna structures are specifically *exempted* from the FAA notification requirements and FCC registration requirements by §17.14 of the FCC rules:

1) Any antenna structure that would be shielded by existing structures of a permanent and substantial character or by natural terrain or topographic features of equal or greater height, and would be located in the congested area of a city, town or settlement where it is evident beyond all reasonable doubt that the structure so shielded will not adversely affect safety in air navigation.

2) Any antenna structure of 20 feet or less in height (except one that would increase the height of another antenna structure).

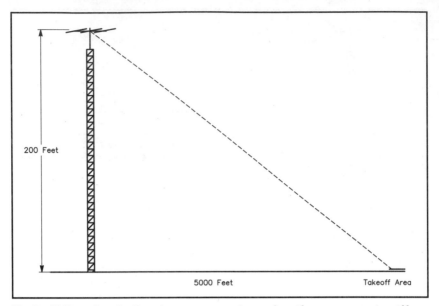

200 Feet

5000 Feet   Takeoff Area

Fig 3—If there is a heliport near your antenna location, you must notify the FAA and FCC if your antenna will exceed heights limited by a slope of 25 to 1.

3) An antenna which is not near an airport and is less than 200 feet tall.

If you are still unsure if your tower needs to be registered, you may call the FCC at 1-888 CALL FCC, contact them by e-mail at **mayday@fcc.gov** or you may use on-line TOWAIR software, available on the FCC's Web site at: **http://www.fcc.gov/wtb/antenna/towair.html**.

If your antenna is near an airport or over 200 feet tall, check this FCC Web site for additional information: **http://www.fcc.gov/wtb/antenna**. Owners of antenna structures required to be registered pursuant to §17.14 of the Commission's rules must first file FAA Form 7460-1 and obtain a final determination of "no hazard" for the structure. The FAA form is available from the Web at **http://www.faa.gov/arp/ace/faaforms.htm**. Second, tower owners must file FCC Form 854 with the Commission either manually or electronically to register the antenna structure. The FCC form is available from **http://www.fcc.gov/formpage.html**. Both forms are available from ARRL HQ for a self-addressed, stamped envelope.

Provided that the owner should register the antenna structure *immediately*, according to the FCC, there is no cause for concern if an amateur misses the filing window deadline. This process provides a measure of safety in air navigation against tall structures that could cause an accident.

If an amateur who has reason to believe that the owner of a tall tower over 200 feet or near an airport is not carrying out his or her antenna structure registration responsibilities is required to (1) notify the owner; (2) notify the site management company (if applicable); and (3) notify the FCC. The FCC will provide additional instructions to the tower owner based on the specifics of the case.

If the tower owner is unable to fulfill the Part 17 requirements for painting and lighting due to negligence, bankruptcy or whatever, the tenants (amateurs, in this case) may be required to carry out these duties *if specifically asked by the FCC*. Amateurs who rent or are given space on tall towers should have a signed legal document addressing maintenance concerns as well as tower access. An ARRL Volunteer Counsel can help with this. See *ARRLWeb* for a list of ARRL Volunteer Counsel—hams who are also lawyers. See: **http://www.arrl.org/ FandES/field/regulations/local/vci.html** and **http://www.arrl.org/FandES/ field/regulations/local/vc.html**.

The National Radio Quiet Zone

You must notify the Director of the National Radio Astronomy Observatory in Green Bank, WV, and the Director of the Naval Radio Research Observatory at Sugar Grove, WV if you intend to put up or make changes to an amateur station in what is called the National Radio Quiet Zone, an area in Maryland, Virginia and West Virginia, the coordinates of which are defined in Chapter 3 [97.203(e), 1.924].

Regional Prohibitions on Interference to Higher Status Services

Most amateurs will never hear transmissions from a non-amateur service, but certain stations will, especially if they are located near certain military bases or near the Canadian border. Spectrum is allocated on the basis of priority and amateurs share many bands or sections of bands with other services on a national and international basis. Some amateur frequency allocations are exclusive. This means that the Amateur Radio Service is the only authorized service in such a band. Other bands are shared with other services on the basis of priority.

In some cases, the Amateur Radio Service is the primary or highest status user service in a particular band. Other bands are shared with other primary occupants on a coprimary basis. In these cases, amateurs operate on a basis of equality: Stations in the Amateur Radio Service must not cause harmful interference to the other primary occupants and they must not interfere with amateurs. In other cases, Amateur Radio is designated a secondary service: Amateurs must not cause harmful interference to, and must tolerate interference from, stations in a primary service. Stations on and above the 70 cm band face additional restrictions based largely on their station location. An amateur station may not operate in the 420-430 MHz band north of Line A to the Canadian border [97.303]. These prohibitions are detailed in Chapter 4.

The Arecibo Observatory

Amateurs planning a new or modified station with 10 miles of the Arecibo Observatory in Arecibo, Puerto Rico, must take reasonable steps to protect the facility from interference [97.203(h), 1.924].

Protection of FCC Field Offices

Permanent, fixed amateur stations within 1.5 miles of FCC Field Offices must take steps to minimize interference to these FCC sites. The coordinates of these FCC sites appears in §0.121. Details of these restrictions appear in Appendix 2 of Chapter 10 of this book.

STATE AND LOCAL RESTRICTIONS ON ANTENNA STRUCTURES

The FCC defines an amateur station as consisting of the apparatus necessary for carrying on radiocommunications [97.3(a)(5)]. As anyone who is familiar with radio knows, an antenna is necessary apparatus. A radio without an antenna is as useless as a car without wheels. The Communications Act requires that the FCC "generally encourage the larger and more effective use of radio in the public interest." It only stands to reason that the FCC must have an interest in ensuring that the stations it licenses include antennas that are appropriate for the services they are expected to render. In the case of the Amateur Radio Service, that interest was formally expressed in 1985 by means of an FCC declaration of limited preemption of state and local regulation commonly known as "PRB-1."

As long as there have been antennas, local governments have adopted zoning ordinances and regulations as part of their duty to protect its citizens and what the law calls the public health, safety, convenience and welfare. The role of local regulators, however, has often proved incompatible with the FCC's interest and the legitimate need of radio amateurs to put up appropriate antennas.

Local restrictions imposed on amateur antennas come in more than one flavor: aside from the local governmental restrictions that will be discussed, public zoning ordinances, non-governmental private deed restrictions and covenants specific to a particular parcel of land are common roadblocks.

PRB-1, The FCC's Limited Preemption of Local Ordinances

PRB-1 mentioned above, cited as "Amateur Radio Preemption, 101 FCC2d 952 (1985)," is a limited preemption of local zoning ordinances. It delineates three rules for local municipalities to follow in regulating antenna structures: (1) state and local regulations that operate to preclude amateur communications are in direct conflict with federal objectives and must be preempted; (2) local regulations that involve placement, screening or height of antennas based on health, safety or aesthetic considerations must be crafted to reasonably accommodate amateur communications; and (3) such local regulations must represent the minimum practicable regulation to accomplish the local authority's legitimate purpose. The heart of PRB-1 is codified in §97.15(b). It states:

> Except as otherwise provided herein, a station antenna structure may be erected at heights and dimensions sufficient to accommodate amateur service communications. [State and local regulation of a station antenna structure must not preclude amateur service communications. Rather, it must reasonably accommodate such communications and must constitute the minimum practicable regulation to accomplish the state or local authority's legitimate purpose. See PRB-1, 101 FCC 2d 952 (1985) for details.]

Of course, what is "reasonable" depends on the circumstances. For suggestions about what to do when you are faced with a restrictive ordinance, see "Interaction with Municipal Officials," below. The full text of PRB-1 can be found in **Appendix 7**. ARRL members can find information on PRB-1 and supplementary materials at **www.arrl.org/FandES/Field/regulations/PRB-1_Pkg/index.html**. The ARRL book *Antenna Zoning for the Radio Amateur*, written by a lawyer, contains the most comprehensive material for amateurs faced with zoning problems and it includes a CD with many documents.

Local Zoning Ordinances

In the past, amateurs relied solely on their powers of persuasion when dealing with local officials. Conflicts between amateurs and local authorities over the antenna height, placement in the yard, number of antennas on a tower and the like were common. In the absence of detailed federal regulations governing amateur antennas (except for those aspects discussed previously), municipal leaders often fill in the void and use their broad discretion in public health and safety matters to enact regulations that limit antennas and supporting structures. The people who write these regulations have a lot of other things on their mind, so these regulations seldom take into account your need for an antenna of certain dimensions and height to be effective, so conflicts arise.

The situation reached epidemic proportions in the early 1980s. Amateurs who invested family savings in fighting local zoning, building codes and covenant restrictions in the courts were losing because the FCC had not issued a clear statement of federal interest in the matter. The courts held that the FCC regulates radio, but because the FCC had issued no statement restraining the zoning power of cities and counties, the traditionally local interest in zoning regulations that protects the public generally superseded the interests of any individual amateur.

By October 1983, the ARRL Board of Directors reviewed the adverse court decisions and recognized that antenna restrictions would continue to be a major stumbling block unless a statement of federal preemption emerged from the FCC. On July 16, 1984, the ARRL filed a formal request asking the FCC to issue a declaratory ruling that would declare void all local ordinances that preclude or significantly inhibit effective, reliable amateur communications. Hundreds of comments were filed when the FCC established a pleading cycle, labeled PRB-1 (PRB being the designation for the FCC's Private Radio Bureau, the bureau that handled Amateur Radio matters at that time). Amateurs, zoning authorities and city planners filed comments.

September 19, 1985, was a red-letter day in the history of Amateur Radio, as the FCC issued its now-famous PRB-1 declaratory *Memorandum Opinion and Order*. It says, in part, that "state and local regulations that operate to preclude amateur communications in their communities are in direct conflict with federal objectives and must be preempted."

May 31, 1989, marked another milestone when the Commission adopted the revised and reorganized Part 97. The new rules codified the essence of the PRB-1 ruling by stating that state or local regulation of amateur antennas may not preclude, but must reasonably accommodate, such communications, and must constitute the minimum practicable regulation to accomplish the local authority's legitimate purpose."

PRB-1 is a good tool and, with a few exceptions, has encouraged open cooperation and dialogue between the communities seeking to regulate amateur antennas and amateurs. With PRB-1 incorporated into the FCC Rules, the federal interest and official FCC policy with respect to amateur communications can be more easily demonstrated to municipal officials. These officials need to be educated by you and your fellow hams.

"Balancing of Interests" Not Enough

In 1996, based on more than a decade of experience with PRB-1, the ARRL requested some clarifications and fine-tuning of the FCC's preemption policy. Four years later, the FCC declined, saying PRB-1 is fine just the way it is. In its denial released November 19, 1999, the FCC said it would not be "prudent" or "appropriate" to set a height standard for amateur antennas and supporting structures "because of varying circumstances that may occur" for differing antenna configurations. "We believe that the policy enunciated in PRB-1 is sound," the FCC said, noting that PRB-1 does not specify a height limit. The Commission also said it did not want to mandate specific provisions that localities must include in zoning ordinances.

"We continue to believe that the standards the Commission set, that is 'reasonable accommodation' and 'minimum practicable regulation,' have worked relatively well," the FCC said. The Commission applied that same philosophy to the imposition of fees, zoning laws and other conditions that localities might impose on amateur antenna installations.

The FCC also said its policy with respect to restrictive covenants already is clearly stated in PRB-1, which excludes restrictive covenants in private contracts as "outside the reach of our limited preemption." The FCC did say that it "strongly encourages associations of homeowners and private contracting parties to follow the principle of reasonable accommodation" with respect to Amateur Radio. But it drew the line at proposing specific rule changes to bring private restrictive covenants under the umbrella of PRB-1.

On a slightly positive note, the FCC did assert that PRB-1 precisely states the principle of "reasonable accommodation." Some courts have held that a local authority can merely balance its own interests against those of the amateur. PRB-1 says local regulations involving placement, screening or height of antennas based on health, safety or aesthetic considerations "must be crafted to accommodate reasonably amateur communications, and to represent the minimum practicable regulation to accomplish the local authority's legitimate purpose." In its Order, the FCC said that given PRB-1's explicit language, "it is clear that a 'balancing of interests' approach is not appropriate in this context." This new tool will be used in an appeal in a Florida court case where the "balancing of interests" approach was inappropriately applied.

At this writing, the ARRL is seeking reconsideration of the FCC's denial on two points: The ARRL wants recognition that the FCC's interest in effective amateur communication extends to those amateurs who must live in homes that are subject to restrictive covenants. In 1985 the FCC went out of its way to exclude these amateurs from PRB 1 protection because it

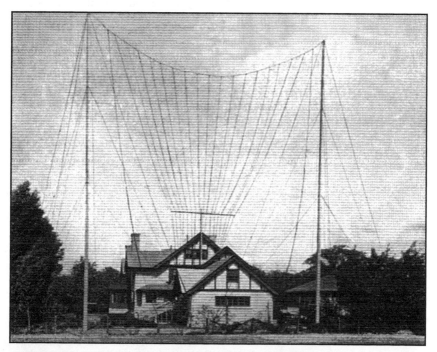

"The Old Man," Hiram Percy Maxim (1AW), didn't have zoning problems when he erected this antenna at his home in Hartford, Connecticut, in the 1920s.

believed it did not have any jurisdiction to preempt private land use regulations. Since that time, however, it has become clear that the FCC does have such jurisdiction if necessary to further an important federal interest.

The second is that some local land use regulations or authorities impose unreasonable costs, either in the form of excessive fees or overly burdensome requirements for screening or the mitigation of the visual impact of an antenna. Guidelines have been developed to control such costs in other services and should also be available to the amateur service.

Interaction with Municipal Officials

Don't be intimidated by the thought of going to city hall to request a building permit for an antenna support structure. Virtually all ham radio operators who own the physical area necessary for the safe installation of a tower should be able to legally erect a tower of *some* size. There are a few steps to take that will enhance your chances of getting as much tower as you wish.

Information Gathering

Since regulations pertaining to antennas and the way building and zoning departments process permits vary from city to city, the first and most important step is information gathering. This means a visit or a phone call to your local building/zoning department, to obtain a copy of the zoning ordinances. Don't settle for anything less than the *whole booklet* of regulations. If the clerk or secretary offers to photocopy for you only the pages that pertain to antennas, keep in mind the sections mentioned, politely thank him or her, and then get the entire booklet (which normally costs between $5 and $15).

The entire booklet will tell you what procedures to follow when you apply for a permit. You also need to know how to appeal an adverse decision if you don't get a favorable ruling from the building inspector or zoning enforcement officer on the first try. Furthermore, if you should need to seek the advice of a lawyer, the first thing the attorney will need to see is the entire body of regulatory law affecting land-use regulations for the town.

Zoning Regs Defined

What are zoning regulations, exactly? Zoning regulations are rules that establish the permitted uses and the minimum and maximum dimensional requirements of structures in established areas or "zones." Ninety-nine percent of the time, a ham will want to put up an antenna/tower at his home, which will be in a residential zone. Because the overwhelming number of jurisdictions hold Amateur Radio to be a normal accessory (as opposed to primary) use of residential property, it is proper in a residential zone. Similarly, such edifices as swimming pools, tennis courts and tool sheds are considered accessory structures on residential property.

In addition to *use* rules, zoning regulations also establish rules as to how *high* structures are permitted to be. You may find your proposed tower being held to the same height standards as other "buildings" or "structures" permitted in a residential zone. Read the definitions section near the beginning of the zoning rules. Sometimes the definition of "building" is broad enough to include a tower, or antennas may be defined specifically. If the regulations do *not* define antennas specifically, see if they mention "accessory structures." Read the definition to see if antennas are included in that definition. You may find a section that defines flagpoles, church steeples and similar structures in language that could easily apply to towers as well.

Your town may be concerned with *building codes*, standards relating to safety that have been agreed upon by engineers from the architectural, structural, civil and other engineering disciplines. Once the building inspector determines that your tower is proper and would not violate zoning regulations pertaining to use and dimensions, your construction must still be carried out in accordance with building codes. Fortunately, this is rarely a problem. Tower manufacturers provide detailed specifications and plans for proper installation in accordance with all building codes.

Meeting the Building Inspector

After you have had a chance to study the regulations, you can probably tell which rules apply to your installation. If the clerk or secretary pointed out certain sections, look at those sections first to see if you agree. The regulations, when read in the context of your proposed antenna installation, should be understandable. If the regulations are full of legal mumbo-jumbo, however, now is the time to consult a lawyer, such as an ARRL Volunteer Counsel. On the other hand, if you feel confident about your level of understanding and have familiarized yourself enough to carry on an intelligent conversation about the regulations, make an appointment with the building inspector (or the appropriate city official). Be prepared to discuss the proposed location, height and purpose of your structure, and take along the basic engineering data provided by the tower manufacturer to satisfy building code concerns. Also, take along a rough drawing of your property that shows your boundary lines, the house and other buildings nearby and the proposed location of the tower.

The building inspector, much like a police officer walking a beat, is the first interpreter of the law, in this case the zoning law. What he or she says will be the first indication of the steps you will have to take to get a permit for your installation. After you present your proposal, listen carefully to what the building inspector says. Building inspectors are often willing to be helpful and grant your permit, provided you follow the correct application procedures. For example, you may need to file a map of your property drawn to scale.

If the building inspector appears negative, pay attention nevertheless to what he has to say, even if his reasoning may be wrong. It is important to thoroughly understand the basis for his opinion. Do not go into the confrontation mode with the building inspector; keep your "grid current" low! Don't wave a copy of PRB-1 or Part 97 in his face and "command" him to give you the permit because of federal law. He's not going to know what you're talking about, nor is he likely to make a snap decision in your favor that might get him into hot water later. If you are going to talk legal issues, he's going to want his lawyer (the town attorney) in on it.

In many situations, the building inspector will have the authority to grant a building permit or other approvals without the involvement of any of the higher-ups. This is why it's important to maintain a good relationship with him if possible.

Sometimes (especially if you're lucky), zoning ordinances specifically exempt antennas from the height restrictions of other structures. Depending on how your town's ordinances are written, it may be necessary for you to seek the permission of a zoning commissioner or land use board. Usually this means that the zoning regulations are set up to allow antennas to a certain height limit without the need of a hearing, but if you want to exceed the "usual" height threshold, you need to apply for a special permit. This means that the drafters of the zoning ordinances decided that certain uses of structures could be permitted only after a public hearing and demonstration of special need.

While this undoubtedly means more red tape and delay if you find yourself in this situation, such a requirement is not illegal in the eyes of the law (including PRB-1). It does provide a forum for potential opposition from neighbors, however, and preparation for the hearing is all-important.

If there is a problem, it will be one of two varieties: It may be a matter of interpretation of the ordinance by the building inspector, or the ordinance may be written in such a way that he is unable to reasonably come up with any other interpretation. If the ordinance is prohibitive under any reasonable interpretation, you should immediately seek the advice of a lawyer.

If the problem is that you disagree with the building inspector's interpretation of the zoning regulations, that's not as serious. While you may ultimately need a lawyer to resolve the issue, you can still carry the issue further yourself. Tell the building inspector in a *nonconfrontational* manner that you have a different interpretation and ask him for his comments. See if you can narrow it down as to where the problem lies. If it is a problem with the way the ordinance is written, that is, under no possible interpretation can you get your permit, that is a more serious problem. It may mean that the ordinance is illegal, and therefore invalid. The town officials won't like that and are more apt to fight vigorously against having their ordinance invalidated. They would rather change an interpretation for a particular situation than throw out their entire ordinance and have to start from scratch. If you run into an unresolvable problem with the building inspector, you should then, as a last resort, calmly tell him about PRB-1 and the rules [97.15(b)]. As mentioned previously, more often than not, you will find that it does not help at the building inspector level. At most, you may get across that the federal government, through the FCC, has acted under a preemption order called PRB-1. You can say that local governments cannot prohibit antenna towers, nor can they unreasonably restrict them in terms of size and height. However, you can't expect the building inspector to be equipped to engage in a lengthy discussion of the nuances of the legalities of federal preemption.

The Appeal

If there is a reasonable interpretation or even a loophole in the regulations under which you should be allowed to put up the antenna/tower, you can usually appeal that decision to your town's Zoning Board of Appeals (ZBA) or equivalent body. If you have absolutely no alternative, you can ask the ZBA for a variance. This means you are asking the ZBA to relax the zoning rules in your case, to give you a special exemption because of some exceptional difficulty or unreasonable hardship. Variances are granted sparingly because it is difficult to establish severe hardship. Remember, too, that if you apply for a variance, you are admitting in the eyes of the law that the ordinance applies to your antenna. This means that you can't contest or challenge the applicability or the jurisdiction of the ordinance in a later proceeding.

The procedure for appealing the building inspector's ruling is outlined in the regulations. You are given a chance to explain what Amateur Radio is and to present your alternative interpretation that would permit you to erect your tower legally or to explain that your hardship is severe enough that you should be allowed to put up your tower despite the zoning rules.

PRB-1 should be used to persuade the ZBA to adopt your more reasonable interpretation because federal law requires it to adopt as reasonable an interpretation as possible. If there is no possible interpretation of the zoning regulations that will allow your tower to go up, then tell the ZBA that PRB-1 and §97.15(b) are binding federal regulations that supersede the ZBA's law if there is a conflict. That is, its interpretation of its own zoning ordinance should be guided by the binding order rendered by the FCC in PRB-1; the local regulations cannot regulate in the "overkill mode." But make no mistake about it; state and local governments can, under the specific language of PRB-1, still regulate antennas for reasons of health, safety and welfare, as long as the regulations are reasonable.

Additional Guidelines for the Presentation

Here are a few other things to keep in mind when you make your presentation before the ZBA: Make sure you can establish the safety factors of your tower. On matters of safety, there should be *no compromise* by the municipality. If your installation does not meet building-code requirements, no board (or court, if it comes to that) will allow it. The manufacturer's specifications must be followed.

On the other hand, aesthetics and welfare, particularly the effect on the surrounding property values, are more likely to be areas of compromise by the ZBA. Your task here is threefold: You have to demonstrate your *need* for the proposed tower and the *safety* of the structure, and you have to show that you have taken reasonable steps to *lessen the impact on the surrounding property.*

As mentioned previously, the ARRL on-line PRB-1 package and the book *Antenna Zoning for the Radio Amateur*, which can be purchased, contains helpful materials to assist you in preparing for any possible zoning hearing. ARRL Volunteer Counsel or Volunteer Consulting Engineers near you can also provide legal or engineering advice. This information is available on *ARRLWeb*: **www.arrl.org/FandES/field/regulations/**.

If you haven't done so, try to gauge the opposition, if any, of your neighbors before the hearing. Neighbors who show up at the hearing can be friendly or adversarial; touching base with your neighbors in advance is a good way to transform adversaries into people who will speak in support of your position. Be prepared to answer all questions that you can anticipate. Although the touchy area of radio-frequency interference (RFI) does not fall under the jurisdiction of the ZBA, it may use your reaction to questions about RFI to judge your character (which could form the unwritten or unstated basis for a denial). A ZBA member is more likely to give the benefit of the doubt to someone who sounds like a responsible, good neighbor.

If neighbors or ZBA members raise concerns about RFI, one of the most effective statements you can make is to explain that, although years ago the home-brew nature of ham stations may have resulted in hams being responsible for RFI, today that is hardly the case. With the present level of Amateur Radio sophistication, RFI is rarely a problem, and when it is, it is usually the fault of the manufacturers of the stereo, TV or other home-entertainment device. But explain to the ZBA members that you will work with your neighbors to resolve any RFI problems in the rare event that RFI problems occur. Also, point out that a tower taller than neighbors' homes will help direct your signals *above* their houses, providing added "insurance" against possible problems.

When you make your presentation, keep it clear, concise and simple. Use a written outline so you don't forget key points, but speak directly and respectfully to the ZBA members in your own words. Avoid technical language or ham radio jargon that's incomprehensible to non-hams. The ZBA does not, and has no reason to, care about dB, SWR, wavelengths, DX or anything else "sacred" to Amateur Radio operators. They care about how big your aerial is going to be and what damage it could do to a neighbor's home if it falls. (You might point out that towers rarely fall or break, and if they do, it is generally not from the bottom.) Emphasize the public service nature of Amateur Radio, and its value to your community in an emergency. Although the ARRL has offered the PRB-1 package for years to assist in making a presentation before a local zoning board, now, even more specialized help is available. *Antenna Zoning for the Radio Amateur*, an ARRL book released in early 2001, was written by a lwayer and even includes a CD with many documents, including "pre-fab" zoning presentations. It is available from ARRL HQ and Amateur Radio book dealers.

Make sure your demeanor is professional, and dress in a conservative businesslike manner (leave your ARES jumpsuit, call-sign cap and painter's pants at home). Make sure, also, not to operate in a vacuum; enlist the support of the local Amateur Radio community and ask as many of your fellow hams as possible to show up for the hearing. A unified show of support will make a profound impression on ZBA members who are, after all, ordinary people yet politicians at heart.

Private Restrictions

There are circumstances under which it is legally *impossible* to erect a tower. Condominium owners are a prime example. A condo owner "owns" only that which exists *within* the confines of the four walls that forms his unit. The rest of the building and the land are owned by someone else or owned in common by all the unit owners. Unless you can persuade the condominium association to allow you to put up an antenna in a common area, you had better concentrate on operating mobile from your car or bone up on so-called "invisible" or limited-space antennas in attics or crawl spaces in the ceiling (although this may also be a violation of the condominium bylaws). You cannot expect to be able to put up a tower on land or a building that you do not own outright.

Private restrictions, commonly called *CC&Rs* (covenants, conditions and restrictions) are another aspect of antenna/tower regulation that exist outside of the zoning regulatory body. CC&Rs are the "fine print" that may be referenced in the deed to your property, *especially* if you are in a planned subdivision that has underground utilities. Your best bet before proceeding with your tower plans is to take a copy of your deed to an attorney to have a limited title search done for the specific purpose of determining whether private restrictions will affect your rights. If you're buying a new home, have a title search done *before* you sign on the dotted line. When you agree to purchase the property, you agree to accept covenants and deed restrictions on the land records, which may preclude you from being able to put up a tower at your new dream home. See Deed Restrictions and Covenants, below.

Summary: State and Local Restrictions

With respect to governmental, as opposed to private, restrictions, it all boils down to one simple fact: Any licensed ham radio operator who has the private property of a sufficiently sized parcel of land, has the right under federal law to erect a tower and antenna, subject to the reasonable regulation of local and state government.

Q&A—PRB-1

Q. How can the federal government limit the local zoning power of the mayor, city council or zoning board, who are much closer to local land-use conditions and the community?

A. PRB-1 recognizes that local leaders can regulate amateur installations to ensure the safety and health of people in the community. This general function has been termed part of a state and local government's "police powers" by legal authorities. But PRB-1, which establishes the federal interest in promoting the Amateur Radio Service, holds that such regulations cannot be so restrictive that amateur communications are impossible. Nor can the regulations be more restrictive than necessary to accomplish the purpose of protecting the community.

The theory of PRB-1 and its incorporation into the rules [97.15(b)] is that there is a reasonable accommodation to be made between the amateur's communications needs and the obligation of the zoning authorities to protect the community's health, safety and general welfare. Just as it is the zoning official's legitimate concern, for example, that your tower doesn't come crashing down on your neighbor's house, it is the FCC's legitimate concern (as delegated by Congress) that you be allowed to legally put up a tower of reasonable size.

Q. Why doesn't PRB-1 or Section 97.15(b) specify a "reasonable" height?

A. Whole legal textbooks have been devoted to trying to define what's "reasonable." As discussed above, the line between legitimate amateur communication goals and the local authority's interests must be determined on a case-by-case basis at the local level. The FCC declined to indicate what it considered a reasonable height below which a city cannot regulate antennas. What might be reasonable in one area might not be reasonable in others. For example, erecting a full-size 80-meter Yagi atop a 150-foot tower behind a townhouse in a densely populated suburb probably would not be considered reasonable. Yet the same antenna might be entirely acceptable in a rural environment. As a general principle, however, a municipality that establishes a blanket height limitation of any type, especially one that doesn't permit at least 65 feet of antenna height, will have a difficult time justifying that limitation as a technical matter in light of PRB-1.

Q. Now that PRB-1 and Section 97.15(b) have put the brakes on local zoning authorities, can I just put my antennas up to what I consider a reasonable height and assume that the ordinance in my city is in violation of the FCC's official policy?

A. Absolutely not! The PRB-1 Order and its codification in 97.15(b) is no more than a statement of policy by the FCC. It's not a panacea; it's not an overnight cure by any means. If you believe your city's ordinance is not valid in light of PRB-1, it's up to you to establish that and get the ordinance changed by the city council or have the existing ordinance declared invalid by the courts. To violate the ordinance or to put up an antenna without a permit can subject you to serious fines and even criminal penalties. In encouraging local municipalities to pay appropriate attention to the federal interest in amateur communications, the FCC said that if you believe the local zoning authorities have been overreaching in terms of interfering with your ability to operate Amateur Radio, you can use the PRB-1 document and the FCC rule [97.15(b)] to bring FCC policies to their attention. The bottom line is that it's still up to you to prove that the existing ordinance is not in accordance with PRB-1.

Q. What do I need to do to prove that the ordinance in my city is in violation of PRB-1?

A. You should be able to establish that you need an antenna of a certain height to communicate reliably on HF, VHF and/or UHF, as the case may be. Your city is usually concerned with aesthetics, safety, property values and RFI. As to the interrelated issues of aesthetics and property values, the city's interests must be balanced against yours. You probably can't convince your neighbor that a three-element tribander looks "good" if he/she feels otherwise. It can, however, be established as to what effect, if any, an antenna of a certain height will have on property values. The written opinion of a local professional appraiser can be a crucial piece of evidence for your side. The safety factor can best be addressed through exhibition of tower manufacturer's specifications for proper installation. Explain that there is no relationship between antenna height and safety. The safety issue is best dealt with by ensuring the integrity of your installation, especially relative to the size of the base section and proper guying. As to RFI, you might assert (although interference is a sensitive subject to your neighbors) that regulation of RFI is an FCC matter and not appropriate for local zoning regulation (see discussion in this chapter). But hasten to add that your modern equipment has less chance of causing interference to television sets than a neighbor's hair dryer or cordless baby monitor.

Materials are available from ARRL HQ to assist you in this regard. The PRB-1 document (11 pages) is available from *ARRLWeb* at **http://www.arrl.org/FandES/field/regulations/local/prb-1.html**. HQ can also refer you to ARRL Volunteer Counsel and Volunteer Consulting Engineers in your area. These are ham attorneys and structural engineers willing to provide an initial consultation about your zoning matter free of charge. See these Web pages for information on the ARRL Volunteer Counsel Program, see: **http://www.arrl.org/FandES/field/regulations/local/vc.html** and **http://www.arrl.org/FandES/field/regulations/local/vci.html**. For information on the ARRL Volunteer Consulting Engineer Program, see: **http://www.arrl.org/FandES/field/regulations/local/vce.html** and **http://www.arrl.org/FandES/field/regulations/local/vcei.html**. *The ARRL Antenna Height and Communication Effectiveness Study* can be found on *ARRLWeb* at: **http://www.arrl.org/FandES/field/regulations/local/antplnr.pdf**. Additional information not found on *ARRLWeb* can be found in the ARRL PRB-1 Package, which consists of over 200 pages of sample ordinances, cases, photocopies from *QST*, the *ARRL Antenna Height and Communications Effectiveness Study* as well as the names and addresses of VCs and VCEs in your area. The cost is $10 for ARRL members and $15 for nonmembers. The same information is available on the *ARRLWeb* at **www.arrl.org/FandES/Field/Regulations/PRB-1_Pkg/index.html**. The ARRL's book, released in early 2001, titled *Antenna Zoning for the Radio Amateur*, is far more comprehensive and even includes a CD full of documents.

Important note: PRB-1 does not directly apply to individuals faced with deed restrictions and covenants. If you are faced with covenants, see **www.arrl.org/FandES/Field/regulations** for information on CC&R restrictions.

(continued on next page)

Q. What if I can't get any satisfaction from the building inspector and/or the Zoning Board of Appeals, and I decide to take the city to court. Has PRB-1 been used in any court cases successfully?

A. Yes. John Thernes, WM4T, successfully sued the city of Lakeside Park, Kentucky, after he initially received an adverse determination by a federal district court judge. Thernes had applied in 1982 for a building permit for a 78-foot tower and antennas. The city denied his application, claiming that the zoning ordinance did not permit antennas and support structures. Thernes sued the city, but a US District Court dismissed his complaint, noting that there was no statement from the FCC preempting local zoning ordinances. Thernes appealed to the US Court of Appeals for the Sixth Federal Circuit (which covers Kentucky) and on the eve of oral argument in that case, the FCC released PRB-1. That was enough for the Appeals Court to send the case back to the District Court for reconsideration.

The same district judge who had ruled against Thernes previously indicated this time around that because of PRB-1, he was inclined to rule in favor of Thernes. By agreement of the parties, judgment was entered against the city and in favor of Thernes, and he was finally able to put up a 73-foot tower. He received an award of attorney's fees, as well. The judge, in the consent decree, noted that PRB-1 obligates municipalities to cooperatively arrive at an accommodation for amateur antennas in local zoning ordinances. [The final disposition of this case is cited at 62 Pike and Fisher Radio Regulations 2d, 284 (1987).]

Q. What if I avoid all the hassle and just put up my antenna, hoping no one will notice?

A. This question is often asked because we all know of cases where one ham simply put up an antenna and didn't have any trouble, while another one in the same town, following the rules like a good citizen, applied for a building permit for his tower and had all kinds of grief from zoning authorities and/or his immediate neighbors. All it takes is one complaint to cause problems not only for you, but possibly all the other radio amateurs in town, if you haven't secured the proper permit when one is required. A ham who has no permit is in a difficult spot if he or she is found to be in violation of the building code or zoning ordinance.

Q. Does PRB-1 mean that I can ignore the "no-antenna" clause in my apartment lease or condo bylaws?

A. No. In PRB-1, the FCC addressed zoning ordinances only; it exercised no federal preemption over restrictive covenants in private contractual agreements (such as your apartment lease). It explained that because these agreements are voluntarily entered into by the buyer or tenant and seller or landlord by contract, rather than established by the government, they don't come under FCC jurisdiction (at least for the time being). The ARRL has asked the FCC to reconsider this. The subject of covenants and deed restrictions is taken up later in this chapter.

Amateurs have spent a substantial amount of money in legal costs in attempts to have courts tell local governments that their idea of reasonable is *not* reasonable under PRB-1. Sometimes a clash cannot be avoided. But if you're like most of us, you want to know how best to go about putting up the highest tower you can without getting into a big legal struggle and alienating your otherwise friendly neighbors.

Emphasis from the start should be on the practical aspects of planning a successful campaign for getting the necessary approvals:

• Be realistic about the physical limitations of your backyard.
• Go on an information-gathering mission at the local town hall to determine which officials and regulations are applicable to your proposed antenna installation.
• Discuss your plans with the local building inspector.
• Determine whether the building inspector's interpretation of how the zoning rules apply to your plans is fair or should be respectfully challenged.
• Then, if you are dissatisfied with the inspector's interpretation, obtain information from ARRL HQ and seek legal advice from a competent attorney as to whether there is any reasonable interpretation of the regulations that would allow you to put up the tower.
• If no such interpretation presents itself, seek a variance or make a frontal assault on the ordinance as being in violation of PRB-1. Once you get into this area of the law, legal advice is often a necessity.

Most amateurs who follow these steps come out of it with a positive result. If a final decision by your local zoning board is unsatisfactory, however, you have the option of taking the matter to court.

Deed Restrictions and Covenants

Deed restrictions and covenants are not meant to be covered by PRB-1. In fact, they are specifically excluded. This is clearly one of the biggest antenna restriction problems affecting amateurs. First, let's examine how deed restrictions came into being.

Long before zoning regulation of land existed, private restrictions in deeds controlled how land could be used. The English system of common law, that we have inherited, permitted a seller of land to impose certain restrictions on the use of that land, which the seller, even after the sale was long past, could enforce in the courts. These restrictions or covenants were included in the deed from seller to buyer. Today, as noted above, deed restrictions are typically referred to as covenants, conditions and restrictions, *CC&Rs*.

Builders or developers commonly use covenants, especially in new housing developments, as a means of controlling land use after individual parcels are sold off. Suppose a builder has a tract of 100 homes and is selling them one at a time. The builder, until he is able to sell all of the lots, wants to maintain uniformity so that, for example, one of the buyers cannot paint his house 20 different Day-Glo colors, making the remaining unsold lots less marketable.

Since the CB boom of the mid-1970s, builders and developers have included antennas in the standard list of things they don't want homeowners to install while the builder is attempting to sell the remainder of the houses in the development. They are concerned that people may find antennas or towers unattractive. So when the subdivision plan is filed in a town's land records, a list of covenants is filed, too. Every deed from the builder makes reference to the list, subjecting every buyer down the line to the restrictions.

Typically, the declaration of covenants provides that enforcement authority passes from the developer to the homeowner's association after the developer sells all the houses in the development and goes on his merry way. The homeowner's association is, among other things, charged with maintaining the aesthetics of the neighborhood and can often determine whether additional structures, such as a tool shed, swing set or antenna can be built. If a homeowner installs an antenna in violation of a covenant, the homeowner's association can bring that owner to court to enforce the covenant.

Although the FCC denied the ARRL request that PRB-1 preempt covenants and deed restrictions for amateur installations, the FCC stated in the November 19, 1999 Order that the FCC will "strongly encourage associations of homeowners and private contracting parties to follow the principle of reasonable accommodation and to apply it to any and all instances of amateur service communications where they may be involved."

The ARRL offers a package that explains the nature of covenants. It also contains suggested language that can be incorporated into a purchase or lease agreement. For more information contact the Regulatory Information Branch at ARRL HQ. See *ARRLWeb* (**www.arrl.org/FandES/field/ regulations/local/prb-1_program.html#private**).

Antenna Restrictions: What's on the Horizon?

Some hams are blessed with living in communities where there are neither zoning nor covenant restrictions on their antenna farms. You can't assume this is the case in your own particular situation, however. The time to start looking into whether it's okay to put up a tower is before, not after, you start pouring the concrete for your base section. If you exercise common sense (that is, resist the temptation to put up a Big Bertha on a city lot) and good-faith compliance with the legal procedures, you will undoubtedly be successful in securing permission for an appropriately sized tower for your antenna system. Keep in mind that what you do, and how you do it, affects not only you, but all other radio amateurs in your town, and perhaps— through precedent-setting court cases—amateurs throughout the country.

PRB-1 has helped Amateur Radio operators faced with antenna restrictions. It is rather vague in places and, as a result, the ARRL continues to ask the FCC to strengthen it. Amateurs have also seen increasing problems from the proliferation of PCS and cellular tall towers across the US. In many cases, communities seek to regulate PCS and cellular towers and inadvertently cause problems for amateurs. In most cases, these problems are resolved favorably. Amateurs aren't quite so lucky when it comes to covenants and deed restrictions since CC&Rs aren't directly covered by PRB-1. ARRL continues to encourage the FCC to preempt covenants and deed restrictions. One ray of hope is that under the Telecommunications Act of 1996, the FCC has preempted covenants allowing consumers to possess satellite dish receivers only smaller than 3 feet in diameter and television antennas no higher than 12 feet above the roofline. Unfortunately, this doesn't include Amateur Radio antennas, so covenants and deed restrictions remain a problem for amateurs. ARRL continues to seek such remedies for amateurs.

APPLICATION FOR NEW LICENSE

In a Report and Order (WT Docket 98-143) restructuring the license classes effective April 15, 2000, the FCC also amended its processes for applying for a new license. Any qualified person or organization is eligible to apply for a new operator/primary station, license grant, club station or military recreation station license grant. *No new license grants will be issued for a Novice, Technician Plus or Advanced Class operator/primary station or RACES station [97.17(a)].* See Table 2 for a complete overview.

In applying for a new license, each applicant must pass the necessary examination elements before the administering VEs, and supply all the information required by the rules prior to the examination. The VEs may collect this information in any manner of their choosing, including creating their own forms. As of this writing, the FCC is planning to privatize the club call sign assignment program [97.17(b)].

Of course, when applying for a new license, no person shall obtain or attempt to obtain, or assist another person to obtain or attempt to obtain, an amateur service license grant by fraudulent means [97.17(c)] and only one unique call sign will be shown on the license of each new primary, club and military recreation station. The call sign will be selected by the sequential call sign system [97.17(d)].

CALL SIGNS

If ever there was a subject whose significance was more apparent to radio amateurs than to nonhams, it is call signs. There's an emotional dimension to that set of letters and numerals by which we're identified that unlicensed people do not fully understand. A person who has been granted an amateur license may apply for a new call sign assigned by the Sequential Call Sign System at any time.

Back in 1978, the FCC closed a call sign assignment program under

Q&A—Deed Restrictions

Q. How can I find out if there are any deed restrictions on my land?

A. Deed restrictions and/or covenants are filed with the town clerk (or the equivalent) in your town (or county, depending on your state). These records are completely open to the public; you don't have to be a lawyer or a real estate broker to examine land records. Some restrictions are mentioned in the deed you received at your closing, so check your paperwork. Such restrictions need not be mentioned in your individual deed, however. A master list of covenants, usually termed "Declaration of Covenants" or something similar, is a list of things that cannot be done on a particular tract of land and may be referred to in subsequent deeds from the seller to the buyer. The land is sold to a buyer "subject to" the covenants on file. Even if you do not buy your land from the original builder who filed them, covenants are considered to "run with the land"; they are referenced in the deed to any particular buyer. Even though you may never have seen the list of covenants on file and even though they are not fully explained in your particular deed, and yes, even though you did not buy your home directly from the builder who established them, you are nevertheless bound by them. Why? Because you voluntarily bought land that is itself subject to those restrictions, and as such, in the eyes of the law (remember, justice is blind!), you have submitted to those covenants and agreed to them. This is why attorneys spend hours looking through boring, old land records; they're trying to find the "land mines" before it's too late. Before you sign a contract to buy a new home, have your attorney or other competent title searcher check the land records for covenants.

Q. How can I avoid antenna covenants when I buy my new house?

A. Make sure your contract for the purchase of land specifies that the sale is contingent on the absence of any deed restrictions, covenants or conditions that would prevent or restrict your ability to install an amateur antenna at least (fill in the blank) feet in height. Require that within two weeks of the signing of the sales contact, the seller must give you a notarized statement to that effect. If it turns out that there are covenants, you could attempt to obtain approval for your proposed antenna from the homeowner's association, architectural control committee or the builder, in accordance with the covenants, before signing a contract to buy the house.

Don't rely on oral representations of anyone involved. Unless you have written, unconditional authorization from whomever has the enforcement authority, don't assume that you will be able to put up your tower after you move in. Your attorney should be consulted before signing anything.

---

which eligible Amateur Extra licensees could request and be granted special consideration in call sign selection. This program was replaced by the present system of computer-assigned call signs. Under the present system, you become eligible (at your option) for progressively more "desirable" (that is, shorter) call signs as you progress up the licensing ladder. Calls are issued alphabetically from the FCC Sequential Call Sign Assignment System. The numeral in the call sign corresponds to the geographic region of the mailing address used when that call sign was first issued. US amateur call signs *must* have only one numeral and between two and five letters. See

Q. In my area, I can't even buy a new or recently built house without finding restrictions in the deed. Can't I use PRB-1 to invalidate them?

A. Sorry, no. The courts and the FCC view antenna covenants as a private contractual matter between a buyer and seller. This may not be the most realistic view today, because more and more amateurs have few alternatives in their home buying because of the pervasiveness of covenants. It may be hard to find real estate in your area without covenants.

Q. The covenants in my development do not prohibit antennas or towers, but do require the approval of the homeowner's association. How do I convince them to approve my antenna?

A. Tactics differ, but generally the best strategy is to prepare in advance for the questions and concerns you are likely to encounter: (1) How you have planned the installation to minimize visual impact; (2) How safety concerns have been addressed; (3) How it will enable you to conduct emergency and public service communications for the neighborhood; (4) How it will not affect property values; (5) How RFI is minimized by higher antennas; and (6) That you need it to communicate effectively and reliably. Also, follow the general guidelines for the ZBA presentation discussed previously, as applicable.

The best thing to do is sit down with your immediate neighbors on all sides, explain in a friendly way what you'd like to do, and assure them that the Voice of America is not being constructed next door to them! If you can obtain the approval of your immediate neighbors, the homeowner's association is less likely to object. If you anticipate opposition, consider the advantages of a crank-up tower and as a compromise, offer to keep it cranked down when you're not using it.

Q. I've heard that the Telecommunications Act of 1996 preempts covenants. Is that true?

A. Yes, the Telecommunications Act of 1996 does preempt covenants, but for television broadcast receivers only. Amateur antennas are not included.

Q. It sounds as though the FCC, in PRB-1, has protected us from some antenna restrictions imposed by my town, but not from my neighbors. What gives?

A. The ARRL considers covenants the most serious cumulative problem that faces amateurs at present. The ARRL has submitted data to the FCC demonstrating that deed restrictions are not simply a matter of contractual agreement between the buyer and seller. The ARRL continues to work on this problem; stay tuned.

Fig 4 for the call sign district map of the US.

The Three Call Sign Systems

During the 15 years prior to 1995, there was only one call sign system: call signs were issued sequentially from the FCC computer in Gettysburg. If you upgraded and didn't like your new call sign, you couldn't obtain your old one. Now, the FCC uses three methods for selecting call signs: the Sequential Call Sign Assignment System, the Vanity Call Sign System and the Special Event Call Sign System.

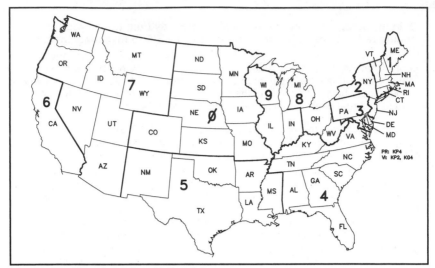

Fig 4—Continental US call districts.

Sequential Call Sign Assignment System

The **Sequential Call Sign Assignment System** is defined in the rules as "The call sign is selected by the FCC from an alphabetized list corresponding to the geographic region of the licensee's mailing address and operator class" [97.3(a)(11)(i)]. This is the call sign you receive when you obtain a license for the first time or when you upgrade your license and request a change of call sign. There is no fee, but the catch is that it is issued by the FCC computer in alphabetical order.

The Vanity Call Sign System

In 1993 the US Congress authorized the FCC to establish a vanity call sign system. In early 1995, the FCC adopted new rules implementing the system by which an amateur may request a call sign of choice [97.3(a)(11)(ii)]. Applicants can list up to 25 possible call signs on FCC Form 605, filed electronically or manually [97.19]. The first assignable call sign will be granted. *The list of call signs must be selected from a group of call signs corresponding to the same or lower class of license held by the applicant under the Sequential Call Sign Assignment System* [97.19(d)]. For example, a Technician is not eligible for a 1×2 call sign. See the sidebar "Amateur Radio Sequential Call Sign Assignment System." Congress authorized the FCC to charge a fee to offset their costs for administering the program.

If none of the requested call signs are available, an applicant will retain his or her original call sign [97.19(d)(2)]. Call signs will be issued in random order by date received.

Amateurs can request previously held call signs, call signs held by deceased close relatives, or any other vacant call sign from the sequential call sign system. Applicants are not limited to call signs from their call district, but may request one from any call district. The applicant may request call signs only from the appropriate call sign group for his or her license class, or a lower one. Applicants may request an available call sign from any call area, except that only applicants with a mailing address in the specific territory may request a call sign reserved for Alaska, Hawaii, American Samoa, Marianas, Guam, Puerto Rico, the US Virgin Islands or other US islands under FCC jurisdiction. This limitation does not apply to applicants requesting a previously held call sign, that of a close relative, or of a deceased club member (with a relative's permission) [97.19(d)(4)].

Assignable Call Signs

Assignable calls under the Vanity Call Sign System must be part of the Sequential Call Sign Assignment System. There are literally millions of unassigned call signs, so the easiest way to determine if a call is available to be reassigned is to check a current copy of the FCC license database. Since calls are deleted from the FCC database two years after the expiration of the license, if the call doesn't appear it is usually available for reassignment. See the sidebar "Sequential Call Sign Assignment System" for a list of acceptable call sign formats.

A call sign shown on an unexpired license is available to the vanity call sign system two years following expiration of the license [97.19(c)(1)]. A call sign shown on a license that is surrendered, revoked, set aside, cancelled or voided is not available for reassignment until two years after this action is taken [97.19(c)(2)].

There is one exception: A close relative of a deceased amateur may apply for the call sign of the deceased *immediately* following cancellation of the license or the date the amateur becomes deceased, whichever is sooner. This also applies to a club applying with the written permission of a close relative. A close relative is defined as a spouse, child, grandchild, stepchild, parent, grandparent, stepparent, brother, sister, stepbrother, stepsister, aunt, uncle, niece, nephew or in-law [97.19(c)(3)].

Clubs Applying for Vanity Calls

A club wishing to apply for a vanity call sign must first have a regular club license. To be eligible for a club license, a club must:

1) Have a trustee designated by an officer of the club who is of Technician or higher class;

2) Be composed of at least four persons;

3) Have a name, a document of organization, management and a primary purpose devoted to amateur service activities [97.5(b)(2)].

Clubs without a station license must first apply for one by sending a completed NCVEC For 605 to a Club Station Call Sign Administrator. The ARRL is a CSCSA. The FCC will not accept applications directly. There is

Amateur Station Sequential Call Sign Assignment System

A unique call sign is assigned to each amateur station during the processing of its license grant. The station is reassigned its same call sign upon renewal or modification of its grant, unless the licensee applies for a change to a new call sign. Each new call sign is sequentially selected from the alphabetized regional-group list for the licensee's operator class and mailing address. The mailing address must be one where the licensee can receive mail delivery by the United States Postal Service. Each call sign has a one letter prefix (K, N, W) or a two letter prefix (AA-AL, KA-KZ, NA-NZ, WA-WZ) and a one, two or three letter suffix separated by a numeral (∅-9) indicating the geographic region (1-13). When the call signs in any regional-group list are exhausted, the selection is made from the next lower group. The groups are:

Group A. For primary stations licensed to Amateur Extra operators.

Regions 1 through ∅: Prefix K, N or W; two letter suffix. Two letter prefix with first letter A, N, K or W; one letter suffix. Two letter prefix with first letter A; two letter suffix.
Region 11: Prefix AL, KL, NL or WL; one letter suffix.
Region 12: Prefix KP, NP or WP; one letter suffix.
Region 13: Prefix AH, KH, NH or WH; one letter suffix.

Group B. For primary stations licensed to Advanced operators.

Regions 1 through ∅: Two letter prefix with first letter K, N or W; two letter suffix.
Region 11: Prefix AL; two letter suffix.
Region 12: Prefix KP; two letter suffix.
Region 13: Prefix AH; two letter suffix.

Group C. For primary stations licensed to General, Technician, and Technician Plus operators.

Regions 1 through ∅: Prefix K, N or W; three letter suffix.
Region 11: Prefix KL, NL or WL; two letter suffix.
Region 12: Prefix NP or WP; two letter suffix.
Region 13: Prefix KH, NH or WH; two letter suffix.

Group D. For primary stations licensed to Novice operators, and for club and military recreation stations.

Regions 1 through ∅: Two letter prefix with first letter K or W; three letter suffix.
Region 11: Prefix KL or WL; three letter suffix.
Region 12: Prefix KP or WP; three letter suffix.
Region 13: Prefix KH or WH; three letter suffix.

The regions and numerals are:

1. Connecticut, Maine, Massachusetts, New Hampshire, Rhode Island and Vermont. The numeral is 1.
2. New Jersey and New York. The numeral is 2.
3. Delaware, District of Columbia, Maryland and Pennsylvania. The numeral is 3.
4. Alabama, Florida, Georgia, Kentucky, North Carolina, South Carolina, Tennessee and Virginia. The numeral is 4.
5. Arkansas, Louisiana, Mississippi, New Mexico, Oklahoma and Texas. The numeral is 5.
6. California. The numeral is 6.
7. Arizona, Idaho, Montana, Nevada, Oregon, Utah, Washington and Wyoming. The numeral is 7.
8. Michigan, Ohio and West Virginia. The numeral is 8.
9. Illinois, Indiana and Wisconsin. The numeral is 9.
10. Colorado, Iowa, Kansas, Minnesota, Missouri, Nebraska, North Dakota and South Dakota. The numeral is Ø.
11. Alaska. The numerals are 7 through 9.
12. Caribbean Insular areas. The numerals are 1 through 5:
    1 - Navassa Island;
    2 - Virgin Islands;
    3 or 4 - Commonwealth of Puerto Rico except Desecheo Island;
    5 - Desecheo Island.
13. Hawaii and Pacific Insular areas. The numerals are Ø through 9:
    Ø - Commonwealth of Northern Mariana Islands;
    1 - Baker or Howland Island;
    2 - Guam;
    3 - Johnston Island;
    4 - Midway Island;
    5 - Palmyra or Jarvis Island; 5 followed by suffix letter K - Kingman Reef;
    6 or 7 - Hawaii; 7 followed by the letter K - Kure Island;
    8 - American Samoa;
    9 - Wake, Wilkes or Peale Island.

Certain combinations of letters are not assignable. These include KA2AA-KA9ZZ, KC4AAA-KC4AAF, KC4USA-KC4USZ, KG4AA-KG4ZZ, KC6AA-KC6ZZ, KL9KAA-KL9KHZ, KX6AA-KX6ZZ; any call sign having the letters SOS or QRA-QUZ as the suffix; any call sign having the letters AM-AZ as the prefix; any 2-by-3 format call sign having the letter X as the first letter of the suffix; any 2-by-3 format call sign having the letters AF, KF, NF or WF as the prefix and the letters EMA as the suffix; any 2-by-3 format call sign having the letters NA-NZ as the prefix; any 2-by-3 format call sign having the letters KP, NP or WP as the prefix and the numeral 6, 7, 8 or 9; any 2-by-2 format call sign having the letters KP, NP or WP as the prefix and the numeral Ø, 6, 7, 8 or 9; any 2-by-1 format call sign having the letters KP, NP or WP as the prefix and the numerals Ø, 6, 7, 8 or 9; and letter combinations that prior recipients have found offensive. Call signs having the single letter prefix (K, N or W), a single digit numeral Ø, 1, 2, 3, 4, 5, 6, 7, 8 or 9) and a single letter suffix are reserved for the special event call sign system.

Further questions can be e-mailed to **fccitd@fcc.gov**.

no fee for a basic club station license. The license received will have a sequentially issued call sign from Group D (2×3). Once the club station license is in hand, the club may apply for a vanity call sign using Form 605 plus Schedule D, Part 1, accompanied by the required fee. Clubs are limited to vanity call signs from the appropriate call sign group for the station trustee's license class, or a lower one (e.g., a General class trustee can't apply for a 1×2 call sign for a club). Military recreation and RACES stations are not eligible to apply for vanity call signs [97.19(a)].

Vanity Applications that are Dismissed

The FCC can process nearly all Vanity applications. They can be dismissed for any of several reasons, including:
• none of the call sign choices requested were available;
• the required fee was not received within 10 days of the application's filing, or
• the application was defective.

Vanity Fee Refunds

After the FCC dismisses an application, the applicant may request a refund.

To apply for a refund, send a signed letter explaining that a vanity fee refund is being requested. Be sure to include the Taxpayer ID Number (which for individuals is often the applicant's Social Security Number; for foreign applicants, indicate in the letter that the applicant is not a US citizen, and therefore that the applicant has no SSN). Send the signed letter, with a copy of the dismissal notice, to: FCC, Amateur Vanity Fee Refund, 1270 Fairfield Rd, Gettysburg, PA 17325-7245.

The Special-Event Call Sign System

Amateurs frequently operate their stations or the stations of others to commemorate special events. One only needs to look at the Special Events column of *QST* to know that this is a popular activity. For many years, the FCC did not issue any type of special event calls. Finally, in 1996, the FCC agreed to a Special Event Call Sign System whereby amateurs or amateur organizations could request a 1×1 call sign (such as W1A) to commemorate an event of special significance.

Upon coordination by a Special Event Call Sign Coordinator (ARRL is one), a specific 1×1 call sign can be substituted for the assigned call sign for a short time to help call attention to the special event. The coordinated call must be transmitted at least every 10 minutes and at the end of the communication. Also, it must not detract from the station making the source of its transmissions known to those receiving them. In addition, the special event station must also transmit its assigned call sign at least once per hour during such operation. A block of 750 call signs is available for use in the special event call sign system [97.3(a)(11)(iii) and 97.119(d)].

The following 1×1 Special Event Call Sign System assignment criteria apply:

- The intention of the Amateur Radio 1×1 Call Sign System is to provide a special call sign for a special event operation which usually commemorates an event that is publicly significant (ideally, this is a one-time, non-recurring celebration, festival, anniversary, holiday, convention, dedication, public demonstration and the like).
- While the 1×1 Special Event Call Sign System is not intended to provide a short call for exclusive use during an upcoming Amateur Radio operating event or contest, should such an operating event or contest timeframe fall within the same timeframe of an event which has been coordinated, the special event 1×1 call sign can certainly be used.
- A 1×1 call sign is normally only assigned for 15 days or less (unless a persuasive showing is made that the event timeframe is so extraordinary that exceeding the 15-day call sign assignment period is appropriate).
- Amateurs may not reserve multiple bordering 15 day periods. Reserving more than one 1×1 call sign during a calendar year is discouraged.

Additional information is available on *ARRLWeb* at **http://www. arrl.org/arrlvec/1x1.html**.

FCC MODIFICATIONS TO YOUR LICENSE

The FCC reserves the right to modify your license at any time if it determines that such action is in the public interest, convenience and necessity. The FCC, however, must give you the opportunity to show why your license should not be modified. If you don't respond adequately or don't take an active interest in the issue, your license and operation may be restricted temporarily or permanently [97.27].

Expired Licenses and the Two-Year Grace Period

If you let your license lapse, you have a two-year grace period to request that it be reinstated. During this grace period, you are not permitted to operate your station or to use your FCC-assigned call sign until your application for reinstatement is granted. It will be backdated to the date of your license's expiration [97.21(b)]. Licenses are no longer renewed automatically when a modification is made.

License Terms

The normal term for a license is 10 years [97.25]. Nowadays, a fresh 10-year term license is issued only to new licensees, to hams who are renewing and to vanity call sign recipients. Before June 1994, FCC renewed *all* licenses for a 10 year term whenever they processed any change. Now, when a license is modified, the expiration date remains the same.

Your Mailing Address

You must always put your mailing address on an application. This

Q&A—Call Signs

Q. How does the FCC's sequential call sign system work?

A. Since the FCC reordered the licensing structure effective April 15, 2000, the FCC Sequential Call Sign Assignment program has changed. After that date, the FCC will only issue new Technician, General and Amateur Extra class licenses, but existing licensees may continue to use their licenses and privileges as they have in the past.

With the exception of vanity call signs, call signs are issued sequentially by the FCC computer in Gettysburg. The computer selects call signs from "blocks" or "groups" of call signs that reflect the licensee's operator class, mailing address and call sign region. In the past, the FCC has issued call signs from four groups. Refer to the Sequential Call Sign Assignment System sidebar. **Group A** call signs are issued only to Amateur Extra operators. **Group B** call signs are assigned to amateurs holding Advanced licenses. **Group C** call signs are issued to Technician, Technician Plus and General operators. **Group D** call signs go to club station licensees and military station licenses.

The FCC sequential call sign assignment system selects only call signs that have not been previously issued. This is the system that automatically issues calls to new licensees and to persons who check. Amateurs who want a new sequentially issued call sign (at random) must complete an FCC Form 605, Schedule D, Part 1. The system assigns call signs from the next lower group after all call signs from one group have been depleted. This has

---

address must be in an area regulated by the FCC. For most of us, that means in the US; see Appendix 1 to Part 97. The mailing address must be one where you can receive mail via the US Postal Service—a street address or post office box, for example. The FCC no longer keeps a record of your station location [97.23].

If your mailing address changes, the FCC requires that you file a timely application for license modification. If FCC correspondence is returned because you failed to provide a correct address, your license can be suspended or revoked [97.23].

Lost or Destroyed Licenses

To get a replacement for a lost, mutilated or destroyed license, complete electronically the FCC Form 605, or manually fill out an FCC Form 605 and

already happened in several areas.

Starting in 1995, the FCC once again began honoring requests for specific call signs. The vanity call sign system allows any amateur to request a specific call sign. The requested call sign must not be currently assigned, and must be available from the sequential call sign system [97.19].

Q. When I upgrade, can I keep my present call sign?

A. Yes, you can keep your present call sign if you want to. Call signs are changed only when you specifically request it after completing an FCC Form 605.

Q. A local ham recently became a Silent Key. Will his call sign automatically be deleted from FCC records?

A. The FCC no longer deletes the call signs of Silent Keys unless cancellation is specifically requested. Because the term of an amateur license is now 10 years, the family of the deceased amateur could continue to receive unwanted correspondence for quite some time. To avoid this, and make the call sign available to the vanity call sign system, the family of the deceased amateur should return the license to the FCC or, in the event that the license can't be found, a letter should be sent to the FCC stating that the amateur is deceased and requesting cancellation of the license.

mail it to FCC, 1270 Fairfield Rd, Gettysburg, PA 17325. They'll provide you with a duplicate license with the same expiration date as the lost/destroyed license [97.29]. The URL for obtaining a duplicate electronically is **http://www.fcc.gov/wtb/uls**.

CONCLUSION

In Part 97, the most basic information appears first—that's why the Basis and Purpose appears before anything else! Consequently, the information in Chapter 1 is from the first part of Part 97 and involves things like the licensing process and the various FCC restrictions on Amateur Radio stations. You may have noticed that this chapter is quite long, but it is because the FCC covers many issues in this section!

2 Station Operation Standards

Subpart B, "Station Operation Standards," covers basic operating practices that apply to all types of operation. Amateurs must operate their stations in accordance with good engineering practice and must share frequencies with others—no one amateur or group has any special claim to any frequency. Amateurs are also required to give priority to emergency communications and never cause willful and malicious interference [97.101].

The requirements of control operators and station control are addressed in Subpart B [97.103, 97.105 and 97.109]. Reciprocal licensing authority is mentioned. Foreign amateurs may operate in the US without filing any paperwork if the US and the foreign country share a bilateral or multilateral reciprocal operating arrangement. Each station must have a control point where operation of the transmitter is effected [97.109(a)]. At the heart of Amateur Radio is the principle of *two-way* communication [97.111(a)]. Although one-way transmissions aren't normally permitted, there are a few exceptions. These will be detailed later in this chapter. A major portion of this subpart, "Prohibited transmissions," covers many "no-no's," such as getting paid for operating your station, conducting communications on behalf of your employer, music, obscenity, news gathering, false signals and ciphers [97.113]. Third-party rules are also covered [97.115].

Station identification, an important aspect of any amateur communication, is addressed in this subpart. The purpose of station identification is to make the source of transmissions known to those receiving them, including FCC monitors. The rules cover ID requirements for the various operating modes [97.119].

SUBPART B RULES SUMMARY:
STATION OPERATION STANDARDS

97.101 General standards.
97.103 Station licensee responsibilities.

97.105 Control operator duties.
97.107 Reciprocal operating authority.
97.109 Station control.
97.111 Authorized transmissions.
97.113 Prohibited transmissions.
97.115 Third-party communications.
97.117 International communications.
97.119 Station identification.
97.121 Restricted operation.

A final section addresses restricted operation and sets forth the conditions that must exist in an interference case involving a neighbor's TV or radio before the Commission can impose "quiet hours" [97.121(a)].

GENERAL STANDARDS

Part 97 is organized logically; the most important material appears in the first section of each subpart and is more general in nature. Consequently, the FCC feels that the Subpart B—General Standards are pretty important!

Under the heading of "General Standards," the FCC outlines four principles that apply to *all* amateur operations:

1) Always follow good engineering and good amateur practice;
2) Make the most efficient use of spectrum since spectrum belongs to everyone equally;
3) Give priority to emergency communications; and
4) Never cause willful or malicious interference.

GOOD ENGINEERING AND GOOD AMATEUR PRACTICE

One of the most significant rules in all of Part 97 concerns good amateur practice. It says, "In all respects not specifically covered by FCC Rules each amateur station must be operated in accordance with good engineering and good amateur practice" [97.101(a)]. You are expected to strive to maintain your equipment, signals and operating practices in a manner consistent with the highest possible standards. The specific technical standards are detailed in Chapter 4. This means complying with the procedures that have evolved within the amateur community to promote efficient use of our limited spectrum resources, and those which promote harmony among amateurs with different operating interests. Such procedures include following band plans and other "gentlemen's agreements" not specifically addressed in the rules. They also include following accepted operating practices. Thus, it is important that you know the actual rules of operating and the various suggestions for promoting efficient spectrum use that have evolved voluntarily within the amateur community.

The amateur frequencies, especially at MF (160 meters) and HF (80-10 meters) tend to be congested; interference is a fact of life. Indeed, it is a positive result of Amateur Radio growth and vitality. As such, a cardinal rule of good amateur practice is always to *listen* before you transmit on any frequency. At best, transmitting without listening is a rude interruption of someone else's conversation. At worst, it could interfere with emergency communications in progress.

EFFECTIVE USE OF SPECTRUM

The FCC Rules clearly state that all amateur frequencies are shared among amateurs and that cooperation is the key to effective use of the bands. The Rules state:

"Each station licensee and each control operator must cooperate in selecting transmitting channels and in making the most effective use of the amateur service frequencies. No frequency will be assigned for the exclusive use of any station" [97.101(b)].

As mentioned before, amateurs should follow the band plans and "gentlemen's agreements" outlined in Chapter 4 because they promote efficient use of limited spectrum. Local and regional band plans supersede the national band plans. In other cases, common sense should prevail: Don't ragchew with your local friend on the choicest DX portion of the 20 or 75-meter phone subband. In that case, VHF, or the high end of 20 meters or 75 meters, would be a better frequency choice and would be more consistent with good amateur practice. Another way of making the most efficient use of spectrum is to use the minimum power necessary to complete the contact [97.313]. Doing so helps reduce the interference on today's crowded bands. Good amateur practice and efficient use of spectrum are important concepts.

GIVE PRIORITY TO EMERGENCY COMMUNICATIONS

No one *owns* any amateur frequency, not even a net or group of amateurs who have been meeting on the same spot on the dial for many years [97.101(b)]. Except in an FCC-declared emergency, no one has any legal right to kick anyone else off a particular frequency, and no one's particular use of the spectrum is any more valid than anyone else's. In emergencies, however, the rules say that each control operator must give priority to stations handling emergency communications [97.101(c)]. Emergency communication is discussed in Chapter 5.

Before making any contact, stations should take precautions to avoid using a frequency occupied by other stations by asking if the frequency is in use. Conversely, non-net operators should ask the same question to determine if a net or another operation is in progress on that frequency. If it's a tossup, consider that many operators in a net using a single frequency is efficient spectrum usage, and it is easier for one or two operators to move than it is for potentially dozens of net operators to move. Guide your operation accordingly.

NEVER CAUSE WILLFUL OR MALICIOUS INTERFERENCE

FCC Rules state: "No amateur operator shall willfully or maliciously interfere with or cause interference to any radio communication or signal" [97.101(d)]. This point is echoed throughout the rules. While this is common sense, a few poor operators can cause major headaches for amateurs on a repeater or on a net on the HF bands.

Malicious interference involves a clearly defined and intensive campaign on the part of the perpetrator. The interference must be sustained and it is best exemplified in the following example: when two or more stations in communication are interrupted by an interfering station on the same frequency, they acknowledge that they can't copy one another through the interference, move to another frequency *and the interfering station follows to resume the interference,* then malicious interference is obviously present.

The FCC has recently been engaged in a vigorous campaign against

---

Q&A—Malicious Interference

Q. How can I fight malicious interference on a personal level?

A. When you experience malicious interference, use the most effective means of combating it at your disposal—ignore it on the air. Above all, keep your on-the-air operation strictly above reproach. Don't engage interfering stations in their own game. By ignoring the offenders, you deprive them of their number one need—attention.

Q. What can we do about a jammer on our repeater?

A. The FCC Amateur Auxiliary incorporates a special function in its program to deal with repeater problems—the Local Interference Committee (LIC). The LIC is organized at the local level to track down repeater jammers and other problem-causers, to exert peer pressure to clear up problems, and when problems persist, to work to gather evidence leading to an enforcement action. The LIC is officially sanctioned by the ARRL Section Manager. If you've got a jammer on your hands, contact your Section Manager and/or Official Observer Coordinator. You can also contact the FCC directly, but remember that the FCC may be reluctant to get involved unless all other options have been tried.

Q. Does the system for shutting down jammers work?

A. Yes. Here's what happened in a recent case in Washington state FCC News Release—"Working closely with the Amateur Auxiliary, the Federal Communications Commission (FCC) was able to issue a Notice of Apparent Liability . . .

The action against the amateur was triggered by numerous complaints from other Amateur Radio operators that [the amateur] was transmitting on 146.04 MHz for the sole purpose of disrupting the communications already in progress on that frequency. The intentional jamming signals were directly observed and identified by members of the Amateur Auxiliary's Local Interference Committee (LIC). The LIC forwarded the pertinent information to the local FCC office for investigation and enforcement."

---

malicious interference, on both HF and on VHF repeaters. Malicious interference is one of the most serious violations of amateur service or any other radio service rules. Review the substantial malicious interference enforcement log on *ARRLWeb*: **http://www.arrl.org/news/enforcement_logs/**.

STATION LICENSE RESPONSIBILITIES AND THE CONTROL OPERATOR

The control operator concept is fundamental in Amateur Radio: Some *person* must be responsible for the proper operation of an amateur transmitter. That's the **control operator**, defined in the rules as "an amateur operator designated by the licensee of a station to be responsible for the transmissions from that station to assure compliance with the FCC Rules" [97.3(a)(12)]. This means that a radio amateur sitting at the mic, key or

---

Q. Our public service net has been plagued with a ham who harasses us. Is this malicious interference, and what can we do about it?

A. Nets are sometimes singled out for abuse because of their perceived "ownership" of a particular frequency. Of course, no individual operator or group has any special privilege to any part of a band.

Although you are suffering a considerable amount of thoughtless remarks, annoying practices and harassment, there seems to be no evidence of maliciousness. To be actionable, interference must be truly malicious (see above). To nail an amateur on a malicious interference charge, Amateur Auxiliary members collect evidence in accordance with comprehensive guidelines. The evidence must include dates, times, frequencies, call signs, local field-strength readings and direction-findings of the offending transmissions so that re-creations of factual occurrences can be made. Conclusions must not be drawn by the monitors—it is for the FCC to determine whether the evidence, taken together, shows that a rule has been violated and that the accused person did it.

The task before the Auxiliary in a case such as yours is not an easy one. There are numerous stations responding to the primary offending operator with their own jamming transmissions, aggravating the situation enormously. The good news is that evidence gathered in accordance with the guidelines can be relied on by the FCC and used directly in enforcement proceedings. It is no longer necessary for the FCC staff to duplicate the monitoring and direction finding done by Auxiliary volunteers.

The best course is to try to avoid confrontation. Use extra caution when choosing a frequency to engage your net. Keep your operation legal and strictly above board. If problems persist, apply peer pressure—try to resolve conflicts through negotiation. If you are unsuccessful, contact a representative of the Amateur Auxiliary to the FCC. Don't call the FCC first.

keyboard, the person running the station from its *control point*, is the one who is legally responsible for the operation of the station, *regardless* of whether it's his or her home station or a station owned by another amateur. When the control operator of a station is someone other than the station licensee, both are equally responsible for the proper operation of the station [97.103(a)].

Unless there is documentation to the contrary, the FCC will assume that the station licensee is the control operator. All amateurs must make the station and the station records available to the FCC for inspection upon

---

Q&A—Who's in Control of Your Station?

Q. My call is being used for Field Day, but I can't be at the station for the duration of the operating event. I like sleeping in my air conditioned house, even during Field Day. Do we have to take the transmitter off the air when I am not present?

A. No, because your appointed control operator(s) should fulfill your duties as the station licensee. In fact, you don't have to be there at all, but you must make sure that your appointed control operator(s) is capable of carrying out your wishes [97.103(b) and 97.105].

Q. Can KA1UFZ, a Novice, operate the station of NU0X, an Amateur Extra operator, during Field Day and can she operate in the Amateur Extra segment even though she holds a Novice license?

A. She may "participate" as a third party outside the Novice bands, but she may not "operate." A control operator *must* be on duty whenever she operates outside of her Novice privileges using the call of NU0X. FCC Rules state that "A control operator must ensure the immediate proper operation of the station..." [97.105(a)]. The rules go on to say, "A station may only be operated in the manner and to the extent permitted by the privileges authorized for the class of operator license held by the control operator" [97.105(b)].

If no control operator is present, the Novice is limited to the Novice segments, since she is the control operator. Use of an Amateur Extra call does not automatically authorize the operator additional privileges without the presence of an Amateur Extra control operator. Note that although no new Novice licenses are issued effective April 15, 2000, existing licensees may operate and renew their licenses indefinitely.

Q. I am an Amateur Extra licensee, but I am going to use a Novice operator's station and call sign during Field Day. Can I legally operate her station and use her call outside the Novice subbands?

A. You, the Amateur Extra, can be designated as the control operator. If you are authorized by the licensee, you may use the call sign of the Novice licensee and operate only within the Novice privileges. However, if an Amateur Extra control operator wants to operate outside the Novice operator privileges, he may do so, but he must identify by appending his call to that of the Novice, such as signing "KA1UFZ/NU0X" on CW or separating the calls by the word "stroke" on phone [97.105(a) and (b), 97.119(e)]. True, this is a long identification procedure, but it is the only way to identify in this case. Why would an Amateur Extra want to use a Novice call, you ask. Well, that may not always be the case, but it clearly illustrates the point.

request [97.103(c)]. The FCC may require amateurs to keep records of station operations if deemed necessary to comply with FCC rules. Keeping such records is required only if you are specifically asked by the FCC, but we are all required to follow all FCC rules at all times [97.103(c)].

Some amateurs are under the impression that the operator of a club station license has all of the privileges granted to the club station trustee, but that is not necessarily the case. The station trustee and the control operator are responsible for the station's operation [97.103(a)]. The control operator may operate the station only up to the privileges of his or her own operator

Q. What about a club that has a General licensee as trustee? There are lots of Amateur Extra amateurs in our club. Can we go outside the General subbands using the club call?

A. Yes, but only if you append your Amateur Extra call to that of the club call as stated in the previous question, and provide a duly licensed control operator who is willing to provide the control operator functions. Remember that the club station trustee and the control operator share responsibility. If the club station trustee doesn't have Amateur Extra privileges, he can't assume responsibility outside his General operator privileges.

Q. Are there any exceptions to the FCC Rules for Field Day?

A. No, all FCC Rules apply 365 days a year. Of course, Field Day participants must also observe additional Field Day rules as set forth by the ARRL.

Q. During Field Day, members of the public wander through as we operate. Many times, these unlicensed individuals want to operate. Can they legally operate our Field Day station?

A. Yes, but only a licensed amateur is eligible to be the control operator. Although an unlicensed person can't be the control operator of an amateur station, they may *participate*. In cases when a third party is participating, the control operator must be present at the control point and must be continuously monitoring and supervising the third party's participation. Third parties may only communicate directly with countries with which the US has signed third-party agreements [97.115(a) and (b)].

Q. During Field Day, our club uses the call sign of one of our Amateur Extra operators and we generally operate in the Amateur Extra subbands. One of our Technician operators made contacts last year with several countries with which the US does not share a third-party traffic agreement. Is that legal?

A. Even though Field Day is primarily an event for US and Canadian stations, an occasional foreign contact may be made. Part 97 states "[The prohibition on third party traffic] does not apply to a message for any third party who is eligible to be a control operator of the station" [97.115(a)(2)]. In this case, the answer is that it is not legal because a Technician operator is not eligible to be a control operator of a station operating outside the Technician segment.

license [97.105(b)]. If the privileges in use exceed those of the station trustee's, however, the station ID must consist of the club station's call sign followed by the home station call sign of the control op: WA1JUY/K1CE, for example [97.119(e)].

Except when a station is operating under automatic control (see Chapter 3), the control operator must be present at the control point. A control operator must always be at the control point when third-party communications are being transmitted, except when a station is transmitting RTTY or data and participating as a forwarding station in a message forwarding system [97.109(e), 97.115(b)]. More on this later.

The control operator must at all times ensure the immediate proper operation of the station, regardless of the type of control [97.105(a)]. The following types of control may be used: local, remote or automatic. A control operator may never operate any station beyond the privileges of his or her operator license [97.105(b)]. Control of, and operation through the various types of amateur stations is discussed in Chapter 3.

Types of Control

The basics of station control are mentioned in Subpart B—Station Operation Standards—although there is much more detail in Chapter 3. The first point is that *every amateur station must have at least one control point*, that is, a location where the control operator function is performed [97.3(a)(13), 97.109(a)]. It can't be an amateur station unless it is being controlled. The three types of control are local, remote and automatic.

Local Control

Local control is defined by the FCC as "the use of a control operator who directly manipulates the operating adjustments in the station to achieve compliance with the FCC Rules" [97.3(a)(30)]. When you sit in front of your rig and twiddle the knobs, that's local control—you are at the control point. Any station may be locally controlled [97.109].

Remote Control

Remote control involves control from a point that is *remote* from the station being controlled. The FCC calls it "the use of a control operator who indirectly manipulates the operating adjustments in the station through a control link to achieve compliance with the FCC Rules" [97.3(a)(38)]. The key words here are *indirectly* and *control link*. According to the FCC, "When a station is being remotely controlled, the control operator must be at the control point" and "Any station may be remotely controlled" [97.109(c)].

Automatic Control

The last type of control is *automatic control*: It is defined by the FCC as "The use of devices and procedures for control of a station when it is transmitting so that compliance with the FCC Rules is achieved without the control operator being present at a control point" [97.3(a)(6)]. This is "hands-off" operation; there's nobody at the control point, *but there must still be a control operator available who is responsible.* Only stations specifically designated elsewhere in Part 97 may be automatically controlled. Only a space, repeater, beacon and auxiliary station can be controlled automatically [97.109(d).

In addition, stations transmitting RTTY/data emissions above 50 MHz or in the following segments may be operated automatically: 3.620-3.635 MHz; 7.100-7.105 MHz; 10.140-10.150 MHz; 14.0950-14.0995 MHz; 14.1005-14.1120 MHz; 18.105-18.110 MHz; 21.090-21.100 MHz; 24.925-24.930 MHz; and 28.120-28.189 MHz [97.221(b)]. A station may not be operated under automatic control while transmitting third-party communications, except a station transmitting a RTTY or data emission. In addition, all messages that are retransmitted must originate at a station that is being locally or remotely controlled [97.109(e)].

Automatic control must cease upon notification by an FCC Field Office District Director that the station is transmitting improperly or causing harmful interference to other stations [97.109(d)].

We will go into more detail of the three types of control in Chapter 3— Special Operations as they apply to the various uses of amateur stations.

RECIPROCAL OPERATING AUTHORITY

Prior to February 12, 1999, foreign amateurs could operate in the US only if their country shared a reciprocal operating agreement with the US and if they applied for and obtained a reciprocal operating permit from the FCC by completing an FCC Form 610-A. US amateurs were required to obtain a reciprocal operating permit from the country they were going to be visiting. Since then, the FCC Form 610-A has been eliminated and the process has been greatly simplified. (US amateurs have been able to operate in Canada and vice versa for many years under the terms of the automatic reciprocal agreement with that country.) The basic points of reciprocal operating authority follow:

1) Foreign amateurs may operate in the US provided that their country has signed a bilateral or multilateral agreement with the US [97.107];

2) US amateurs may operate in Canada under the terms and conditions of the agreement with that country (see Appendix 4);

3) Canadian amateurs may operate in the US under the terms and conditions of the agreement with the US (see Appendix 4);

4) US amateurs may operate in foreign countries in certain circumstances without applying for a permit. If the US and the foreign country have signed a bilateral or multilateral agreement, the US amateur may operate under the terms and conditions of that agreement, which will be outlined later in this chapter. If there is no such agreement between the two countries, the US amateur may still

apply for a permit from the foreign host government.

5) In addition, the FCC may modify, suspend, or cancel the reciprocal operating authority granted by 97.107 to any person [97.107(c)].

FOREIGN AMATEUR OPERATION IN THE US

In 1999, sweeping changes were made to the reciprocal operating rules. Effective February 12, 1999, foreign amateurs who are citizens of their home country may operate temporarily in the US without any paperwork—provided that the US and the foreign country share a bilateral or multilateral reciprocal operating agreement. A list of countries that hold reciprocal operating agreements with the US is in Chapter 1. Foreign amateurs who are citizens of countries that have a reciprocal operating agreement with the US must carry with them proof of their citizenship and their foreign amateur license.

FCC Rules state that foreign amateurs, other than Canadians operating in the US under reciprocal operating authority, must identify by using an indicator consisting of the appropriate letter-numeral designating the station location. It is to be included *before* the call sign issued to the station by the licensing country and separated by a slant bar ("/" if on a non-phone mode or "stroke" or similar words if on phone, such as W1/G5RV) [97.119(g)]. For a map of US call districts, see Chapter 1 or **http://www.arrl.org/awards/was/map.gif**. For a text listing, see **http://www.fcc.gov/wtb/amateur/amateur.html**.

No US citizen is eligible to operate under this reciprocal operating authority since all US citizens must obtain a full US license [97.107].

A "multilateral" arrangement refers to the International Amateur Radio Permit (IARP) under the CITEL Convention and the European Conference of Postal and Telecommunications Administrations (CEPT) agreement, also known as the CEPT Recommendation T/R 61-01.

The privileges granted to a foreign amateur who is operating in the US are limited by:

1) The terms of the agreement between the alien's government and the United States;

2) The operating terms and conditions of the amateur service license granted by the alien's government;

3) The applicable rules of Part 97, but not to exceed the control operator privileges of an FCC-granted Amateur Extra Class operator license [97.107].

Specifically, if the foreign amateur holds a CEPT or IARP license of any class (Class 1 or 2) issued to him by his government, he may operate in the US on all amateur frequencies above 30 MHz. If the foreign amateur has been granted a CEPT Class 1 or a Class 1 IARP license, he may operate with all US privileges. A Class 1 multilateral agreement means that the foreign amateur has proven to his national licensing authority that he is proficient in Morse code at a minimum of 5 WPM. The foreign amateur must be careful to follow all US band/mode restrictions [97.301(a), (b)].

If there is no bilateral or multilateral reciprocal operating arrangement between the US and the foreign country of which the ham is a citizen, the only option for the foreign amateur is to obtain a US license. There are no citizenship requirements. For information on obtaining a US amateur license, contact ARRL HQ or see **http://www.arrl.org/hamradio.html**. Any person, other than a representative of a foreign government, can do so. Once a person is prepared to take the US license examinations, licenses are granted in as little a few days. A US mailing address is required for FCC license application and license information mailing purposes.

US OPERATION UNDER CEPT

In years past, US amateurs who traveled to foreign countries were required to obtain a reciprocal operating permit from the government of the country visited. This could be time consuming and often required payment of fees. This changed when the US became a participant in the CEPT arrangement. The European Conference of Postal and Telecommunications Administrations (CEPT) Recommendation T/R 61-01 benefits foreign and US amateurs whose governments are participants in the arrangement. A CEPT radio amateur license is issued to an amateur by the country of which the person is a citizen. The US is a non-European participant in the CEPT arrangement. A US amateur may operate in most European CEPT countries with the following items: US license, proof of US citizenship and a copy of the FCC CEPT Public Notice. US amateurs *may not* operate under CEPT in *countries outside of Europe* regardless of whether the country has been accepted into CEPT unless there is a bilateral reciprocal agreement between the US and the other country. If a certain European country doesn't participate in CEPT, they may be able to apply to the foreign government for a permit.

CEPT license: The FCC defines a CEPT license as "a license issued by a country belonging to the European Conference of Postal and Telecommunications Administrations (CEPT) that has adopted Recommendation T/R 61-01 (Nice 1985, revised in Paris 1992 and by correspondence August 1992)" [97.3(a)(15)].

Classes of license or permit: There are two classes of CEPT Radio Amateur License:

Class 1—This class permits utilization of *all* frequency bands allocated to the Amateur Service and Amateur-Satellite Service and authorized in the country where the amateur station is to be operated. It will be open only to those amateurs who have proven their competence in Morse code to their own Administration. The European Radiocommunications Office (ERO) has determined that for the purposes of Recommendation T/R 61-01, the FCC Amateur Extra, Advanced, General, and Technician Plus licenses are equivalent to CEPT Class 1. A US amateur who has proven proficiency in Morse code at a minimum of 5 WPM may operate on all frequencies in CEPT countries (excluding "non-CEPT countries").

Class 2—This class permits utilization of all frequency bands allocated to the Amateur Service and Amateur-Satellite Service *above 30 MHz* and autho-

---

CEPT Countries that Recognize US Participation in T/R 61-01 Recommendation (March 7, 2001)

Country	Call Sign Prefix(es)	
	CEPT Class 1	CEPT Class 2
Austria	OE	OE
Belgium	ON	ON
Bosnia and Herzegovina	T9	T9
Bulgaria	LZ	LZ
Croatia	9A	9A
Cyprus	5B	5B
Czech Republic	OK	OK
Denmark	OZ	OZ
Faroe Islands	OY	OY
Greenland	OX	OX
Estonia	ES*	ES*
Finland	OH	OH
France	F	F
Corsica	TK	TK
Guadeloupe	FG	FG
Guiana	FY	FY
Martinique	FM	FM
St-Bartholomew	FJ	FJ
St-Pierre/Miquelon	FP	FP
St-Martin	FS	FS
Reunion	FR	FR
Mayotte	FH	FH
French Antarctica	FT	FT
Local permission also required:		
Glorieuse	FR	FR
Jean de Nova	FR	FR
Tromelin	FR	FR
Crozet	FT	FT
Kerguelen	FT	FT
St. Paul & Amsterdam	FT	FT
Terre Adelie	FT	FT
French Polynesia	FO	FO
Clipperton	FO	FO
New Caledonia	FK	FK
Wallis & Futuna	FW	FW
Germany	DL	DC
Hungary	HA	HG
Iceland	TF	TF
Ireland	EI	EI
Italy	I	I
Latvia	YL	YL

rized in the country where the amateur station is to be operated. The ERO has determined that for the purposes of Recommendation T/R 61-01, the FCC Technician license (without the 5 WPM element) is equivalent to CEPT Class 2.

CEPT identification: When transmitting in the foreign CEPT country, the

Country	Call Sign Prefix(es)	
	CEPT Class 1	CEPT Class 2
Liechtenstein	HBØ	HBØ
Lithuania	LY	LY
Luxembourg	LX	LX
Monaco	3A	3A
Netherlands	PA	PA
Netherlands Antilles	PJ	PJ
Norway	LA	LC
Poland	SP	SP
Portugal	CT	CT
Azores	CU	CU
Madeira	CT	CT
Romania	YO	YO
Slovak Republic	OM	OM
Slovenia	S5	S5
Spain	EA	EB
Sweden	SM	SM
Switzerland	HB9	HB9
Turkey	TA	TA
Ukraine	UT	UT
United Kingdom	M	M
Isle of Man	MD	MD
Northern Ireland	MI	MI
Jersey	MJ	MJ
Scotland	MM	MM
Guernsey	MU	MU
Wales	MW	MW

Amateurs can see a detailed list of CEPT member countries that have implemented the Recommendation by visiting the European Radio-communications Office Web site at **www.ero.dk** and clicking "ERC-WG Activities" and then "RR-WG" and then on the "Special Area on Radio Amateurs." More detailed information, far too voluminous to appear in this book on the type of operating privileges the visiting amateurs license equates to in the country visited can be found by clicking "Documentation" then "ERO Recommendation." Scroll to "T/R 61-01" and click on "Implementation." Technician Plus, General, Advanced and Amateur Extra Class amateurs have CEPT Class 1 privileges and a US Technician class amateur (who has not passed the 5 WPM exam) has CEPT Class 2 privileges. Amateurs who have not demonstrated proficiency in Morse code may not operate below 30 MHz.

PUBLIC NOTICE

FEDERAL COMMUNICATIONS COMMISSION
445 12TH STREET, S.W.
WASHINGTON, D.C. 20554   **DA 99-2344**

News media information 202/418-0500   Fax-On-Demand 202/418-2830   Internet: http://www.fcc.gov   ftp.fcc.gov

Released: October 29, 1999

AMATEUR SERVICE OPERATION IN CEPT COUNTRIES

Subject to the regulations in force in the country visited, a U. S. citizen holding a Technician, Technician Plus, General, Advanced, or Amateur Extra Class amateur radio service operator license grant by the Federal Communications Commission (FCC) is authorized to utilize temporarily an amateur station in a European Conference of Postal and Telecommunications Administration (CEPT) country that has implemented CEPT Recommendation T/R 61-01 with respect to the United States. CEPT Recommendation T/R 61-01 is available on the internet at http://www.ero.dk/.

While operating an amateur station, the person must have in his or her possession a copy of this Public Notice, proof of U. S. citizenship, and evidence of the FCC license grant. These documents must be shown to proper authorities upon request.

When the privileges authorized by the FCC license grant are Technician Plus, General, Advanced, or Amateur Extra Class operator privileges, the corresponding CEPT operator privileges are CEPT radio amateur Class 1. When the privileges authorized by the FCC license grant are Technician Class operator privileges, the corresponding CEPT operator privileges are CEPT radio amateur Class 2. When the privileges authorized by the license grant are Novice Class operator privileges, the licensee is not authorized any corresponding CEPT radio amateur privileges. As mentioned above, operator privileges are subject to the regulations of the country visited.

Participating CEPT countries as of October 25. 1999, are: Austria, Belgium, Bosnia and Herzegovina, Bulgaria, Croatia, Cyprus, Czech Republic, Denmark, Estonia, Finland, France,* Germany, Hungary, Iceland, Ireland, Italy, Latvia, Liechtenstein, Lithuania, Luxembourg, Monaco, Netherlands, Netherland Antilles, Norway, Portugal, Romania, Slovak Republic, Slovenia, Spain, Sweden, Switzerland, Turkey, and the United Kingdom.**

*   Participating for France, Corsica, Guadeloupe, Guiana, Martinique, St. Bartholomew, St. Pierre/Miquelon, St. Martin, and Reunion/Dependencies.

** Participating for Great Britain, Northern Ireland, the Channel Islands, and the Isle of Man.

This CEPT Public Notice must be carried by US amateurs who are operating under CEPT in certain European countries. US amateurs who operate in these countries must also carry proof of US citizenship and a US amateur license. Although the Notice is written in three languages, only the English version is reproduced here. The complete Public Notice is available on *ARRLWeb* or from ARRL HQ. A few countries have joined CEPT after the FCC Notice was issued, but, as of this writing, the FCC has not issued an updated notice.

license holder must use his or her national call sign preceded by the CEPT call sign prefix such as EI/KB1EEE. The CEPT call sign prefix and the national call sign must be separated by the character "/" (telegraphy) or the word "stroke" (telephony). For a mobile Amateur Radio station the national call sign must be followed by the characters "/M" (telegraphy) or the word "mobile" (telephony). For a portable Amateur Radio station the national call sign must be followed by the characters "/P" (telegraphy) or the word "portable" (telephony). There is no

CEPT equivalent to the FCC Novice license. Operation by Novices is not authorized under a CEPT Radio Amateur License.

Conditions of Utilization: Amateurs must follow the following terms and conditions when operating in a country that is a participant in the CEPT agreement:

On request, the license holder shall present his CEPT radio amateur license to the appropriate authorities in the country visited. For US amateurs who are citizens of the US, a CEPT "license" consists of a copy of the FCC license, proof of US citizenship and a copy of the FCC CEPT Public Notice.

Authorization is granted for utilization of a portable or mobile station only. A portable station shall, for the purposes of the CEPT Recommendation, include any station using main electricity at a temporary location, e.g. a hotel or a camping site.

Authorization is also granted for utilization of the station of a radio amateur holding a permanent license in the host country.

The license holder shall observe the provisions of the ITU Radio Regulations, the CEPT T/R 61-01 Recommendation and the regulations in force in the country visited. Furthermore, any restrictions concerning national and local conditions of a technical nature or regarding the public authorities must be respected. Special attention should be paid to the difference in frequency allocations to the radio amateur services in the three ITU Regions. Amateur allocations vary according to ITU Region. For a map showing how the Earth is divided into three ITU "Regions," see the map in Chapter 4.

The use of the Amateur Radio station aboard an aircraft is prohibited.

The license holder cannot request protection against harmful interference.

Information for US Amateurs: For US citizens who are US amateurs, a "CEPT Radio Amateur License" consists of the following:

• FCC Public Notice (DA 99-2344, released October 29, 1999) entitled "Amateur Service Operation in CEPT Countries," written in three languages, English, French and German; The FCC Public Notice can be found at **http://www.arrl.org/field/regulations/io/#cept** and elsewhere in this chapter.

• their original license document (Form 660) issued by the FCC and

• proof of US citizenship (typically with a Passport or similar photo ID plus Birth Certificate).

In addition, Part 97 states that a foreign amateur operating in the US on the basis of a CEPT license may not be a resident alien or a citizen of the US. The non-US amateur may not hold an FCC-issued amateur operator license nor reciprocal permit for alien amateur licensee. The non-US amateur may not be a prior amateur service licensee whose FCC-issued license was revoked, suspended for less than the balance of the license term and the suspension is still in effect, suspended for the balance of the license term and relicensing has not taken place, or surrendered for cancellation following notice of revocation, suspension or monetary forfeiture proceedings; be the subject of a cease and desist order that relates to amateur service operation and which is still in effect [97.5].

For a list of countries that recognize US participation in the CEPT Radio Amateur License, see the reciprocal operating agreement countries list.

US OPERATION UNDER IARP

The FCC and US State Department now authorize Amateur Radio licensed citizens of certain countries in the Americas to operate their amateur stations while on short visits in the US. (The concept is similar to the International Driving Permit.) Likewise, citizens of the United States may now operate amateur stations in certain countries within the Americas while on short visits. A new arrangement makes it easier for US amateurs to operate stations temporarily in several South American countries. US amateurs must first apply for and obtain an International Amateur Radio Permit (IARP) from the ARRL. Foreign amateurs must obtain an IARP or CEPT license from their country of citizenship. Amateurs who are citizens of countries that have signed a Reciprocal Operating Agreement may operate with no paperwork. So far, an IARP is valid only in a handful of South American countries. They are listed in this section.

International Amateur Radio Permit (IARP): The Inter-American Convention on an International Amateur Radio Permit (CITEL/Amateur Convention) allows visitors to operate stations temporarily in other countries of the Americas. The August 21-25, 1995, meeting of the Inter-American Telecommunication Commission (CITEL) Permanent Consultative Committee III: Radio Communications adopted a resolution submitted by the US urging members to sign the CITEL/Amateur Convention. Participation in the CITEL/Amateur Convention allows US citizens to operate amateur stations in five countries within CITEL (seven if you count the US and Canada), a component of the Organization of American States. Under the CITEL/Amateur Convention, US amateur operators with an International Amateur Radio Permit (IARP) have reciprocal operating privileges for *one year*, or until their FCC license expires, whichever occurs first. A new permit must be obtained each year for IARP operations in certain South American countries.

The IARP may be issued by a member-society of the International Amateur Radio Union (IARU)—for the US, the IARU member-society is ARRL. The permit describes its authority in three different languages. The FCC presently recognizes the ARRL as the issuing body for such permits. The ARRL offers this service to US citizens for their use when they travel to CITEL countries. The ARRL provides this service on a non-discriminatory basis, at no expense to the United States Government.

FCC Rules: An IARP is only issued to the amateur by the country of which the person is a citizen. In order to obtain an IARP, an amateur:

1) Must not be a resident alien or citizen of the visited country, regardless of any other citizenship also held;

2) Must not hold an FCC-issued amateur operator license nor reciprocal permit for alien amateur licensee;

3) Must not be a prior amateur service licensee whose FCC-issued license was revoked, suspended for less than the balance of the license term and the suspension is still in effect, suspended for the balance of the license term and relicensing has not taken place, or surrendered for cancellation following notice of revocation, suspension or monetary forfeiture proceedings;

IARP Fee Information...

❑ IARP ($10 shipped)   ❑ IARP ($10) plus Rush delivery ($10) = ($20 total)   Total enclosed $_____ (US dollars) [up to $20 maximum]

If payment by credit card, indicate the card type, number and expiration date here:

VISA MC AMEX DISC (Circle card type), Card # (all 16 digits) _ _ _ _   _ _ _ _   _ _ _ _   _ _ _ _   Card Expiration date (mm/yy) _ _ / _ _

Cardholder name if different from below:

IARP Application Form for US Amateurs
(US Citizens Only)
(Print Legibly)

Applicant name: _____
(include first name, middle initial, last name, any surnames and/or any suffix {eg, Jr, Sr, i, ii, iii, etc})

US FCC-License Call Sign: _ _ _ _ _ _   US FCC-License Expiration Date: _ _ / _ _ / _ _ _ _
(up to 6 characters)   Month   Day   Year

FCC License, License Class: _____
(Technician, Technician Plus, General, Advanced or Extra)

Postal Address: _____

City: _____ State or Country: _____ Postal/Zip Code: _____

Telephone number (day): _____ (night): _____

Email address: _____ Fax phone number: _____

Certification: By signing this application, I certify that I am a US Citizen; that I understand and will comply with any regulations
or operation guidelines/limitations that may be required by the host country (or countries) I will visit; I understand that the IARP authorization is valid only while my US FCC license is in effect, or for a period of 365 days, whichever is less.

_____   _____
            (signature)   (date signed)

The following items must be supplied with each IARP application (feel free to use this as a check-off list) –
allow 30 days for processing and delivery -- for an additional fee, courier delivery can be chosen for stateside street addresses

❑ Application completed above, along with checking the appropriate fee payment box and writing in the total fee paid.

❑ Clear readable copy of applicant's photo-ID.

❑ Applicant's photograph -- limit size of photo to 1.5 inches high by 1.5 inches wide.

❑ Clear readable copy of applicant's FCC license.

❑ Application fee (made payable by check or money order to "ARRL", or credit card charge {Visa/MC/Discover/Amex only}).

❑ If the credentials must be directed to a different address, other than the applicant's mailing address above,

indicate the ship to address here: _____
_____
_____
_____

Submit your application with the above Items to: ARRL-IARP, 225 Main St, Newington CT 06111-1494 USA

Questions can be directed to ARRL at 860-594-0300 (8 am to 5 pm Eastern, weekdays), or email: wirwin@arrl.org

ARRL Form IARP Application 06/1999 - Page 2 of 2

The International Amateur Radio Permit application form for US amateurs, available from ARRL HQ or on *ARRLWeb*. The application fee is $10. Send the completed application to ARRL.

Q&A— Operation Away from Home

Q. My wife and I are setting sail on a luxury liner for a cruise among the Caribbean islands. I'd like to bring my ham rig with me. When I operate, whose rules do I follow?

A. The first determinant is the country of registry for the vessel. When you operate on the high seas (i.e., international waters) on a US-registered vessel, you must follow the FCC Rules. US and Canadian licensees need no special permit or authorization other than their own amateur licenses for operation aboard a US-registered vessel; these two countries share an automatic reciprocal operating agreement.

Q. Whose rules do I follow when my US ship sails into the territorial waters of another country?

A. When sailing or anchored in the territorial waters of another country, you must check the radio rules of that country before you operate your station. CEPT and IARP have greatly simplified overseas operating. If the country you are visiting does not participate in the CEPT or IARP arrangements, you will have to apply for and obtain a reciprocal permit from the government of that country. This information appears on the ARRL Web page at **http://www.arrl.org/FandES/ field/regulations/io/recip-country.html** is available for an SASE from ARRL HQ.

Q. What US rules apply when I'm flying or sailing over/in US territory?

A. Concerning your equipment aboard a ship or plane, the rules require that the installation and operation of your station must be approved by the master of the vessel or the pilot [97.11(a)]. You must keep your radio gear separate from and independent of all radio equipment installed on the ship or plane, except a common antenna may be shared with a voluntary ship radio installation.

Your transmissions must not cause interference to any equipment installed on the ship or plane [97.11(b)]. Your station must not pose a hazard to the safety of life and property [97.11(c)].

You must not operate your rig on a plane when it is flying under Instrument Flight Rules (IFR), unless you can be sure your station complies with all applicable FAA Rules [97.11(c)]. When you operate in ITU Region 2, frequencies used must be consistent with US frequency bands and if you are a US licensee,

---

4) Must not be the subject of a cease and desist order that relates to amateur service operation and which is still in effect [97.5(e)].

Classes of license or permit: There are two classes of IARPs:

Class 1 requires knowledge of the international Morse code and proven proficiency in CW. It carries *all* operating privileges (Technician Plus, General, Advanced or Extra Class US licensees qualify for Class 1). For foreign amateurs, Class 1 is equivalent to the US Amateur Extra Class.

Class 2 does not require knowledge of telegraphy and carries *all operating privileges above 30 MHz*. It is, therefore, equivalent to the US current (codeless) Technician Class operator license. There is no equivalent Class description for the US Novice license; therefore, the Novice licensee is not eligible to operate under IARP [97.301].

IARP Station identification: When the station is transmitting under the

you must operate within the privileges of your license. Outside Region 2 and subject to the limitations of your license class, other frequency segments may apply [97.301]. For example, on 40 meters in Region 2, 7.0-7.3 MHz is allocated to the Amateur Radio Service, but in Regions 1 and 3, the amateur allocation is only 7.0-7.1 MHz.

Q. What ITU Region am I in?

A. If you're operating from Europe or Africa or the adjoining waters, you are in ITU Region 1. North and South America and the adjoining waters comprise Region 2. The rest of the world (the countries of southern Asia and the islands of the Pacific and Indian Oceans) make up Region 3. See the map in Chapter 4.

Q. What type of station ID procedure should I use when I operate maritime mobile in international waters?

A. Amateur FCC Rules place no special identification requirements on a station in maritime (or aeronautical) mobile operation. It is helpful to listeners, however, if you follow your call sign with the words "Maritime (or aeronautical) Mobile" followed by the ITU Region in which you are operating if on a phone mode. If operating on a non-phone mode, you can send your call sign followed by the fraction bar, then the indicator MM (for maritime mobile) and the number of your ITU Region, such as KB1MW/MM2. Your ITU Region will always be 1, 2 or 3 (don't confuse ITU regions with domestic US call areas).

Q. How far do the territorial waters of a particular country extend?

A. The territorial limits extend to wherever that particular country says they do. The US, Canada and Mexico claim 12 nautical miles. Most Caribbean island nations claim 3-12 miles, although there are exceptions. The territorial limits of certain Caribbean nations and other island nations whose area consists of many small islands often overlap, creating a larger territorial area than one would assume.

Q. A ham friend of mine told me that FCC-licensed amateurs within international waters could operate on all frequencies, regardless of their license class. Is this true?

A. No way. If an FCC-licensed station operates outside the privileges of his/her license class, it's a violation of FCC Rules [97.105(b)].

authority of an IARP, an indicator consisting of the appropriate letter-numeral designating the station location must be included *before, after, or both before and after the call sign issued to the station by the licensing country.* At least once during each intercommunication, the identification announcement must include the geographical location as nearly as possible to the city and state, commonwealth or possession of the station operation. An example of station identification under IARP by a US amateur operator while traveling in or near Lima, Peru might be, "This is OA1/W1XYZ, near Lima Peru." If on CW, a sample ID procedure would be "de OA1/W1XYZ nr Lima Peru."

Facilitator: ARRL provides these services on a non-discriminatory basis, at no expense to the US Government. A processing fee (US dollars) of $10 is charged by ARRL to cover IARP credentials/authority creation and delivery to applicants. For domestic rush/courier delivery, add $10 (street addresses only) for a total of $20.

Application: Credentials will be issued to US amateurs and citizens upon receipt of a completed and signed application, along with a photocopy of the applicant's US FCC amateur license, a copy of the applicant's legal photo-ID and a 1 inch × 1 inch (up to 1.5 × 1.5 inch) color or black/white photo of the applicant (to be affixed to credentials), and the application fee (payable by check or money order to "ARRL," or by credit card). US amateurs who are US citizens can obtain an IARP application from ARRL HQ by sending a SASE. An IARP application appears on *ARRLWeb* at **http://www.arrl.org/FandES/field/regulations/io/index.html#iarp**.

Participating countries: The ARRL issues International Amateur Radio Permits (IARP) that allows US amateurs to operate from certain South American countries:

Argentina
Brazil
Peru
Uruguay
Venezuela

OPERATION BY CANADIANS IN THE US

The US and Canada have shared an automatic reciprocal operating agreement for many years. A control operator who holds an amateur license in Canada and who is a citizen of Canada may operate in the US under the auspices of the automatic reciprocal agreement the US holds with Canada. The privileges granted to the control operator by that authorization are made under the following conditions:

1) The operator must abide by the terms of the agreement with the US, formally known as: the Convention Between the United States and Canada (TIAS no. 2508) Relating to the Operation by Citizens of Either Country of Certain Radio Equipment or Stations in the Other Country;

2) Canadian amateurs must follow the operating terms and conditions of the amateur service license issued by the Government of Canada; and

3) Canadian amateurs must follow the applicable provisions of the FCC Rules, but not to exceed the control operator privileges of an FCC-issued Amateur Extra operator license. For example, a Canadian operating in the US can't operate phone in the 14.100-14.150 MHz segment even though he or she may have been able to do so in Canada [97.107(a)]. See Appendix 4 for the agreement.

Canadian amateurs need not file any paperwork with the FCC when operating in the US because the two countries share an automatic reciprocal agreement. A Canadian amateur may operate indefinitely provided that the amateur continues to renew their Canadian license and provided that they remain Canadian citizens. Canadian amateurs may have additional privileges available to them in Canada, but when operating in the US, they must abide by all FCC Rules, including the appropriate band/mode restrictions.

When a Canadian amateur is operating under the automatic reciprocal agreement with the US, a station location indicator must be included *after* the call sign. Also, at least once during each intercommunication, the identification announcement must include the geographical location as nearly as possible by city and state, commonwealth or possession, for example, "VE8RCS/W1 mobile 20 miles west of Hartford, Connecticut" [97.119(g)].

OPERATION BY US AMATEURS IN CANADA

Because the US and Canada hold an automatic reciprocal agreement, US amateurs do not need to apply for a permit or file any paperwork provided that they maintain their US license and remain US citizens. The same identification procedures apply as for Canadian amateurs operating in the US (mentioned above), such as "N1KB/VE6 portable near Lake Louise, Alberta." US amateurs may operate in Canada under the following control operator conditions:

1) US amateurs must abide by the terms of the Convention Between the United States and Canada (TIAS no. 2508) Relating to the Operation by Citizens of Either Country of Certain Radio Equipment or Stations in the Other Country;

2) US amateurs must follow the operating terms and conditions of their US license; and

3) US amateurs must follow the applicable provisions of Canadian amateur rules.

Additional information is available on the World Wide Web at **http://www.rac.ca/rcip.htm** or at **http://strategis.ic.gc.ca/sc_mrksv/spectrum/engdoc/spect1.html**. These Web sites, as is the case with any other Web site URLs, are subject to change.

OPERATION BY US AMATEURS IN FOREIGN COUNTRIES

When US amateurs travel to a foreign country, there are several possibilities for operating. US amateurs should first check to see if the foreign country participates in the CEPT or IARP agreements. If that is the case, operating is greatly simplified. To participate in the CEPT arrangement, the US amateur must carry proof of his or her US citizenship, a copy of the US license and a copy of the FCC CEPT Public Notice which can be found at **http://www.arrl.org/FandES/field/regulations/io/**. A copy of the FCC Public Notice appears elsewhere in this chapter. To obtain an application for an International Amateur Radio Permit, US amateurs who are also US citizens must apply to the ARRL. For a copy of the application, see **http://www.arrl.org/FandES/field/regulations/io/iarp-app.pdf**. You can also write ARRL HQ or fax at 1-860-594-0259.

If the country you are travelling to does not participate in CEPT or IARP, US amateurs may apply for and obtain a reciprocal permit for amateur operation in a foreign country. The presence of a reciprocal operating agreement with the US ensures that a US amateur will be able to obtain a permit in the foreign country, but the absence of such an agreement doesn't always preclude a US amateur from obtaining a permit in a foreign country. US amateurs must abide by the terms and conditions as dictated by the foreign government. Reciprocal licensing information is available on the ARRL Web page at: **http://www.arrl.org/field/regulations/io/recip-country. html**. Information on obtaining a permit for operation in foreign countries is also available from ARRL HQ for a business-sized, self-addressed stamped envelope with two units of postage per country.

AUTHORIZED COMMUNICATIONS

Amateur Radio is a two-way radio service. FCC licensed amateurs may contact amateurs in any country except stations in countries whose administrations have banned such communications. Although there are currently no "banned" countries, the FCC will detail any changes in a public notice [97.111(a)(1)].

Speaking of international communications, use plain language, and confine your conversations to technical and personal comments when contacting amateurs in other countries. The content of your conversation must be such that no party would be compelled to use the public telecommunications system to communicate the same information [97.117]. This protects foreign governments' interests in public telecommunications revenue.

You may communicate with stations in other FCC-licensed radio services while providing communications during emergencies and disasters. For example, it may be necessary to contact a station operating in the Commercial Land Mobile Service to save lives in emergencies [97.111(a)(2)]. This is very rare, however, and your actions must be justified in the event of an FCC inquiry. Further, you may communicate with US Government stations when operating under RACES, the Radio Amateur Civil Emergency Service [97.111(a)(3)]. We will discuss RACES in Chapter 5.

Amateur stations may make two-way transmissions "necessary to exchange messages with a station in a service not regulated by the FCC, but authorized by the FCC to communicate with amateur stations. An amateur station may exchange messages with a participating US military station during an Armed Forces Day Communications Test. During such tests, amateurs transmit on designated amateur frequencies while certain military stations listen there and transmit on designated government frequencies. Armed Forces Day occurs once a year for a 24 hour period, usually in May [97.111(a)(4)].

Because Amateur Radio is primarily a two-way communications service, there are only a few cases when you may send a one-way transmission. You may send short transmissions for [97.111(b)]:

1) Adjustments to the station;

2) Establishing two-way communications with other stations (e.g. calling CQ);

3) Telecommand;

4) Providing emergency communications;

5) Assisting persons in learning, or improving proficiency in, the international Morse code;

6) Disseminating information bulletins;

7) Telemetry.

PROHIBITED COMMUNICATIONS

Amateurs can transmit any sort of communications when in a two-way contact with another amateur unless Part 97 specifically says we can't. The Amateur Radio Service is unlike any other authorized radio service because Part 97 is set up to allow flexibility and experimentation. Amateurs can experiment with new ideas, help the public enjoy and participate safely in events such as parades and walk-a-thons by providing support communications, and promote goodwill between the US and the peoples of other nations, to name just a few. The rules allow for providing emergency communications in support of disaster relief efforts, a major reason for the existence of Amateur Radio.

Now, we'll examine the types of transmissions amateurs *can't* conduct. The FCC calls them "prohibited transmissions" [97.113]. Many of these are common sense, black-and-white rules, needing little explanation or interpretation. But others lie in the gray area and are not so clearly defined. These require interpretation and clarification for specific situations. We will also look at specifically authorized transmissions.

We will present comprehensive discussions of FCC letters, news releases, public notices, approved interpretations and so forth that will help you understand the gray area rules and apply them to your activity.

The rules we will be looking at are important. Some are required to preserve the core of Amateur Radio: the prohibitions against broadcasting to the public, and operating your station for compensation and on behalf of your employer, for example.

BUSINESS COMMUNICATIONS:
WHAT YOU CAN AND CAN'T DO

Between 1972 and 1993, the FCC laid down stringent "no business" rules. "Talk-ins" to conventions and hamfests weren't legal, among many other things! Effective September 13, 1993, the "no business communications" language was replaced with a prohibition on communications for compensation on behalf of one's employer or in which the amateur has a pecuniary interest [97.113(a)(2), (3)]. The current language is almost, but not quite, as relaxed as the pre-1972 rules. Now, instead of a flat prohibition on providing an alternative to other radio services, there is a less restrictive one against doing so on a regular basis [97.113(a)(5)].

These rules permit wider use of Amateur Radio to satisfy personal communications needs. To cite a classic example, as far as the FCC is concerned you may now use an autopatch to order a pizza. You may call your dentist's office to let them know you'll be late, or even to make an appointment. On your way home you may ask your spouse if you should pick up a loaf of bread on the autopatch without worrying about whether this will "facilitate the business affairs" of the grocery store. Repeater owners or trustees may set tighter standards if they want, but it's no longer an FCC issue.

The FCC doesn't want to hear questions about whether such-and-such is permitted. The FCC Report and Order, which carries the weight of a regulation, said:

"We [the FCC] have decided to amend the amateur service rules substantially...to allow amateur operators more flexibility to provide communications for public service projects as well as to enhance the value of the amateur service in satisfying personal communications needs. Amendment of the rules as proposed by the League will allow licensee to use amateur service frequencies, for example, to facilitate such events as races and parades, to support educational activities, to provide personal communications such as making appointments and ordering food, to collect data for the National Weather Service, and to provide assistance voluntarily even where there are other authorized services available. We believe that this action will expand the benefits derived from the amateur service by the general public as well as amateur service licensees."

The Report and Order also said, in part, that ". . .any amateur-to-amateur communication is permitted unless specifically prohibited, or unless transmitted for compensation, or unless done for the pecuniary benefit of the station control operator or his or her employer" [PR Docket 92-136, Report and Order].

How can you tell if something is allowed? A simple check list may help you determine if a communication is permissible under 97.113:

1) Is it expressly prohibited in the rules (music, obscenity, etc) [97.113(a)(1)]?
2) Is it transmitted for compensation [97.113(a)(2)]?
3) Does the control operator have a pecuniary interest; that is, could he or she benefit financially [97.113(a)(3)]?
4) Does the control operator's employer have a pecuniary interest [97.113(a)(3)]?

If you can answer "No" to all of these questions, the communication is okay as far as the FCC is concerned.

DIRECT AND INDIRECT PAYMENT

You must never accept any money or other consideration for providing communications services [97.113(a)(2)]. This is consistent with one of the main bases and purposes of the Amateur Radio Service:

"Recognition and enhancement of the value of the amateur service to the public as a *voluntary, noncommercial* communication service, particularly with respect to providing emergency communications" [97.1(a)].

If your club is providing communications support to the town of Needham for a parade, you cannot accept their offer of payment for your work. You are volunteers, providing a community service on a noncommercial basis, period.

You should never accept anything in exchange for providing Amateur Radio communications. The FCC prohibits operation of an amateur station "for hire, or for material compensation, direct or indirect, paid or promised" [97.113(a)(2)]. This includes direct payment (money, goods, food, and so on) and indirect payment (publicity, advertising, and so on).

Back to our example, the Needham town officials may, however, provide you with items to verify the identity of participating amateurs. Badges, caps, T-shirts, signs and other incidental items are not considered to be material compensation; amateurs would have provided the communications regardless of whether such an item is received.

Exceptions to the No Compensation Rule

How is it that W1AW (the ARRL HQ station) operators are allowed to be paid? The rules provide for such an activity. Control operators of a club station may be compensated when the club station is operated primarily for code-practice transmissions or for transmitting bulletins consisting of Amateur Radio news having direct interest to hams. To qualify under this provision, however, the station must conduct code-practice sessions for at least 40 hours per week, schedule operations on at least six medium and high-frequency amateur bands, and publish the schedule of operating times and frequencies at least 30 days in advance of the actual transmissions. Control operators may accept compensation only when the station is transmitting code practice and bulletins [97.113(d)].

The best-known one-way bulletins come from W1AW. For decades, W1AW has transmitted brief information bulletins. It is common practice for other amateur stations to conduct similar operations, usually on a localized basis, and as part of a scheduled net or on some other limited, scheduled basis. Such bulletins are important to the dissemination of timely and accurate information to radio amateurs.

W1AW and other stations providing this service generally have been careful to make such bulletins brief and factual. Occasionally, such as during the launch of an Amateur Radio satellite or space shuttle or a transmission from the International Space Station, some amateur stations using phone have been put into a quasi-broadcast operation to provide real-time information about a developing situation of special interest to radio amateurs. Such events are rare and amateurs have exercised restraint [97.113(b),(e)].

Normally, amateurs are prohibited from benefiting monetarily from amateur communications, but there are several narrow exceptions. Amateur operators may notify other amateur operators of the availability for sale or trade of apparatus normally used in an amateur station, provided that such activity is not conducted on a regular basis [97.113(a)]. A "regular basis" means "not every day." The FCC staff has also said that mentioning the price over the air is okay, but the "haggling" should be handled on the telephone.

There is another exception to the "no-compensation" rule:

Amateurs aren't usually permitted to provide communications on behalf of their employers or to be paid for such communications. In limited circumstances, the fact that amateurs are still on the payroll is incidental. FCC Rules state "A control operator may accept compensation as an incident of a teaching position during periods of time when an amateur station is used by that teacher as a part of classroom instruction at an educational institution" [97.113(c)]. A professional teacher may let his or her students speak to a farmer in Brazil or a cowboy in Argentina as part of classroom instruction. There must, however, be a third party agreement between the US and the other country if unlicensed persons would like to speak to the foreign amateur directly.

ALTERNATIVES TO THE AMATEUR RADIO SERVICE

Amateurs frequently provide communications for the benefit of the general public (although amateurs are prohibited from making transmissions to be *received* by the general public since that constitutes broadcasting). These can include events like walk-a-thons. Even though event sponsors, such as the March of Dimes, are in the "business" of coordinating such events, they aren't held "on a regular basis"—the FCC declined to define what it means by "regular" but it can be reasoned that "a regular basis" is *not* every day. FCC Rules state: "No amateur shall transmit: Communications, on a regular basis, which could reasonably be furnished alternatively through other radio services" [97.113(a)(5)].

There are times when amateurs are asked to provide communications by nonamateur groups because these individuals view the Amateur Radio Service as a cheap alternative to communications in the service they should be using on a regular basis. If communications are required every day, amateur communications should not be used. In 1997, for example, amateurs in Alaska were asked by the local sheriff to provide communications for the local sheriff's department since they didn't have enough police radios to conduct the regular business of the department. The sheriff asked amateurs to modify their amateur transceivers to make them capable of transmitting on sheriff frequencies while providing communications on behalf of the department. Few questioned this because "if the sheriff said it, we must comply." In that case, the local sheriff wasn't aware of Part 97 and wasn't aware of the capabilities of amateurs. He simply saw a need and saw Amateur Radio as an easy way to solve his problem. In addition, modification of

Q&A— Music

Q. At last night's club meeting, a fellow member told me that he could hear my car radio playing in the background during our repeater QSO. I didn't even think about it at the time, but was I in violation of the rules?

A. What the FCC is really concerned about is the deliberate playing of music on Amateur Radio for purposes of providing entertainment. The FCC doesn't want the general public tuning in to your amateur station to listen to music!

As a practical matter, you won't go to jail for an isolated incident if you're talking on 2 meters, but, if the background radio music was loud enough to cause your friend to mention it to you, it was too loud. It might have disturbed others, too. Just keep it down next time!

Q. My friend and I are music composers. Can we trade compositions in ASCII code across town on 2 meters?

A. The music prohibition concerns the playing of music itself, not information about music. As long as no musical notes can be detected on the air, you're okay.

Q. What if we send commands to each other's MIDI synthesizers over the air?

A. Again, no problem, as long as no actual music is played on the air and the transmission took place on 50 MHz or higher [97.307(f)(5)].

Q. Can we sing "Happy Birthday" to our friend on the local 2-meter repeater?

A. No. Singing is music, and is prohibited, no matter how badly you sing.

amateur transceivers to transmit outside the amateur bands is a violation of the FCC certification (formerly called "type acceptance") rules; amateur transceivers don't require FCC certification, but police radios do!

There are instances such as the one above in which other authorized radio services should be used such as the Private Land Mobile Radio Service where many business band radios operate. If an individual or group has a need for communications on a daily basis, services other than Amateur Radio should be used. It is up to amateurs to know when use of Amateur Radio is appropriate and when it is not, since the person or group requesting communications may not know.

MUSIC

The transmission of music is strictly prohibited in the amateur bands [97.113(a)(4)]. For example, expect some mail from the FCC if you transmit Rossini's *The Barber of Seville* on your favorite 75-meter phone net. The FCC mail will not be a critical review of the performance; rather, it may be a Notice of Apparent Liability requiring a formal reply within 10 days of receipt!

The FCC has specifically stated that incidental music on space shuttle retransmissions is okay [97.113(e)].

CRIMINAL ACTIVITIES

Amateur Radio may not be used for any purpose or in connection with any activity contrary to federal, state or local law. This means that if you use your 2-meter hand-held to communicate to your getaway car during a bank heist, you'll not only be in trouble with the local law enforcement, but with the federal government (FCC) as well. [97.113(a)(4)].

CODES AND CIPHERS

You may not hide the meaning of your communications by putting them into codes or ciphers [97.113(a)(4)]. There are certain exceptions, however. In this context, codes and ciphers refer to text that has been transformed to conceal its meaning. This restriction is consistent with the Commission's obligation, under international regulations, to ensure that amateur communications be made in plain language. Universally accepted abbreviations may be used, however, when the intention is not to hide the meaning of the transmission; common Q signals, for example.

The rules do not apply to the legitimate use of secret telecommand codes used to protect the security of a satellite [97.207(f)]. When we use the word "codes" in this context, we aren't referring to the digital codes used in the RTTY and data modes [97.309], or to Spread Spectrum transmissions [97.311].

Also, repeater trustees may use authentication codes to secure access to

---

FCC Cites Amateur for Indecent Speech

On September 21, 1992, the Commission fined a Tennessee amateur $2000 for violation of §97.113(a)(4). The notice stated, "On June 29, 1992, between 3:53 and 4:22 PM CST, the Commission's Kingsville Office monitored a conversation on frequency 14300 kHz which included transmissions by an individual identifying with the call sign. We find that the words and language transmitted are indecent within the meaning of Section 97.113(a)(4) and prevailing Supreme Court and Commission precedent." The release went on to state, "Speech is considered indecent if it describes sexual or excretory activities and organs in patently offensive terms. It need not depict or describe 'hard core' sexual conduct as required for a finding of obscenity. We find that the transmissions describe sexual acts and organs in a patently offensive manner and go well beyond what an average adult person in any community would consider to be worthy of protection."

The Commission stated further, "One of the Commission's goals is to protect children from exposure to sexually explicit communications over the airwaves. The Commission has previously stated that 'the concept of indecency is intimately connected with the exposure of children to material that most parents regard as inappropriate for them to hear.' Amateur transmissions are accessible to homes over a large area and a significant number of licensed amateurs are children in their formative years. Additionally, the transmissions were made in the summertime in the afternoon when there is a real likelihood that children are listening."

The Commission's action signals the amateur community that the agency will continue to enforce its rules in this arena.

the control functions of their hilltop repeater. (Authentication codes are sent by control operators to control repeater functions—the repeater checks, or authenticates, the code to ensure that the commands are coming from an authorized control operator.) Universally accepted touch-tone pad tones are not considered to be codes and ciphers; their use in traditional repeater and other applications is fine.

OBSCENITY AND INDECENCY

The rules say you may not transmit obscene or indecent words, language or meaning [97.113(a)(4)]. But when is the line crossed? In April 1987, the FCC notified licensees of standards that would be applied in these cases:

Obscenity: (1) An average person, applying contemporary community standards, must find that the material, as a whole, appeals to prurient interest; (2) The material must depict or describe, in a patently offensive way, sexual conduct specifically defined by the applicable state law; and (3) The material, taken as a whole, must lack serious literary, artistic, political, or scientific value.

Indecency: Language or material that depicts or describes, in terms patently offensive as measured by contemporary community standards for the broadcast medium, sexual or excretory activities or organs.

Is the use of an expletive in itself indecent? According to the Commission, "deliberate and repetitive use of such expletives in a patently offensive manner would be a requisite to a finding of indecency." The context is also important.

FALSE SIGNALS

False or deceptive messages, signals and identification are clearly prohibited in the amateur bands. You may not use someone else's call sign without authorization, or transmit a communication intended to deceive listeners. Don't retransmit other amateurs' communications without their knowledge or without properly identifying such retransmissions. Sending a false "SOS" or "MAYDAY" won't win you any friends, either—and it may expose you to significant fines from the FCC and other federal agencies [97.113(a)(4)].

BROADCASTING

Broadcasting is prohibited in the Amateur Radio Service [97.113(b)]. But isn't that what we amateurs do—broadcast? No, not in the eyes of the FCC. *Broadcasting* is defined as "Transmissions intended for reception by the general public, either direct or relayed " [97.3(a)(10)]. As such, broadcasting must be left to those services directly authorized to do so by the FCC—commercial television and radio, for example. Even amateur bulletins and code practice must be aimed at an amateur audience, not a nonamateur one.

You can't transmit anything intended to be received by the public directly or by intermediary relay stations. It's important to note the difference, however, between broadcasting and the permitted one-way transmissions of bulletins. Bulletins dealing directly with Amateur Radio matters may be transmitted one-way to amateurs only; they may not be transmitted for the benefit of the general public. For example, an amateur may recite the latest ARRL bulletin or retransmit the ARRL Audio News over his local repeater, but may not target the bulletin for the ears of the general public with home scanners. You may not retransmit AM or FM broadcast programs or television audio or video. You may, however, retransmit NOAA weather broadcasts, propagation bulletins originated by US Government stations, and space shuttle communications or International Space Station (with NASA's approval) on an occasional basis, as an incident to normal amateur activity [97.113(e)].

NEWSGATHERING AND THE MEDIA

Occasionally, at a Field Day or other operating activity, a local commercial broadcast station may want to record your station's transmissions and receptions for the local evening news. This is fine since the station is simply reporting on an amateur activity (e.g. Amateur Radio is the news).

Working with the Media

Sooner or later, your amateur activity may come to the attention of the media. For example, a local TV station may want to interview you at your station concerning the latest ham transmissions from a hurricane-devastated Caribbean island.

Reporters, especially those working on breaking emergency stories, have to work quickly and they'll be eager to cover all possible news angles. That's where you may come in.

The ARRL has come up with guidelines to keep in the back of your mind when under the hot, bright camera lights:

• Amateur Radio operators may assist news media representatives in their efforts to gather information for relay to the public from areas where normal communications have been disrupted.

• Amateurs may ask questions of, or relay media questions to, amateurs in the emergency area. The responses may be electronically recorded by media representatives.

• Amateur Radio should not be used to assist the news media in gathering information when telephones or other commercial means of communication are available.

• Amateur Radio must not be used to facilitate the operation of any business.

• Amateur Radio operators should depend on their own judgment when dealing with the news media and when operating their stations in the public interest, convenience and necessity.

A press kit, which includes a "backgrounder on news gathering and Amateur Radio" is available from ARRL's Public Relations Department. You may want to have one on hand when a reporter pays you a visit. To get a kit, contact ARRL Media Relations Manager Jennifer Hagy, N1TDY at ARRL HQ.

You must not allow your amateur station to be used as a medium for any activity directly related to program production or newsgathering for broadcast purposes [97.113(b)]. Commercial broadcast stations must have their own systems for gathering news and they don't involve Amateur Radio. There is only one exception. You may provide news information about an event if the following requirements are met. The information:

• Involves safety of life and/or property;
• Is directly related to the event;
• Can't be sent by any other means because normal systems are disrupted or aren't available at the site where the information is originated; and
• Other communications could not be reasonably provided before or during the event.

These rules protect the amateur service from encroachment by commercial news media that would use Amateur Radio as an inexpensive alternative to its more expensive systems [97.113(b)].

RETRANSMITTING RADIO SIGNALS

Amateurs can't normally retransmit the signals of other radio services, but there are two narrow exceptions:

• Propagation and weather forecast information intended for use by the general public and originated from United States Government stations;
• Communications, including incidental music, originating on United States Government frequencies between a space shuttle and its associated Earth stations where NASA permission has been granted. Such retransmissions must be for the exclusive use of amateur operators.

Propagation, NOAA weather forecasts, and shuttle retransmissions may not be retransmitted on a regular basis, but only occasionally, as an incident of normal Amateur Radio communications [97.113(e)].

In addition, you must never record someone else's transmissions and play them back over the air without permission [97.113(a)(4)].

AUTOMATIC RETRANSMISSION OF AMATEUR SIGNALS

Automatic retransmission of amateur signals may only be conducted by space, repeater or auxiliary stations [97.113(f)]. Message forwarding stations participating in a message forwarding system may be automatically controlled when transmitting third party communications [97.109(d), (e)].

THIRD-PARTY COMMUNICATIONS

Communications on behalf of third parties has been a part of Amateur Radio from its earliest beginnings in the United States. The very basis for the creation of the ARRL in 1914 was to organize amateurs to relay messages on one another's behalf in order to overcome the limited range of the amateur stations of the day. In that simpler time, there was essentially no limit to the content of such messages nor on whose behalf the messages could be sent.

It was not until the 1930s that international limitations were placed on amateur traffic, at the insistence of European governments for whom the telecommunications monopoly was a source of considerable revenue. While handling messages or providing communications for material compensation always has been prohibited in Amateur Radio, it was not until 1972 that the FCC specifically prohibited "business communications" in Docket 19245. Thus, the FCC began for the first time to regulate amateur traffic on the basis of its content.

Confusion developed in the amateur community when it came to provid had difficulty interpreting the rules, and in some cases felt they were too restrictive. As a result, the Commission changed its rules once again. The focus of the new rules is no longer on content, but on whether the amateur or his employer stand to gain financially. This has greatly simplified and expanded public service and personal communications opportunities for hams [97.113(a)].

THIRD PARTY COMMUNICATIONS DEFINED

So, who is this third-party person? Part 97 defines *third party communications* as "A message from the control operator (first party) of an amateur station to another amateur station control operator (second party) on behalf of another person (third party)" [97.3(a)(46)]. Third-party messages include those that are spoken, written, keystroked, keyed, photographed or otherwise originated by or for a third party, and transmitted by your Amateur Radio station, live or delayed. A third party may also be a person permitted by the control operator to participate in Amateur Radio communications [97.115(b)].

An amateur station may transmit traffic for a third party to (1) Any station within the US, and (2) Amateurs in any foreign country that has entered into a third-party agreement with the US. Third-party messages *can't* be sent to countries which haven't entered into such agreements. This assumes that the third party isn't an amateur. For example, if you've just found out that your long lost non-ham Aunt Minnie is alive and well and living in Ethiopia, you *can't* contact her through a phone patch with your ham Cousin Larry in Addis Ababa because the US and Ethiopia do not share a third-party agreement. There is an exception if the third party is an amateur. The Rules state "This prohibition does not apply to a message for any third party who is eligible to be a control operator of the station" [97.115(a)]. If your Aunt Minnie obtains her ham license and if you're chatting away with Cousin Larry, you (the first party) can tell Cousin Larry (second party) to tell Aunt Minnie (third party) to get on the air. It's still a third-party message, but because all involved are amateurs and eligible to be control operators, the third-party prohibitions don't apply.

TYPES OF THIRD-PARTY TRAFFIC

There are three main types of third-party traffic:

Third-Party Messages

The first type involves *third-party messages,* those sent via traffic nets, packet networks, or other means. Message fairs and displays at shopping malls provide sources for this type of routine message. Not all messages need be as formal as this, such as the example above.

Phone Line Interconnections

The second type of third-party traffic involves *phone-line interconnection,* so-called "phone patch" and "autopatch" operation. This type of operation allows third parties to communicate directly with second and first parties via the telephone system. If you decide to call a non-amateur friend in Cheraw, South Carolina, through a ham friend in the same town, that's through a phone-line interconnection. See the section on Phone Patch and Autopatch Guidelines in Chapter 3.

Direct Participation

The third type of third-party traffic is *direct participation* by interested third parties in actual Amateur Radio communications [97.115(b)]. If you allow your non-ham friend to participate in amateurs' communications from your ham shack, that's direct participation. Note that a non-amateur *can't operate an amateur station*! He or she is limited to making contact with other amateurs in the US and with countries that have entered into third-party agreements with the US. But, there's more!

THIRD-PARTY COMMUNICATION RULES

The rules provide for these three types of third-party communications, provided that specific rules are met by the control operator. The control operator must continually monitor and supervise the third party's participation [97.115(b)(1)]. At no time may a control operator leave a third party unattended at a transmitter that is on the air. As long as the control operator is present and monitoring the communications, however, the third party may key the transmitter and identify the station; there is no requirement that the control operator actually do so.

The rules prohibit participation in this type of third-party traffic by a former amateur whose license was revoked; suspended for less than the balance of the license term and the suspension is still in effect; suspended for the balance of the license term and relicensing has not taken place; surrendered for cancellation following notice of revocation, suspension or monetary forfeiture proceedings; or who is the subject of a cease-and-desist-order that relates to amateur operation and is still in effect [97.115(b)(2)].

Third-party traffic involving payment for the communications service to any party is not allowed [97.113(a)(2)]. Third-party traffic in which the operator stands to gain financially or on behalf of the operator's employer is not permitted [97.113(a)(3)].

INTERNATIONAL THIRD-PARTY TRAFFIC

International third-party traffic is traffic exchanged between control operators in different countries in certain circumstances. It is prohibited for US operators except where:

• The US has a special third-party agreement with the other country [97.115(a)(2)]; or
• The third party is a licensed amateur and eligible to be a control operator of the station [97.115(a)(2)]; or
• In cases of emergency where there is an immediate threat to lives and property [97.403].

Traffic carried over a message forwarding system must conform to the international regulations when the originating (first party) and receiving (second party) control operators are in different countries. If both first and second parties are in the same country, the international prohibition does not apply, even if the third party is in a different country. For example, if an amateur in California sends a message to an amateur in New York who then sends the message via the Internet to a third party in England, there is no violation because the over-the-air portion was within the US. In such a situation, the communication is delivered to or received from the third party

---

On the Road

While most of your ham radio activity will probably take place at your home station, you may operate from other locations—your car, your vacation spot, at Field Day or even outside the country. Amateurs are permitted to operate their stations portable or mobile anywhere in the US, its territories and possessions. There is no need to notify the FCC, or keep a log of your portable operation in these areas (note that when there is a *permanent* change in your mailing address, you must notify the FCC on Form 605—note that the FCC no longer accepts 610's). You don't have to sign "mobile" or "portable." If you're operating your station away from home for a long time, arrange to have your mail forwarded to your temporary location, in the unlikely event that the FCC sends a Notice of Violation or other official correspondence to your permanent mailing address.

Drawing a distinction between mobile and portable operation is sometimes helpful. Mobile refers to talking on your 2-meter FM rig while driving your pickup truck, or while jogging or backpacking. Portable means operating for an extended period at a specific, definable location, such as your cabin in the mountains or condo in Florida.

US amateurs sometimes forget that when they go to American Samoa, the US Virgin Islands or any other place where Amateur Radio is regulated by the FCC, they may operate normally under the terms of their license. When operating from US territory that has a distinctive prefix such as Guam (KH2), you are not required to sign with that prefix, but you may do so to let others know you're "DX."

Table 1

International Third-Party Traffic—Proceed With Caution

Occasionally, DX stations may ask you to pass a third-party message to a friend or relative in the States. This is all right as long as the US has signed an official third-party traffic agreement with that particular country, or the third party is a licensed amateur. The traffic must be noncommercial and of a personal, unimportant nature. During an emergency, the US State Department will often work out a special temporary agreement with the country involved. But in normal times, never handle traffic without first making sure it is legally permitted.

US Amateurs May Handle Third-Party Traffic With:

C5	The Gambia	TI	Costa Rica
CE	Chile	T9	Bosnia-Herzegovina
CO	Cuba	V2	Antigua and Barbuda
CP	Bolivia	V3	Belize
CX	Uruguay	V4	St Christopher and Nevis
D6	The Comoros	V6	Federated States of
DU	Philippines		Micronesia
EL	Liberia	V7	Marshall Islands
GB*	United Kingdom	VE	Canada
HC	Ecuador	VK	Australia
HH	Haiti	VP6/VR6**	Pitcairn Island
HI	Dominican Republic	XE	Mexico
HK	Colombia	YN	Nicaragua
HP	Panama	YS	El Salvador
HR	Honduras	YV	Venezuela
J3	Grenada	ZP	Paraguay
J6	St Lucia	ZS	South Africa
J7	Dominica	3DAØ	Swaziland
J8	St Vincent and	4U1ITU	ITU Geneva
	the Grenadines	4U1VIC	VIC Vienna
JY	Jordan	4X	Israel
LU	Argentina	6Y	Jamaica
OA	Peru	8R	Guyana
PY	Brazil	9G	Ghana
TA	Turkey	9L	Sierra Leone
TG	Guatemala	9Y	Trinidad and Tobago

Notes

*Third-party traffic permitted between US amateurs and special-events stations in the United Kingdom having the prefix GB only, with the exception that GB3 stations are not included in this agreement.

** Since 1970, there has been an informal agreement between the United Kingdom and the US, permitting Pitcairn and US amateurs to exchange messages concerning medical emergencies, urgent need for equipment or supplies, and private or personal matters of island residents.

Please note that the Region 2 Division of the International Amateur Radio Union (IARU) has recommended that international traffic on the 20 and 15-meter bands be conducted on the following frequencies:

14.100-14.150 MHz	21.150-21.200 MHz
14.250-14.350 MHz	21.300-21.450 MHz

The IARU is the alliance of Amateur Radio societies from around the world; Region 2 comprises North, South and Central America and the Caribbean.

Note: At the end of an exchange of third-party traffic with a station located in a foreign country, an FCC-licensed amateur must transmit the call sign of the foreign station as well as his own call sign.

via normal communications systems and thus there is no revenue loss to the foreign communications system.

In almost all cases, amateurs are not required to give the call sign of the person with whom they are engaged in a QSO, but there's one exception: At the end of any international third-party communications, a station must identify with its own call sign and that of the foreign station with which traffic was exchanged [97.115(c)].

INTERNATIONAL COMMUNICATIONS

The international Radio Regulations as well as the FCC's Rules apply to international communications. FCC Rules state "Transmissions to a different country, where permitted, shall be made in plain language and shall be limited to messages of a technical nature relating to tests, and, to remarks of a personal character for which, by reason of their unimportance, recourse to the public telecommunications service is not justified." [97.117].

STATION IDENTIFICATION

There is a simple reason for station identification: You must clearly make known the source of your transmissions to anyone receiving them. No station may transmit unidentified communications or signals, or transmit as the station call sign any call sign not authorized to the station. Specifically, FCC rules state: "Each amateur station, except a space station or telecommand station, must transmit its assigned call sign on its transmitting channel at the end of each communication, and at least every ten minutes during a communication, for the purpose of clearly making the source of the transmissions from the station known to those receiving the transmissions. No station may transmit unidentified communications or signals, or transmit as the station call sign, any call sign not authorized to the station [97.119(a)]."

You must identify with your call sign *at the end of each contact, and every 10 minutes during the contact.* You may use any emission authorized for the frequency you're using [97.119(a), (b)]. You are not required to identify at the beginning of a QSO.

You must identify with your complete call sign in the manner described above. Some net and DX operators encourage callers to use just the "last two" letters of their call sign. This is fine as long as every US operator identifies with his or her full call sign in accordance with the FCC requirements outlined above. If a person calls on a frequency with their "last two," they must give their full call sign at least every 10 minutes and before leaving the frequency, even if they don't make the desired contact. Riley Hollingsworth, the FCC's Special Counsel for Amateur Radio Enforcement, has stated that to be strictly legal, stations using a suffix-letter ID, should always identify within the first 10 minutes of the communication (and each 10 minutes thereafter) with a complete call sign.

Except when exchanging international third-party communications, there is no requirement to identify the other station(s) with which you are communicating. In the case of international third-party communications, at the end of the contact you must give the call sign of the station with which you exchanged third-party traffic, as well as your own call sign [97.115(c)].

PERMISSIBLE METHODS OF IDENTIFICATION

There are different FCC Rules for identification when using various modes. Other than the general guidelines specified in §97.119(a), more specific identification rules apply for each individual mode. Proper identification must be made in the following ways when using one of the following modes when operating with [97.119(b)]:

• CW—when keyed by an automatic device used only for identification, the speed must not exceed 20 words per minute;
• Phone—when using the English language, use of a standard phonetic alphabet as an aid for correct station identification is encouraged;
• RTTY—using a specified digital code, when all or part of the communications are transmitted by a RTTY or data emission;
• Image—must conform to the applicable transmission standards, either color or monochrome, of §73.682(a) of the FCC Rules, when all or part of the communications are transmitted in the same image emission.

CALL SIGN INDICATORS

Hams normally use only their call sign when operating within the US, its possessions and territories. US amateurs aren't required to identify their call sign region if it is different from the one indicated by their call sign. Sometimes amateurs are required by the FCC to append their call with a special indicator. The FCC Rules state "One or more indicators may be included with the call sign. Each indicator must be separated from the call sign by the slant mark (/) or by any suitable word that denotes the slant mark" [97.119(c)]. When amateurs upgrade their license, they are required to append their call with an indicator to show that they have upgraded and it must be used until the license is processed by the FCC. When the control operator upgrades his or her license, the operator may begin operating immediately. The amateur must use this ID procedure until the upgrade appears on the FCC database, at which time the special identifier may be dropped. When operating in the recently gained privileges, the following indicators must be used after the call sign and separated by a stroke as follows [§97.9(b), 97.119(f)]:

1) When upgrading to Technician Class: KT;
2) When upgrading to General Class: AG;
3) When upgrading to Amateur Extra Class: AE, such as KA1JO/AE.

If an indicator is self-assigned, it must be included before, after, or both before and after the call sign, but a self-assigned indicator may not conflict with any other indicator specified by the FCC Rules or with any prefix assigned to another country [97.119(c)]. For example, when ARRL volun-

Q&A— Station Identification

Q. Do I have to give my call sign at the beginning of the contact?

A. You only have to ID at the *end* of the QSO and at least once every 10 minutes during its course [97.119(a)]. There is no requirement to transmit your call sign at the beginning of a contact.

Q. How often do I have to give the call sign of the station I'm talking to?

A. You are not legally required to mention the other amateur's call at all [97.119(a)]. The only exception is when handling traffic with foreign stations—you must then give the other station's call sign at the end of an exchange of third-party traffic [97.115(c)].

Q. When my ham friends from the local radio club come to visit my home and operate my rig, or vice versa, whose call sign is used? What frequency privileges may they (I) use?

A. Every control operator is bound by the frequency privileges of his or her license, regardless of what class of license is held by the station owner [97.105(b)]. For ID purposes, let's use an example. If Joanne, KA1SIP, a Technician, visits the shack of Steve, WV1X, an Amateur Extra, Joanne uses Steve's call sign, but must stay within her Technician privileges. If Steve authorizes it, she may use her own call at his station, but must stay within her Technician privileges. She could also operate as a third party (that is, as an unlicensed individual) outside her Technician privileges as long as Steve acts as the control operator and remains at the control point continuously monitoring and supervising the operation [97.115(b)]. On the other side of the coin, if Steve visits Joanne's shack and is using his Amateur Extra privileges, Steve must add his own call sign to the end of the station ID, for example, KA1SIP/WV1X [97.119(e)]. Joanne could also "lend" Steve her station, and then Steve operates his "temporary" station under his own station/operator license and call sign—no special ID needed.

Q. I regularly conduct my QSOs in Esperanto. Is it okay to identify in Esperanto?

A. Sorry, Esperanto doesn't cut it. When operating phone, you must identify your station in the *English* language [97.119(b)(2)].

Q. What's this "Temporary AG" stuff I've heard on the HF bands?

A. If you have a license and pass an upgrade examination, the Volunteer Examiners will issue a Certificate of Successful Completion of Examination (CSCE), a temporary permit that allows the use of your new privileges immediately [97.9(b)]. In the interim period after passing the exam but before the FCC grants the upgrade, you must add a special designator to your call sign whenever you use your new privileges. For example, if you just upgraded from Technician to General and you are operating in the General subband, you must give your call sign followed by the words "Temporary AG," or the slant mark (/) followed by the letters "AG" on CW. AG is the FCC's indicator for General class (the other indicator is AE for Amateur Extra) [97.119(f)].

Q. This summer, G5BFU from England and VE3GRO from Ontario, Canada are coming to visit me and my family. How should G5BFU and VE3GRO identify while they're here in the States?

A. Because the US and England share a reciprocal operating agreement, G5BFU may operate without any paperwork. He must bring his English license and proof of his citizenship. If he is on the air from California, his station ID consists of the US letter prefix and number followed by his home call sign: "W6/G5BFU." This is the "reverse ID" method that the FCC adopted in June of 1988. Because of treaty constraints, however, proper identification for VE3GRO is in the traditional manner—Canadian call sign *followed by* US prefix. VE3GRO in 6-land would ID as "VE3GRO/W6." The "W6" portion of the identification is considered the "indicator" by the FCC. The call sign and the indicator are separated by the slant bar (/) on CW or RTTY/data, or the words "stroke," "slant," "slash" or "portable" if on phone. The rule also requires that at least once during the QSO, the actual geographical location must be mentioned, in English, such as "14 miles west of Bakersfield, California" [97.119(g)]. If they have CEPT documentation, they may use it.

Q. Is it okay to give my call sign in phonetics when identifying?

A. Yes. The FCC encourages the use of a nationally or internationally recognized standard phonetic alphabet *when necessary* as good amateur practice [97.119(b)(2)]. The International Telecommunication Union (ITU), an agency of the United Nations, has developed such a list, and the ARRL encourages its use when phonetics are necessary to make the *initial* identification (such as when signals are weak, or in a DX pileup when there is interference). The ITU list is as follows:

For example, Shelly, WB1ENT, may phonetically identify on phone by giving her call sign as "Whiskey Bravo One Echo November Tango."

A—Alfa	N—November
B—Bravo	O—Oscar
C—Charlie	P—Papa
D—Delta	Q—Quebec
E—Echo	R—Romeo
F—Foxtrot	S—Sierra
G—Golf	T—Tango
H—Hotel	U—Uniform
I—India	V—Victor
J—Juliette	W—Whiskey
K—Kilo	X—X-Ray
L—Lima	Y—Yankee
M—Mike	Z—Zulu

teers celebrated the 130th anniversary of the birth of ARRL Founding President Hiram Percy Maxim in 1999, they were authorized to append "/130" to their calls if on CW or RTTY/data or "stroke" followed by their call if on phone. FCC permission isn't required.

SPECIAL EVENT CALL SIGNS

Amateurs like to operate their stations to commemorate special events and calls used can take several forms: amateurs may use their own call, such as N1KB; they may use their call with a self-assigned identifier *after* the call, such as N1KB/125; or they may obtain a 1×1 call sign, such as W1A, from a Special Event Call Sign Data Base Coordinator.

Special identification rules apply to amateurs or amateur organizations who have obtained a 1×1 call sign: "When transmitting in conjunction with an event of special significance, a station may substitute for its assigned call sign a special event call sign as shown for that station for that period of time on the common data base coordinated, maintained and disseminated by the special event call sign data base coordinators. Additionally, the station must transmit its assigned call sign at least once per hour during such transmissions" [97.119(d)]. These special event call signs are only assigned for short terms for events of special significance. If, for example, the Newington Amateur Radio League obtains N1N to commemorate the 130th anniversary of the founding of the Town of Newington, the operators may substitute N1N in place of the club call of W1OKY and it must identify every 10 minutes and at the end of the communication. The normally assigned call of W1OKY *must* be given at least once per hour. For information on obtaining a 1×1 call sign, contact ARRL HQ or one of the other Special Event Call Sign Data Base Coordinators. The database can be found on the World Wide Web at **http://ncvec.spindle.net/html/show_all.cfm**.

OTHER IDENTIFICATION PROCEDURES

Under all circumstances except one, amateurs use one call sign and it can be appended by special indicator as detailed above. The one exception is when the operator license class held by the control operator exceeds that of the station licensee. In that case, an indicator consisting of the call sign assigned to the control operator's station must be included after the call sign [97.119(e)].

If, for example, N1KB, an Amateur Extra, operates the station of KA1UFZ, a Novice, N1KB can't exceed the Novice class frequencies using the call KA1UFZ unless the following identification procedure is given: KA1UFZ/N1KB. If KA1UFZ allows it, N1KB may use his own call sign at the station of KA1UFZ.

RESTRICTED OPERATION AND QUIET HOURS

In rare cases, the FCC will assign quiet hours to amateurs if his or her station "causes general interference to the reception of transmissions from stations operating in the domestic broadcast service when receivers of good engineering design, including adequate selectivity characteristics, are used to receive such transmissions, and this fact is made known to the amateur station licensee, the amateur station." In other words, if a consumer's television is properly shielded and if the amateur knows it, yet still causes interference from spurious emissions or other unwanted emissions, the FCC has the authority to assign "quiet hours." In this case, the amateur station can't be operated during the hours from 8 PM to 10:30 PM local time, and on Sunday for the additional period from 10:30 AM until 1 PM local time, on the frequency or frequencies used when the interference was created [97.121(a)].

Quiet hours are not usually applicable to cases of telephone, stereo or other home electronic interference, but only to broadcast receiver interference. Even then, there are usually no quiet hours applicable, except when there has been an actual finding that the broadcast receiver is of good engineering design and has adequate selectivity.

The FCC may impose quiet hours for interference to other radio services, and the ARRL has received sporadic reports of quiet hours imposed by FCC field offices. These are usually cases where the amateur did not cooperate with the FCC and did not offer any cooperation to bona-fide attempts by a neighbor trying to cure the interference. If the FCC intends to put an amateur on "quiet hours," or to impose other operating restrictions, it is obliged to afford the amateur an opportunity for a hearing before the restrictions are effective [§§303(f) and 316, Communications Act of 1934, as amended].

Concerning interference to other services, the FCC states: "In general, such steps as may be necessary to minimize interference to stations operating in other services may be required after investigation by the FCC" [97.121(b)].

INTERFERENCE

A combination of FCC-mandated and voluntary restrictions are intended to keep us out of one another's way help, but these cannot completely eliminate interference between amateur stations—nor should we expect them to.

Let's put interference into perspective. Note that we're referring only to interference from one amateur station to another, not RFI/TVI or to nonamateur intruders into exclusive ham bands.

Except when it concerns emergency communications, amateur-to-amateur interference is not, in and of itself, illegal. Each amateur station has an equal right to operate; just because you've used the same frequency since 1947 doesn't mean you have any more legal right to it than the person who received their license in the mail five minutes ago. The rules specifically prohibit willful or malicious interference [97.101(d)].

What's malicious interference? Here's an example. If two hams, or groups of hams, find themselves on the same frequency pursuing mutually exclusive objectives, that's happenstance, not malicious interference. On the other hand, if one moves to another frequency and the other follows for the purpose of continuing to cause QRM to the first, the second has crossed the line. If he does it enough, he'll put his license in jeopardy. Of course, what sometimes happens is that they'll all sit on one frequency and argue about who has more right to be there. All it accomplishes is to keep the frequency from being used by anyone for anything worthwhile.

Other FCC Rules are intended to minimize (but not to eliminate) interference. One says, ". . . amateur stations must use no more than the minimum transmitter power necessary to carry out the desired communications" [97.313(a)]. There's also a requirement that ". . . each amateur station shall be operated in accordance with good engineering and good amateur practice" [97.101(a)]. But hams' obligations to each other don't end with the rules; even more important is the need for common sense and common courtesy, when hams share common spectrum resources.

Radio amateurs have the right to pursue legitimate objectives within the privileges conveyed by their licenses, but they also have the obligation to minimize the inconvenience and loss of enjoyment hams cause to others. If there's a tiny segment of a band used for international communication, it's not too much to ask that local ragchews take place elsewhere. If establishing a beacon in the middle of a densely populated area is going to cause interference to nearby weak-signal enthusiasts, an amateur can find another place to put it. And surely, in such cases amateurs don't need the FCC to tell us what growing up in a civilized society should already have taught us to do.

CONCLUSION

With the exception of §97.107, Reciprocal Licensing Authority, Subpart B has not changed in recent years. Many questions concerning this subsection arrive at ARRL HQ each year, however. It gives amateurs broad guidelines as to what the FCC expects of them, including what amateurs *can't* do. The FCC gives amateurs the latitude to experiment, something many other services do not have. It is the responsibility of all amateurs to follow all Part 97 rules at all times.

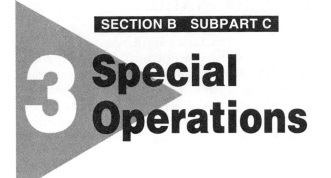

3 Special Operations

Subpart C, "Special Operations," addresses specialized activities of Amateur Radio: Auxiliary links, beacon operation, repeater operation, space and Earth station operation, telecommand (remote control) operation and message forwarding systems. These are not "modes" of operation, but "uses" for amateur stations using whichever mode is appropriate and legal.

Here are some of the questions this chapter answers: What are auxiliary stations? How are auxiliary links, remote bases, repeaters and telecommand operation related? Why aren't repeaters the same as remote bases? How can I legally make my H-T into a crossband repeater? What's the difference between a repeater and a digipeater? Why is frequency coordination important?

Some of the concepts in this chapter are quite complex, but by the time you finish reading it, you'll be able to answer these questions with authority, plus a whole lot more!

SUBPART C RULES SUMMARY: SPECIAL OPERATIONS

97.201 Auxiliary station.
97.203 Beacon station.
97.205 Repeater station.
97.207 Space station.
97.209 Earth station.
97.211 Space Telecommand station.
97.213 Telecommand of an amateur station.
97.215 Telecommand of model craft.
97.217 Telemetry.
97.219 Message Forwarding System.
97.221 Automatically controlled digital station.

AUXILIARY STATIONS

When an amateur station, such as a repeater, is remotely controlled over a radio link, there is another station involved—the station doing the controlling. This "control" station is, under the FCC rules, called an *auxiliary station*. Here's how the FCC defines an auxiliary station: *an amateur station, other than a message forwarding system, that is transmitting communications point-to-point within a system of cooperating amateur stations* [97.3(a)(7)]. There are a few important rules that apply to auxiliary stations:

1) All amateurs, except Novices, may put auxiliary stations on the air and be control operators for auxiliary stations [97.201(a)].

2) Auxiliary stations may transmit only in ham bands above 222 MHz, except 222.0-222.15, 431-433 and 435-438 MHz [97.201(b)].

3) Licensees of auxiliary stations causing interference to each other are equally responsible for solving the interference, except where one station is coordinated and the other is not [97.201(c)]. This is why it's important to have repeater control links coordinated as well as the input and output frequencies. This is the FCC's way of recognizing the importance of frequency coordination. We'll discuss this critical topic later in this chapter.

4) An auxiliary station may, under certain circumstances, be automatically controlled and may send one-way transmissions [97.201(d),(e)].

The easiest way to explain the operation of an auxiliary station is to use several examples.

USES FOR AUXILIARY STATIONS

There are several forms of auxiliary operation, encompassing a number of different types of activities, such as:

1) Remote control of a station at a different location (such as a repeater on a mountaintop), where a radio link is used to make one-way transmissions of DTMF tones to change its operating parameters, turn it on or off, change frequencies or power, or rotate antennas. These commands are considered to be a form of "primary" control and may be performed only by designated control operator(s). **Fig 1** shows how an auxiliary station can be used to remotely control a remote base.

2) Voice links between two or more stations within a system of stations, such as:

(a) Point-to-point links from a repeater's remote receiver(s) back to the main repeater site.

(b) Dedicated point-to-point links between different repeaters in a "system" of either full-time or part-time linked repeaters.

(c) A combination of remote control and point-to-point voice links intended to control *and* carry the voice signals from the control point to the transmitter(s) of a remotely controlled station. (This is the equivalent of replacing the wire between the microphone and the transmitter's mike input with a radio link from the microphone to the remotely located transmitter.)

This is commonly referred to as an "uplink."

(d) Point-to-point links from the receiver(s) of a remotely located station back to the station's control operator(s) at their control point(s). This is the equivalent of replacing the wire between the receiver's audio output terminals and its loudspeaker with a radio link from the receiver to a remotely located loudspeaker. This is commonly referred to as a "downlink."

WHAT IS A "SYSTEM" OF "COOOPERATING" AMATEUR STATIONS?

The FCC uses the terms "system" and "cooperating" in its definition of "auxiliary stations." A repeater transmitter, its associated receivers, link transmitters and receivers, and any associated control stations and control receivers, constitute such a "system" [97.3(a)(7)]. *"Users" of the repeater are not part of the "system."* This is a very important point. See also the section on "Relaying Signals in a Repeater System" later in this chapter. Remember that all of the different combinations of stations described in

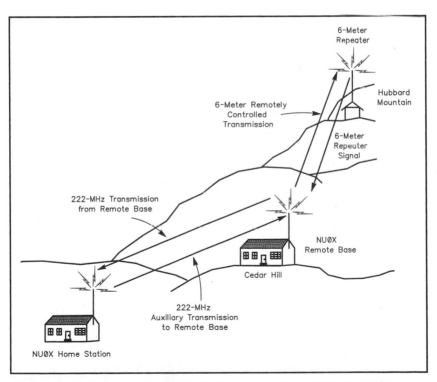

Fig 1—Jay, NUØX, uses an auxiliary station to remotely control the NUØX remote base atop Cedar Hill. This enables him to check into the nightly net on the Hubbard Mountain 6-meter repeater.

items 2(a) through 2(d), in the section on "Uses for Auxiliary Stations" elsewhere in this chapter, form closed "systems" of stations.

There may be several different licensees for all of the individual stations that make up this interconnected "system," all of whom must work together to make the system work. Thus, they are "cooperating," as the FCC likes to call them.

"REMOTE BASE" STATIONS

Auxiliary stations are also used in what have come to be known as "remote bases." The term "remote base" does not appear anywhere in the FCC rules. But, if you combine items 2(c) and 2(d) in the section on "Uses for Auxiliary Stations," you can create the basics of a radio remotely controlled base station, or a "remote base." There are *many* possibilities for remotely controlled amateur stations.

REMOTE BASES *AREN'T* REPEATERS

It is important to recognize that a "remote base" is not the same as a repeater [97.3(a)(38)]. With a repeater, the users don't need to send any sort of primary control signals in order to use the repeater; and normally, *anyone* can be a user. Users transmit and receive on the repeater's input and output frequencies, which must be in appropriate repeater segments of the 29.5 MHz or higher frequency bands.

With a repeater, *users* are *not* a part of its "system," but the control operator(s) for a radio remotely controlled repeater *are* a part of its "system." They must conduct all of their primary control functions for the repeater by a form of auxiliary operation on authorized frequencies above 222.15 MHz, except 431–433 and 435–438 MHz [97.201(b)].

With a remote base, all users are conducting a form of auxiliary operation to remotely control *and use* the station. *All* of these users *are* control operators of the remote station. Therefore, they are all a part of the "system," and all of them must conduct their control and voice links to and from the remote base on authorized (and hopefully coordinated) auxiliary frequencies above 222.15 MHz [97.201(b)].

A remote base always operates under the rules for remotely controlled stations. The rules for local control and automatic control do not apply. Just as there must be a control operator at your home station whenever it's in operation, there must also be an acting control operator whenever the remote base is in operation. This includes periods when the remote receiver and downlink are active, but none of the control operators are actually talking, i.e., when the remote station is in a "listening only" mode.

"OPEN" REMOTE BASES AREN'T LEGAL

Remember that there is no such thing as an "open" remote base. Just as you wouldn't allow any unknown ham to just walk into your shack and start talking on your radio without your permission, the same rule applies to the use of a remote base. *Every* user must be specifically authorized by the station's licensee to use the station, thus making each of them "designated control operators" of the station. By the way, the receiver(s) and transmitter(s) at the remotely controlled station may operate on any frequency for which the acting control operator has license privileges. For instance, if the control operator holds an Advanced Class license, the operator may use a remote base which operates on any appropriate HF phone band, provided that he or she doesn't exceed his or her own privileges. The control operator may allow other amateurs to talk over the remote base while he is in control, but even though they may hold amateur licenses, these other people are only talking over the station under provisions of the "third party" rules, not as control operators.

Finally, if you look at the rules regarding the frequencies available for auxiliary operation, you will conclude that there is no such thing as a legal "remote base" which uses frequencies anywhere in the 2-meter band for the "uplink" and "downlink." Those systems that go from 2-meter FM to 10-meter FM, or from 2-meter FM to 6-meter FM, for example, are not technically "remote bases," even though some hams like to call them that. They are really "crossband repeaters" and they are legal only if *both* ends are within authorized repeater segments of both bands. Repeater operation (including all input and output frequencies) is prohibited on *all* HF amateur bands, except the top end of 10 meters. Likewise, there is no such thing as a legal 2-meter FM to 75-meter SSB "remote base," since auxiliary uplinks and downlinks must *all* be above 222.15 MHz [97.201(b)].

MAKING YOUR STATION A "CROSSBAND REPEATER"

Modern dual-band or tri-band VHF/UHF rigs often have the capability to do crossband linking. When operating in this mode, the users may call them "crossband repeaters." Actually they are often remote bases, such as when they are used to allow an operator with a hand-held radio to access a repeater from a location where he or she would normally not be able to do so. For example, a hiker in a remote location might leave his car where his dual-band mobile rig can access a distant 2-meter repeater. Leaving the mobile rig on, he then takes his UHF H-T with him, and can access the 2-meter repeater via his mobile rig.

MAKING IT LEGAL

A crossband repeater (or "portable remote base") is okay as long as several conditions are met:

1) The user communicates with his crossband rig via the UHF side. Since this serves as his control and voice uplink, it is a form of auxiliary operation and must be conducted on authorized auxiliary frequencies above 222.15 MHz. Since the operator is the control operator, *that person* must actually be able to

control the station! That person must be able to turn it off remotely if a problem develops. If the operator can't control it, it's not legal [97.7, 97.201, 97.213].

2) If the control link fails, the remote station must shut down within three minutes which means a 3-minute timer is required [97.213].

3) The unattended station must be identified on *all* frequencies it transmits on. Since this is a form of remote base, the user's ID over the UHF uplink to the dualband radio also serves to ID the VHF output of the mobile rig. In the other direction, however, there is no way for the control operator to ID the UHF downlink from the mobile remote base, so some form of automatic ID must be employed [97.119].

Unfortunately, few manufacturers include the capabilities listed above in their rigs. Hence, to be fully legal, some form of add-on controller may be necessary.

Another use for crossband operation is to link together two existing repeaters on different bands. This is usually done on a temporary basis during an emergency, a drill or a special event. Again, the requirements for proper station identification and control on *both sides* of the dualband radio's transmissions still apply. If both the VHF and UHF transmitters are not properly identified and controlled, the operation is not legal.

In both examples cited above, the control requirement can be satisfied by having a control operator at the station, thus making it a locally controlled station. Although this may not always be convenient, it is a way to satisfy all of the station control requirements.

CONTACT YOUR FREQUENCY COORDINATOR FIRST

One other thing—when setting up your "crossband repeater," or portable "remote base," don't just plop down on just any old UHF frequency which appears to be "vacant." It might be a repeater input, or a link or control frequency for some unknown repeater. The UHF output from your mobile rig might cause severe interference to someone else's coordinated operations, and you wouldn't be aware of it. Contact your local frequency coordinator for a recommendation as to what frequencies to use. Many coordinators have set aside frequency pairs which are designated specifically for temporary, portable or emergency repeaters. For the name and address of your frequency coordinator, see the latest edition of *The ARRL Repeater Directory* or check the listing on *ARRLWeb* at: **http://www.arrl.org/field/regulations/freqcoord.html**.

RELAYING SIGNALS IN A REPEATER SYSTEM

Having the repeater's receiver and transmitter at one site can cause problems. These problems can often be solved with filters and duplexers, but an alternative is to separate the transmitter and receiver using a link between the two sites. Since filters and duplexers for 10 and 6 meters can be quite large and expensive, many repeaters on these bands use the "split-site" technique whereby a dedicated wire line or an auxiliary link on a band above 222.15 MHz is used to relay signals from the receiver to the transmitter. The latter is shown in **Fig 2**.

Some repeaters even have multiple remote receivers to expand or improve their receiving coverage. The signals from each of these remote receivers are then relayed on auxiliary frequencies back to the repeater transmitter site where a "voter" selects the best signal to be retransmitted. Note that *every* one of these auxiliary transmitters must be properly controlled, just like the main repeater transmitter. They cannot just be plopped down somewhere out in the "boonies" and left to fend for themselves!

Auxiliary stations are also used to link separate repeaters into a repeater network spanning a much larger geographic area than can be covered by one repeater alone, such as the Evergreen Intertie in the Northwest.

BEACON STATIONS

A *beacon station* is simply a transmitter that alerts listeners to its presence. In the Radionavigation Service, beacons are used to provide navigational guidance. In the Amateur Radio Service, beacons are used primarily for the study of radiowave propagation—to allow amateurs to tell when a band is open to different parts of the country or world. Accordingly, the FCC defines a beacon as *an amateur station transmitting communications for the purposes of observation of propagation and reception or other related experimental activities* [97.3(a)(9)].

The rules address beacon operation [97.203]. A few key points:

- Any license class, except Novice, can operate a beacon station [97.203(a)].

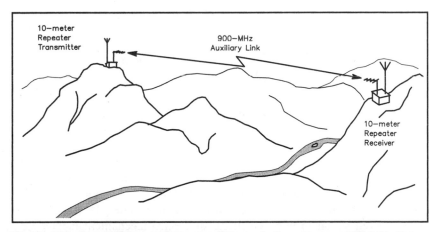

Fig 2—This is another use for an auxiliary station. Here, a 902-MHz link relays signals from a 10-meter repeater receiver to the repeater transmitter, located a few miles away.

Table 1

Frequencies Authorized for Automatically Controlled Beacon Stations [97.203(d)]

28.20-28.30 MHz
50.06-50.08 MHz
144.275-144.300 MHz
222.05-222.06 MHz
432.300-432.400 MHz
All amateur bands above 450 MHz

- A beacon may transmit only on one frequency band from the same location [97.203(b)].
- The transmitter power of a beacon must not exceed 100 W [97.203(c)].
- Automatically controlled beacon stations are limited to the frequencies shown in **Table 1**. Beacons that are manually controlled are not subject to the same restrictions as automatically controlled beacons [97.203(d)].
- Before establishing or modifying a beacon in the National Radio Quiet Zone, beacon owners must notify the National Radio Astronomy Laboratory [97.203(e)]. See the map of the National Radio Quiet Zone later in this chapter.
- A beacon may transmit one way communication [97.203(g)].
- The operator of a new beacon within 10 miles of the Arecibo Observatory in Arecibo, Puerto Rico must give written notification to the Observatory. See §1.924, found in Appendix 2, for details.

There is one exception to the rules laid out in §97.203. The FCC has issued a special license for an automatically controlled beacon operating on 14.100 MHz and a few other HF frequencies. This network is part of the Northern California DX Foundation and IARU sponsored worldwide system of beacons on those frequencies.

REPEATER STATIONS

A *repeater station* is *an amateur station that simultaneously retransmits the transmission of another amateur station on a different channel or channels* [97.3(a)(39)]. Only repeaters, some types of auxiliary stations, and space stations may automatically retransmit the radio signals of other amateur stations [97.113(f)].

Although the term "automatic retransmission" is not defined in the current version of the FCC rules, in past versions it was defined as follows: "Automatic retransmission. Retransmission of signals by an amateur radio station whereby the retransmitting station is actuated solely by the presence of a received signal through electrical or electro-mechanical means, i.e., without any direct, positive action by the control operator." Holding your mike in front of the loudspeaker of a receiver so you can retransmit the signals of another station is not "automatic," so this is not "repeater" operation.

WHAT IS A REPEATER?

A repeater normally consists of a receiver, a transmitter, an antenna and a repeater controller (which controls the retransmission and various other functions). Many repeaters also use a duplexer, which allows the use of a single antenna for simultaneous transmitting and receiving. Operation generally occurs on the VHF amateur bands, although there is 10-meter repeater activity and repeaters are becoming more common on the UHF and microwave bands. The most popular band for repeaters is the 2-meter band (144 MHz), with the 440, 222 and 50 MHz bands following closely behind. FM voice is the most common mode of repeater operation, although there are also quite a few amateur television (ATV) repeaters.

A typical "machine" sits on top of a mountain or tall building and retransmits signals from small hand-held or mobile rigs. The result is an increase in communications coverage for the user. Some repeaters extend coverage to entire states and more! Others have much more localized coverage.

An individual repeater may be part of an interconnected "network" of repeaters which are linked together by wireline or auxiliary radio stations, extending the coverage area of the network far beyond that of a single repeater. Except for the geographic range involved, the same rules apply to the entire system as to the individual repeater and auxiliary stations that make it up.

A REPEATER'S "PRIMARY" CONTROL SYSTEM

When transmitting, every amateur station must have a control operator who must have access to the primary control functions of the station [97.7]. There is a special exception to this rule, as described in the following section on automatic control.

TYPES OF REPEATER CONTROL:
LOCAL, REMOTE AND AUTOMATIC

There are three types of "primary" control for a repeater.

Local Control

1) *Local control* is when the control operator is physically located at the repeater site and is actually monitoring and controlling the repeater's operation whenever it's on. This is the simplest form of control, and is typical where the repeater is located at the licensee's home or place of business. It is defined by the FCC as *the use of a control operator who directly manipulates the operating adjustments in the station to achieve compliance with FCC rules* [97.3(a)(30)].

Since most people need to sleep once in a while, it is usually not convenient for the licensee to be able to "babysit" the repeater 24 hours a day. Thankfully, the FCC rules have made provision for alternative forms of control, as described below.

Remote Control

2) *Remote control* is used when the repeater is located away from the control operator(s), such as on a tall building, a tower or a mountain. The FCC defines "remote control" as *the use of a control operator who indirectly manipulates the operating adjustments in the station through a control link to achieve compliance with the FCC Rules*. [97.3(a)(38)]. Under remote control, the licensee has implemented a means by which the repeater's control operator(s) can monitor and control its operation by some form of control link from one or more distant locations. The duties of monitoring and controlling the repeater can be shared by several amateurs, all of whom have been designated by the repeater's licensee as "control operators." They have been given access to the remote control system, and also been given the "secret" codes used to control the repeater's various functions.

Such a remote control link can take any of several forms. There are three basic types:

A *dedicated wireline from the remote control point(s) to the repeater site*. Although such a system might be somewhat expensive, since renting a dedicated line from the telephone company is not cheap, it is very secure! Nobody else has any access to this type of line. One limitation is that it can only be accessed from those specific locations where it terminates.

A *non-published telephone line into the repeater site*. Such a line can be accessed from any telephone, so precautions must be implemented such that an accidentally dialed "wrong number" won't inadvertently cause the repeater to do something the control operator doesn't want it to do. The simplest form of controller is a "ring counter" which counts the number of times the telephone rings then performs some function. This is not very secure, however, and should not be used as a means by which a repeater can be turned on. A more secure controller usually answers the telephone line, after which the control operator must send a non-published sequence of DTMF tones to perform the desired control function.

Note that in both cases (a) and (b), in the earlier section, "Uses for Auxiliary Stations," the control link must be available 100% of the time! Therefore, a telephone control line cannot also be used for an autopatch. This is because if the autopatch is in use, the telephone line is busy, in which case the control operator could not gain access to the repeater's control system if he needed to.

A *radio control link* uses auxiliary stations, operated by designated control operators and transmitting on authorized auxiliary frequencies above 222.15 MHz. Again, this control link must be available to the control operator(s) 100% of the time, so it cannot be used for any other purpose. The frequency and control codes are not published and are known only by the licensee and control operators (and the frequency is known by the area frequency coordinator).

Automatic Control

3) *Automatic control* is used when no control operator is available to "babysit" the repeater. This is the exception mentioned earlier. *Automatic control* is defined by the FCC as *the use of devices and procedures for control of a station when it is transmitting so that compliance with the FCC Rules is achieved without the control operator being present at a control point* [97.3(a)(6)].

Under automatic control, the licensee has installed a control device which continuously monitors the technical operation of the repeater. If the controller detects a malfunction, it shuts the repeater down. From a practical standpoint, most repeaters operate under some form of automatic control most of the time. However, they also have a control link as described in the preceding section on remote control of a repeater which allows the repeater to be disabled by remote control if necessary. This remote control link also allows the control operator(s) to enable or disable various repeater functions such as an autopatch or links.

Note that such a controller cannot detect and correct improper use of the repeater. The licensee is always responsible for the proper operation of the station, even when not monitoring its operation. In the event of improper use of the machine, the licensee is responsible for correcting the problem as soon as practicable and for making sure that the problem will not happen again. *Although no control operator is required to be present at a contol point while the repeater is operating under automatic control, it is still the station licensee's responsibility to see that the repeater operates properly at all times* [97.103(a)]. The repeater's licensee should prevent unauthorized tampering with the equipment by implementing various security procedures and devices, such as having an unpublished remote control link frequency and unpublished primary remote control codes for the control operator(s) to use. The licensee should use padlocks on the repeater housing and try to protect the feedlines and antennas from tampering. Finally, the licensee should make sure word gets out quickly if something is wrong, and that authorized individuals have quick access to the repeater shutdown function.

One more note on accountability: the rules do say that the control operator of a repeater that inadvertently retransmits communications that violate the rules is not accountable for the violative communications. [97.205(g)]. If a user transmits obscene words, for example, the control op is not responsible for the violation. However, if the obscene transmissions continue for any length of time, the repeater should be shut down until the problem is solved.

From this discussion of the three basic types of primary station control, you can correctly conclude that a repeater is *not* restricted to *only one* form of control. During those periods when a control operator is awake and "on duty," the repeater is operating under either "local" or "remote control." When the maintenance crew is working at the repeater site, it is also operating under "local control." When all the control operators are asleep or at work and there is nobody around to babysit the machine, it can be operated under "automatic control."

"ANCILLARY" FUNCTIONS

The FCC makes a distinction between *functions repeater users can perform* (activating a crossband link, getting a weather or time-of-day report, or making a phone call via the autopatch, for example), and those *primary control functions reserved exclusively for the control operators in effecting basic control of the station.* The rules state that "ancillary (which also means "secondary") functions of a repeater that are available to users on the input channel are not considered remotely controlled functions of the station" [97.205(e)]. These "user" functions are conducted on the repeater's input frequency. However, the primary control functions (turning the repeater on or off, for example) must be performed via the repeater's primary control system, which is separate from the input frequency. By the way, there is nothing to prevent implementing some form of "emergency backup" means to shut down a repeater via its regular input frequency, as long as the turn-on function can be performed only via the primary control system.

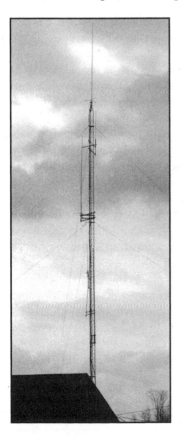

This distinction applies to crossband links and other functions. If the control operator enables a crossband link for use by a user by changing the repeater's command state through the control link, then users, including Technicians on a 2-meter repeater, may turn on and use the crossband link on the repeater input

The W1KKF repeater, located at the firehouse atop Cook Hill in Wallingford, Connecticut, allows operators to communicate throughout central Connecticut. It provides communications during emergencies for both local and area Emergency Operations Centers. *(photo by WA1CCQ)*

frequency to communicate with other hams on 10 meters. Changing the command state to allow users access to the crossband link is a "primary" control function. The user accessing the crossband link on the repeater input frequency is an "ancillary" function.

AMATEUR "PAGING"

Many modern amateur transceivers have "paging" capability. Paging opens the squelch of another radio that has been programmed by the control operator to accept such a command. Paging is just another form of calling a specific station to initiate a conversation. It is no different than calling CQ, or calling another specific station using his or her call sign. It is not telecommand, which is a form of one-way transmission that applies only to "devices," not operators, and it is not "communication." In other words, telecommand is a transmission in which the end result is intended to perform some function.

Paging is for the purpose of establishing communication, or for conveying information from one station to another. Although "paging" is not defined in Part 97, it is defined in Part 90 of the FCC Rules as "A one-way communications service from a base station to mobile or fixed receivers that provide signaling or information transfer by such means as tone, tone-voice, tactile, optical readout, etc." As such, it is an ancillary function and is no different than sending tones to activate an autopatch, which can be done on any appropriate amateur frequency, including 2 meters. It's not limited to frequencies where auxiliary operations must be conducted. It's the end result for which the transmission was made that counts. In this case, it's calling another station to initiate a conversation, not controlling a "system."

CONTROL DURING AUTOPATCH OPERATION

The distinction may be subtle: Although John Q. Ham, a user, can access an autopatch by sending the proper touchtones (use the patch to make a call, then turn it back off, all on the input frequency), this is an "ancillary" function. He is *not* "controlling" the repeater. The act of changing the command state of the repeater to enable the autopatch function, thus making it available for John Q. Ham to use in the first place, is a "primary" control function, which is reserved only for the control operators.

The point of this discussion of repeater control is that the licensee and control operators are responsible for the emissions of the repeater at all times [97.103(a)]. They must be able to shut off the repeater if there is a problem. If the only means of control is on the repeater input frequency, there may be times when jamming or unintentional interference make control unuseable. Therefore, they must have a different means of primary control that is available 100% of the time, such as a dedicated wireline, a telephone line or a radio link on an auxiliary frequency above 222.15 MHz separate from the repeater input frequency.

WHO MAY USE A REPEATER OR REMOTE BASE?

The licensee of *any* amateur station has the right to limit the use of his station to only certain other licensees! When it comes to repeaters, the FCC states this explicitly in Part 97. This rule states "limiting the use of a repeater to only certain users is permissible." [97.205(e)]. "Closed" repeaters may use CTCSS or other techniques to limit access to designated users. However, a repeater does not have to be listed as being "closed" in *The ARRL Repeater Directory* in order to have a limited access.

REASONS FOR LIMITING REPEATER ACCESS

There are several reasons for limiting the use of a repeater or a "remote base" to a certain list of users. Building and operating such a station is not cheap. In addition to the cost of all of the equipment (receivers, transmitters, controllers, duplexers, housing, tower, antennas and feed lines), there may also be ongoing expenses such as site rental fees, utility bills, phone line expenses, property insurance, equipment maintenance and so forth. Building and maintaining such a system takes a lot of time and effort. Because of the effort and expense, the sponsors and users of some systems may legitimately feel that they are the only people who should be able to enjoy the fruits of their labors. Contact the sponsor to find out how you might be able to join the group and become a welcome user.

It should also be noted, however, that just because a repeater may use some form of coded access, such as CTCSS, this does not necessarily mean that it is a "closed" repeater. Many "open" repeaters employ coded access, either full-time or part-time, in order to eliminate, or reduce, various types of interference, *not* to restrict who is welcome to use the machine. If in doubt, check with the sponsor.

Another important point is that a repeater user, more than likely, is *not* a control operator for the repeater. What this means, as an example, is that a Technician licensee who is operating on a repeater frequency authorized for Technician use (such as a 440 MHz repeater) may use a system that is crosslinked to a 10-meter repeater where he is not authorized to operate directly. In this case, the Technician is the control operator of only his own station on 440 MHz, not the repeater he is using. The Technician is not transmitting on 29 MHz. The repeater station is, and it is operating under the repeater licensee's or control operator's license privileges.

One final note about using a repeater: There is no FCC rule that requires a repeater's licensee or sponsor to build a repeater. And if he does, there's no rule which requires the person to let you use it. A repeater is *not* a public utility—you don't have a "right" to use it! When you are using someone else's repeater you are, in effect, a visitor in the owner's station. So, you should conduct yourself accordingly. If you use that station in a manner that the owner finds objectionable, that person has every right to revoke your privilege of using it!

OTHER REPEATER RULES

In addition to the somewhat complex rules mentioned thus far, amateurs must be aware of a few more, though simpler, repeater station rules:

1) A Novice licensee may not operate or be the control operator of a repeater. Any other licensed operator may put up a repeater as long as the outputs are all on frequencies authorized to the licensee [97.205(a)].

2) Specific frequencies are available for repeater operation. Repeaters may operate on any frequency authorized to the Amateur Radio Service above 29.5 MHz except for 50.0 - 51.0, 144.0 - 144.5, 145.5 - 146.0, 222.0 - 222.15, 431 - 433 and 435 - 438 MHz [97.205(b)]. Note that these frequencies include *both* the input *and* output frequencies of all repeaters.

3) Two repeater licensees must work together to solve an interference problem between the repeaters, unless one repeater is coordinated and the other is not. The licensee of an uncoordinated repeater bears the primary responsibility for solving an interference problem. This is the FCC's way of recognizing and encouraging repeater sponsors' participation in local or regional frequency coordination programs [97.205(c)].

4) If the control operator is someone other than the licensee, *both* are equally responsible for the proper operation of the station [97.103(a)].

5) The licensee and control operator(s) of a repeater that inadvertently retransmits communications which violate the rules in Part 97 are not normally held accountable for the violative communications [97.205(g)]. However, they will be held accountable if they become aware of the illegal communications and allow them to continue, because they are no longer "inadvertent." They must make an effort to prevent such communications from continuing. If they are unsuccessful, they must shut the repeater off until the problem can be corrected. The operator of the station originating the illegal communications will be held accountable at all times by the FCC.

6) Before establishing a repeater within 10 miles of the Arecibo Observatory in Arecibo, Puerto Rico, the facility must be notified. See details in Appendix 2 of Chapter 10 [1.924].

"SIMPLEX REPEATERS"

The availability of digital devices that can store a limited amount of audio has led to the development of devices called *simplex repeaters*. These devices are used to extend the range of low power rigs such as H-Ts by storing the signal transmitted on a frequency and then retransmitting it through a more powerful or better situated transmitter on the same frequency.

According to the rules, however, such a device is *not* a repeater. It does not *simultaneously* retransmit the signals of another station and it might not retransmit the signals on a *different* channel or channels, as specified in the FCC's definition of a repeater. Since it isn't a repeater, such a device *can not* be operated under automatic control. If a control operator is present and controlling the device, either locally or by remote control, then it can be used. But it cannot be left unattended! On the other hand, it is not limited by the other repeater rules, such as repeater frequencies.

SIMPLEX AUTOPATCHES

The simplex autopatch ("simpatch") is a device that allows you to connect to a telephone line. You transmit control commands to your remotely controlled home station to activate and control the simpatch. This makes your station an auxiliary station. The simpatch base station transmits the audio from the phone line back to you, so your home station is also operating as a form of auxiliary station [97.201]. It is not a repeater, so none of the repeater rules apply. Since both the "uplink" and "downlink" constitute a form of auxiliary operation in a closed system, all such operations must be conducted *on frequencies authorized for auxiliary operation* (above 222.15 MHz, except 431 to 433 and 435 to 438 MHz). Also see the sections "Control During Autopatch Operation" and "Phone Patch and Autopatch Guidelines" in this chapter for control operator and other requirements and guidelines.

Note that if you operate a simplex autopatch on the 2-meter band, it is only legal if there is a control operator at the base station or at a designated remote control point using an appropriate remote control link. It is not legal to remotely control such a station on 2-meters. Since it's not a repeater, it cannot be operated under automatic control [97.3(a)(38)].

NATIONAL RADIO QUIET ZONE

If you're putting up an automatically controlled beacon or repeater in the National Radio Quiet Zone (see coordinates in this section), you must give written notification of your plan to the Director, National Radio Astronomy Observatory, PO Box 2, Green Bank, WV 24944. You must also notify the Director if you're planning to modify (change frequency, power, antenna height or directivity) an existing repeater or beacon in the zone. If you are in this zone, you must also notify the Director of the Naval Radio Research Observatory at Sugar Grove, WV.

Notification must include the geographical coordinates of the antenna, antenna height and directivity, proposed frequency, emission type and power. If the NRAO or NRRO objects within 20 days, the FCC will consider the problem and take appropriate action. Details appear in Appendix 2 of this book.

The National Radio Quiet Zone

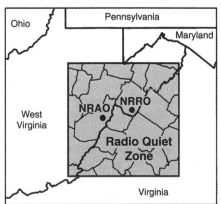

Fig 3—The National Radio Quiet Zone.

Phone Patch and Autopatch Guidelines

As with any privilege, phone patch and autopatch can be abused, and the penalty for abuse could be the loss of the privilege for all amateurs. Since phone patches and autopatches can constitute third-party operation, see the section titled "Third Party Communications" in Chapter 2. What constitutes abuse of phone patch and autopatch privileges? In the absence of specific regulations governing their use, the answer to this question depends on one's perspective. Consider these facts: To other amateurs, phone patching activities that result in unnecessary frequency congestion or which appear as a commercialization of Amateur Radio operation are an abuse of their privilege to engage in other forms of amateur activities.

To the telephone company, which needs to protect its massive investment in capital equipment, anything that endangers its equipment, its personnel or its revenues is an abuse.

To the Federal Communications Commission, which is responsible for the efficient use of the radio spectrum by the services it regulates, any radiocommunication that could be handled more appropriately by wire is an unnecessary use of a valuable resource.

To the commercial suppliers of radiocommunication for business purposes (Radio Common Carriers), competition from a noncommercial service constitutes a possible threat to their livelihood.

At one time or another, threats to radio amateurs' interconnect privileges have come from each of these sources. And threats may come from another quarter: The governments of certain nations that prohibit amateurs from handling third-party messages internationally in competition with government-owned telecommunications services. If illegal phone patching to and from their countries cannot be controlled, they reason, the solution may be to ban all international third-party traffic by amateurs and to permit no such special arrangements.

The question facing amateurs is this: Should phone patches and autopatches be subject to reasonable voluntary restraints, thereby preserving most of our traditional flexibility, or should we risk forcing our government to define for us specifically what we can and cannot do? Experience has clearly shown that when specific regulations are established, innovation and flexibility are likely to suffer.

The Amateur Radio Service is not a common carrier, and its primary purpose is not the handling of routine messages on behalf of nonamateurs. Third-party communications as an incidental part of Amateur Radio, however, adds an important dimension to amateur public-service capability.

It is the policy of the American Radio Relay League to safeguard the prerogative of amateurs to interconnect their stations, including repeaters, to the public telephone system. An important element of this defense is encouraging amateurs to maintain a high standard of legal and ethical conduct in their patching activities. It is to this end that these guidelines are addressed. They are based on standards that have been in use for several years on a local or regional basis throughout the country. The ideas they represent have widespread support within the amateur community. All amateurs are urged to observe these standards carefully so amateurs' traditional freedom from government regulation may be preserved as much as possible:

1) International phone patches may be conducted only when there is a special third-party agreement between the countries concerned. The only exceptions are when the immediate safety of life or property is endangered, or where the third party is a licensed amateur.

2) Phone patches or autopatches involving the pecuniary interest of the

originator, or on behalf of the originator's employer, must not be conducted at any time. The content of any patch should be such that it is clear to any listener that such communications are not involved. Particular caution must be observed in calling any business telephone. Calls to place an order for a commercial product may be made such as the proverbial call to the pizza restaurant to order food, but not calls to one's office to receive or to leave business messages since communications on behalf of one's employer are not permitted. Calls made in the interests of highway safety, however, such as for the removal of injured persons from the scene of an accident or for the removal of a disabled vehicle from a hazardous location, are permitted.

3) All interconnections must be made in accordance with telephone company tariffs. This means that your equipment must not affect the proper functioning of the telephone system; if it does, you are responsible for correcting the problem. If you have trouble obtaining information about the tariffs from your telephone company, they are available for public inspection at the telephone company office.

4) Phone patches and autopatches should never be made solely to avoid telephone toll charges. Phone patches and autopatches should never be made when normal telephone service could just as easily be used.

5) Third parties should not be retransmitted until the responsible control operator has explained the nature of Amateur Radio to them. Control of the station must never be relinquished to an unlicensed person. Permitting a person you don't know very well to conduct a patch in a language you don't understand amounts to relinquishing control.

6) Make sure the third parties know they are participating in radio communications, and that such communications are not private, and may be heard by people other than the parties involved.

7) Phone patches and autopatches must be terminated immediately in the event of any illegality or impropriety.

8) Autopatch facilities must not be used for broadcasting. If a repeater can transmit information of general interest, such as weather reports, such

is the area in Maryland, West Virginia and Virginia bounded by 39° 15' N, 78° 30' W, 37° 30' N and 80° 30' W. See **Fig 3** [97.203(e)].

RADIO ASTRONOMY COORDINATION ZONE

Amateurs planning to operate new repeaters or beacons or change the operational parameters of existing repeaters or beacons on wavelengths longer than 1.2 cm or frequencies below 24 GHz (including 6 m, 2 m and 70 cm) within a 10 mile radius of the Arecibo Radio Astronomy Observatory in Puerto Rico must notify the Observatory in writing of the technical parameters of the proposal. Notification must include the geographical coordinates of the antenna, antenna ground elevation above mean sea level (AMSL), antenna center of radiation above ground level (AGL), antenna directivity, proposed frequency, type of emission and transmitter power [97.203(h), 1.924]. You can find details in Appendix 2, in Chapter 10.

FREQUENCY COORDINATION

Although it is not "required" by the FCC Rules, most repeater operators

transmissions must occur only when requested by a licensed amateur and must not conform to a specific time schedule. The retransmission of radio signals from other services except for NOAA weather, government propagation bulletins and space shuttle communications, is not permitted in the Amateur Radio Service.

9) Station identification must be strictly observed. In particular, US stations conducting international phone patches must identify in English at least once every 10 minutes, and must give their call signs and the other stations' call signs at the end of the communication.

10) In selecting frequencies for phone patch work, the rights of other amateurs must be considered. In particular, patching on 20 meters should be confined to the following frequency segments in accordance with the IARU Region 2 recommendation: 21.300-21.450 MHz and 14.250-14.350 MHz.

11) Phone patches and autopatches should be kept as brief as possible, as a courtesy to other amateurs; the amateur bands are intended to be used primarily for communication among radio amateurs.

12) No unlicensed person may initiate an amateur transmission without the knowledge and approval of the station's control operator. Incoming "reverse autopatch" calls must be answered and screened off the air by the control operator to ensure rule compliance. If an incoming call automatically causes the repeater to transmit, even if it's just a signal tone or notification message, then it is possible for an unlicensed person to initiate a transmission without the control operator's knowledge or approval, which is not permitted. The use of a reverse autopatch is permitted only under very limited conditions. This is not to restrict the Amateur Service unduly, but to protect the character of the Service.

13) If you have any doubt as to the legality or advisability of a patch, don't make it.

Compliance with these guidelines will help ensure that hams' interconnection privilege will continue to be available in the future, which will in turn help amateurs contribute to the public interest.

coordinate the input and output frequencies for their repeaters, as well as any auxiliary link and control frequencies, with their local or regional frequency coordinators.

The FCC defines a *Frequency Coordinator* as ***An entity, recognized in a local or regional area by amateur operators whose stations are eligible to be repeater or auxiliary stations, that recommends transmit/receive channels and associated operating and technical parameters for such stations in order to avoid or minimize potential interference.*** [97.3(a)(22)]. The primary function of frequency coordinators is to help amateurs who desire to put up new repeaters select frequencies that will cause, and receive, a minimum amount of interference within the limited number of repeater frequency pairs available. Coordinators are volunteers who serve with the approval of the amateurs within their region. They have no authority to "assign" frequencies—they make recommendations. They maintain an accurate database of information on every coordinated station within their area (this data is held in strict confidence), and they use this data in forming their recommendations. If repeater users do experience harmful interference, coordinators are happy to assist in resolving the problem.

The rules state that if one repeater is coordinated and the other is not, the uncoordinated repeater's licensee must assume the primary responsibility in resolving any interference [97.205(c)]. This also applies to auxiliary stations [97.201(c)]. Putting it another way, the FCC considers participation in your regional frequency coordination program to be "good amateur practice."

Here is the rationale behind the current rules that affect amateur frequency coordination. This is taken from the FCC's Report and Order in PR Docket 85-22 in 1986, in which they said:

Repeater operation in the amateur service inherently requires operation on established frequencies. Amateur repeater operation is not frequency agile, as are other types of amateur station operation. As a result, most amateur operators have been willing to voluntarily cooperate to avoid interference to frequencies designed for repeater operation...in favor of the greater good, particularly because many amateur repeaters are open to all amateur operators who desire to use them. The cooperation has taken the form of adherence to the determination of local frequency coordinators. While no amateur operator or amateur station 'owns' a frequency, this type of coordination is the minimum joint effort by the amateur community needed to facilitate repeater operation...

Several coordinators urged us to establish some mechanism to officially recognize local or regional coordinators. Others were concerned about the potential for abuse of power at the local level. Another concern was the exclusive right to coordinate within a geographical area. It is essential that repeater coordinators respond to the broadest base of local amateurs and consider the concerns not only of repeater owners, but also of those users of spectrum affected by repeater operation. Their authority is derived from the voluntary participation of the entire amateur community; their recognition must be derived from the same source. We believe the new rules will assure that a coordinator is representative of all local amateur operators.

Several commenters urged us to abolish closed repeaters in the amateur service or alternatively, to permit coordinators to relegate closed repeaters to secondary status or to give open repeaters preference when coordinating. We are not of the view, as were these commenters, that closed repeaters are any more or less desirable than open repeaters.

We proposed to make noncoordinated repeaters primarily responsible to resolve interference associated with coordinated repeaters. The ARRL commented that we should go further and make noncoordinated repeaters solely responsible to resolve such interference and require noncoordinated repeaters to cease operation if the interference is not resolved. Although the focus must be placed in the first instance upon the noncoordinated repeater to resolve such interference, we are adopting our proposed rules which continue to make the coordinated repeater secondarily responsible. This permits local coordinators and the FCC to consider technical alternatives, questions of equity, and spectrum efficiency in reaching the most reasonable solution.

Most frequency coordinators are certified by the National Frequency Coordinator's Council, Inc. (NFCC), an association of coordinators. The NFCC has established a set of criteria which each coordinator must abide by in order to become certified. These certification criteria include both technical and performance standards, which comprise the minimum necessary to perform the coordination process at an acceptable level of competence. You can obtain more information about the NFCC on *ARRLWeb* at: **http://www.arrl.org/nfcc/**.

If you are planning to put up a repeater, contact your frequency coordinator first! He or she will be happy to help you. For a list of frequency coordinators nationwide, see *The ARRL Repeater Directory* or check *ARRLWeb* at: **http://www.arrl.org/field/regulations/freqcoord.html**.

VHF/UHF BAND PLANS

"Band plan" is a term you will encounter in the world of VHF/UHF and repeaters. It refers to agreements between concerned VHF and UHF operators as to how each VHF and UHF Amateur Radio band should be used. With the exception of 50.0-50.1 and 144.0-144.1 MHz where CW only is permitted, amateurs may use any mode on any VHF, UHF or microwave band. Clearly there is a need for a system so that operators of one mode, FM simplex, for example, won't cause interference to people operating incompatible activities such as Earth-Moon-Earth (EME). The goal of a band plan is to systematically minimize interference between users of the various emission modes that share each band. Aside from FM repeater and simplex activity, you can find CW, SSB, AM, satellite, digital, TV, spread spectrum and R/C (radio control) operations, among others, on many of these bands.

Band plans *are not* mandated or dictated by the FCC, but the FCC does dictate where CW/RTTY/data and phone/image transmissions may be conducted on HF. For example, RTTY can't be transmitted where phone/image can according to FCC rules. The only national band plan is that created by ARRL, and following the band plans is "good amateur practice."

The most popular band for FM use is 2 meters. The FM and repeater part of the band plan generally looks like this: The spacing between 2-meter repeater channels is either 15 or 20 kHz, depending upon what area of the country you're in. The standard spacing between each repeater input and its output is 600 kHz. For example, the input (the repeater's receiving, or your transmitting) frequency of 146.34 MHz is paired with an output (the repeater's transmitting, or your receiving) frequency of 146.94 MHz (146.34 MHz + 600 kHz = 146.94 MHz). Under this plan, repeaters in the 144/145 and 146 MHz portions of the band have a low-input/high-output split; that is, the lower frequency (such as 146.01) is the input and the higher frequency (146.61) is the output. Conversely, repeater pairs in the 147 MHz segment, such as 147.81/147.21 MHz, generally follow a high-input/low-output standard. The simplex frequencies between 144.90 and 145.10 MHz are generally used for digital operation. Those frequencies between 146.40 and 146.58, and between 147.42 and 147.57 MHz, are generally designated for voice simplex operation. However, some frequencies within these subbands are used for repeater inputs or outputs in a few parts of the country.

Generalized band plans for every amateur band can be found in Chapter 4. However, there may be regional or local variations to these band plans as determined by the local amateur community. These local plans take precedence over the regional or national band plans.

HF BAND PLANS

Band plans are not limited to VHF and UHF, however. Since HF signals cross countries and continents, they are established through International Amateur Radio Union (IARU) meetings on an international basis. In addition to the material in Chapter 4, you can find information on band plans in *The ARRL Repeater Directory* and on *ARRLWeb* at: **http://www.arrl.org/field/regulations/bandplan.html**.

SPACE STATIONS

The FCC defines a *space station* as *an amateur station located more than 50 km above the Earth's surface* [97.3(a)(40)]. This includes amateur satellites, amateur operation from a space shuttle, the International Space Station and any future operations by astronauts in space.

When you build a repeater, you try to put the antenna on a tall tower or on top of a tall building. The higher you get the antenna, the better coverage your repeater will have. What about a repeater with an antenna more than 50 kilometers high? An amateur satellite is a repeater in space with a large "footprint" on the Earth. Except for geostationary orbits, satellites don't stay in one spot, either. They cross international borders all the time. A satellite is not your average amateur station.

Consequently, special rules apply to space stations:

• Any licensed amateur can be the licensee of a space station [97.207(a)]! Likewise, any amateur can be designated as the control operator of a space station. However, in both cases, the licensee and the control operator's privileges will dictate which frequencies the satellite can operate on. For that reason, most satellites are licensed to Extra class licensees. If you have a Technician class license, for example, you can't be the control operator of a satellite that has a control uplink in the Amateur Extra class subband of 15 meters.

• It must be possible to make the space station stop transmitting if the FCC orders this [97.207(b)]. This is done by telecommand, another type of specialized operation examined later in this chapter. The FCC wants to make sure someone can shut off OSCAR-29's transmitter if it's interfering with the guidance system on the Jupiter 2 as it leaves for Alpha Centauri!

• A space station may automatically retransmit the radio signals of Earth stations and other space stations. An amateur satellite wouldn't be very useful without this provision [97.207(d)].

Is the Operator a "Licensee" or "Trustee?"

There seems to be a lot of confusion as to whether the person whose name is on the license for a repeater or a remote base is the "licensee" or the "trustee" of the station. The operator could be either one! It depends upon the type of license the station is operating under.

If the repeater or remote base is operating under the auspices, and using the call sign of an individual amateur's personal station license, then the operator is the "licensee" of the station, not the "trustee."

If it is operating under the auspices of an FCC-issued club station license, and using the FCC-issued club call sign, then the person whose name appears on the license is the "trustee," not the "licensee."

- Space stations are exempt from some rules that apply to ordinary amateur stations. Space stations do not have to identify themselves, and are permitted to transmit one-way communications [97.119(a), 97.207(e)].
- If space stations transmit telemetry (the results of measurements made in the station) [97.3(a)(44)], they may use special codes to facilitate communications without worrying about the "codes and ciphers" provisions in Part 97 [97.207(f)].
- Space stations may transmit only on certain frequencies authorized in Part 97. **Tables 2** and **3** show the transmit and receive frequencies authorized to space stations [97.207(c)].
- The licensee of a space station must notify the FCC. This is an important part of placing an amateur satellite in orbit. Notification allows the FCC to keep track of US-licensed amateur satellites so that it can respond to any interference complaints registered with the ITU. A satellite is an "international" station and its licensee must remember that he has international responsibilities. The FCC specifies in Part 97 when they must be notified, but rather than spell out what information must be provided, the FCC defers to the ITU Regulations. The appropriate sections of the ITU Regulations are available from ARRL HQ.

If you want to use your station as a space station, such as launching a satellite, not just using your station to make contacts *through* a satellite, these rules are required reading! In accordance with Articles 11 and 13 of the international Radio Regulations, the FCC must be notified four times [97.207(g),(h),(i)]:

1) You must notify the FCC's International Bureau *no less than 27 months before the space station will begin transmissions.* This notification must include the information specified in Appendix 4 of the ITU Regulations. This includes the name of the satellite, the date it will commence operations, the name and address of the organization responsible for the satellite and the satellite's orbital parameters (where it will travel in space). Notification must include technical information about any radio links the satellite will use: Earth-to-space, space-

Table 2

Frequencies Authorized to Space Stations [97.207(c)]

Bands

Wavelength	Frequency
40 m	7.0-7.1 MHz
20 m	14.00-14.25 MHz
17 m	18.068-18.168 MHz
15 m	21.00-21.45 MHz
12 m	24.89-24.99 MHz
10 m	28.0-29.7 MHz
2 m	144-146 MHz
70 cm	435-438 MHz
23 cm	1260-1270 MHz
13 cm	2400-2450 MHz
9 cm	3.40-3.41 GHz in ITU Regions 2 and 3 only
5 cm	5.83-5.85 GHz
3 cm	10.45-10.50 GHz
1.2 cm	24.00-24.05 GHz
6 mm	47.0-47.2 GHz
4 mm	75.5-81.0 GHz
2 mm	142-149 GHz
1 mm	241-250 GHz

to-Earth and space-to-space as appropriate [97.207(g)(1)].

2) You must notify the FCC's International Bureau again *no less than five months before the space station starts transmitting.* This time, Appendix 3 and Resolution 642 are the relevant parts of the ITU Regulations. This notification must include more detailed information about the RF links the space station will use [97.207(g)(2)].

3) Once the space station is in space and operating, you must notify the FCC's International Bureau *within seven days* to let them know your station has commenced in-space operation. This notice must update the pre-space notifications [97.207(h)].

4) Finally, when the satellite fails or the shuttle lands and space operation is terminated, you must notify the FCC's International Bureau *within three months.* If the FCC orders you to terminate space operation, you must let them know that you have complied *no later than 24 hours after the operation ends* [97.207(i)].

EARTH STATIONS

The FCC defines an *Earth station* as *an amateur station located on, or within 50 km of, the Earth's surface intended for communications with space stations or with other Earth stations by means of one or more objects*

KD4JL and KC4NEQ work on the AMSAT Phase 3D satellite, which was launched in 2000. Amateurs worldwide contributed to this effort. *(photo courtesy Ed Richter, KD4JL and Rod Davis, KC4NEQ)*

in space [97.3(a)(16)]. Any radio amateur can be the control operator of an Earth station, subject to the limitations of his license class [97.209(a)]. Specific transmitting frequencies are authorized for Earth stations [97.209(b)]. These are shown in **Table 3**.

Generally, when you operate your amateur station, you are operating in the Amateur Radio Service, but in some cases, you may operate in the Amateur Satellite Service. What this means is that when you are talking to one of the astronauts aboard the Space Shuttle or the International Space Station, or when you are using one of the OSCAR satellites, you are no longer operating your station in the Amateur Radio Service. During these periods, your station is actually an "Earth station" operating in the Amateur Satellite Service!

SPACE TELECOMMAND STATIONS

A *telecommand station*, according to the FCC, *transmits communications to initiate, modify or terminate functions of a space station* [97.3(a)(44)]. A few special rules apply to a space telecommand station:

- Any amateur station designated by the licensee of a space station is eligible to transmit as a space telecommand station to the space station. This is a simple precaution that protects the space station from unauthorized control. This privilege is limited by the privileges of the operator's license class [97.211(a)]. Like the space station control operator requirements, if you have a Technician license, you can't control a space telecommand station on 20 meters.
- A space telecommand station may transmit special codes intended to obscure the meaning of telecommand messages [97.211(b)]. This protects the space station from unauthorized control commands. One wrong command could turn an expensive satellite into just a piece of orbiting space junk!
- Space telecommand stations may transmit only on certain frequencies [97.211(c)]. **Table 3** shows the frequencies authorized for telecommand stations.

The International Space Station is an impressive and valuable orbiting laboratory. It is particularly valuable to Amateur Radio operators, who can communicate through it as it passes over their locations. *(photo courtesy NASA)*

Table 3

Frequencies Authorized to Earth and Space Telecommand Stations [97.209 and 97.211]

Band

Wavelength	Frequency
40 m	7.0-7.1 MHz
20 m	14.00-14.25 MHz
17 m	18.068-18.168 MHz
15 m	21.00-21.45 MHz
12 m	24.89-24.99 MHz
10 m	28.0-29.7 MHz
2 m	144-146 MHz
70 cm	435-438 MHz
23 cm	1260-1270 MHz
13 cm	2400-2450 MHz
9 cm	3.40-3.41 GHz in ITU Regions 2 and 3 only
5 cm	5.65-5.67 GHz
3 cm	10.45-10.50 GHz
1.2 cm	24.00-24.05 GHz
6 mm	47.0-47.2 GHz
4 mm	75.5-81.0 GHz
2 mm	142-149 GHz
1 mm	241-250 GHz

TELECOMMAND AND CONTROL OF AN AMATEUR STATION

When dealing with the specialized operating modes, we must discuss the concept of "control." The terms *control operator* and *control point* were introduced in Chapters 1 and 2, but the FCC specifically states that control of an Amateur Radio station can be done in one of three very different ways, as discussed below. Every station, regardless of the type of control used, must have at least one control point [97.109(a)] and at least one control operator [97.109(b),(c),(d)]. Any station may be locally or remotely controlled [97.109(b),(c)]. Only certain types of stations may be automatically controlled [97.109(d)]. As mentioned before, there are three types of control of an amateur station: local, remote and automatic.

Local control is the simplest kind of control. When you sit in front of your rig and twiddle the knobs, controlling the station *directly*—that's *local control* [97.3(a)(30)].

Remote control, logically enough, involves control from a location that is remote from the station being controlled. If you control your station *indirectly*, it's *remote control* [97.3(a)(38)].

Another FCC definition applies in remote control situations: *Telecommand* is defined by the FCC as *a one-way transmission to initiate, modify or terminate functions of a device at a distance* [97.3(a)(43)]. If you are using a radio or wire line link to remotely control a station, this is "telecommand."

The rules contain several requirements for remote control and telecommand operation:

1) Provision must be incorporated to limit transmissions to no more than three minutes if the control link fails. This is a common-sense provision. If the control link fails while your transmitter is keyed, the transmitter could be seriously damaged (not to mention the interference it would cause) if there was no three-minute timer to shut if off [97.213(b)]. But this also means that if the control link is functioning properly, there is no requirement for the station to have a three-minute "reset" or turn-off timer.

2) The station must be protected so that unauthorized transmissions cannot be made, whether deliberately or accidentally. This refers to providing safeguards on your remotely controlled station so it cannot be used by unauthorized operators. Most remote station licensees incorporate the use of DTMF tones or CTCSS systems to limit access to the control system to only those people who know the codes. You, as the licensee, are responsible for all transmissions from your remote station, just as you are responsible for your home station [97.213(c)]. This responsibility applies all the time, even if you share the control operator duties with other amateurs.

3) A photocopy of the station license and a label with the name, address, and telephone number of the station licensee and at least one designated control operator must be posted in a conspicuous place at the station location [97.213(d)].

4) Control (or telecommand) links may be wire (a telephone or fiber optic line, for example) or radio. The FCC says that if a radio link is used, the station where the control commands are performed is an auxiliary station [97.213(a)] and an auxiliary station is "an amateur station transmitting communications point-to-point within a system of cooperating amateur stations" [97.3(a)(7)]. All auxiliary operations must be conducted on appropriate frequencies above 222.15 MHz.

Automatic control takes place when there is no control operator locally or remotely and it uses "devices and procedures for control of a station when it is transmitting so that compliance with the FCC Rules is achieved without the control operator being present at a control point" [97.3(a)(6)]. This is "hands-off" operation; there's nobody home (at the control point). Most repeaters operate, at least part of the time, under automatic control.

Only a few types of stations may be operated by automatic control. These include space stations, repeaters, auxiliary stations which are part of a repeater system, certain beacons and stations transmitting RTTY/data emissions. Automatically controlled beacons are limited to operation in certain subbands of the HF, VHF and UHF bands (see Table 1 earlier in this chapter) [97.203(d)]. Stations transmitting RTTY/data emissions above 50 MHz and in certain segments of the HF bands may be operated automatically

[97.221(b)]. "Remote base" stations can not be operated under automatic control. Automatic control must cease upon notification by an FCC Field Office District Director that the station is transmitting improperly or causing harmful interference to other stations, and cannot be resumed without prior approval of the District Director [97.109(d)]. Refer to the section on "A Repeater's 'Primary' Control System" earlier in this chapter for additional details on the various types of station control.

TELECOMMAND OF MODEL CRAFT

Amateurs are also permitted to use radio to control "model craft," such as model airplanes and model boats. Certain restrictions apply [97.215] on this kind of operation:

1) Station identification is not required for transmission directed only to the model craft. The control transmitter must bear a label indicating the station's call sign and the licensee's name and address [97.215(a)].

2) Control signals are not considered codes and ciphers [97.215(b)].

3) Transmitter power cannot exceed 1 W [97.215(c)].

4) Only licensed amateurs may operate telecommand transmitters using amateur frequencies. See the next section concerning third party and telecommand operation.

"THIRD PARTIES" AND REMOTE CONTROL/ TELECOMMAND OPERATION

While unlicensed persons may participate as "third parties" in most amateur operations, they *may not* participate in any type of remote control or telecommand operation. This is true even when a licensed amateur is closely supervising the operation. The FCC says that the one-way transmissions involved in remote control and telecommand do not constitute communications exchanged between control operators because there is no "second" party! In other words, there is not a second amateur control operator to receive the one-way transmissions. Since there is no "second" party, there can't be a "third" party! Non-amateurs who wish to remotely control model airplanes or boats cannot use Amateur Radio equipment or frequencies to do so. They must use equipment that operates in the Radio Control Service under Part 95 of the FCC Rules, on frequencies in the 27, 72 or 75 MHz bands.

TELEMETRY

Telemetry is defined as *a one-way transmission of measurements at a distance from the measuring instrument.* [97.3(a)(45)]. Although it's not common in the amateur service, the FCC does allow amateurs to transmit telemetry. The best known use of telemetry is by the amateur satellites [97.207(f)]. These usually send telemetry as a series of numbers denoting temperatures, voltages, currents or other sensor measurements, or the on/off state of various spacecraft systems.

One of the simplest forms of down-to-earth telemetry is where a repeater will respond to a command, sent on the control link by one of its control operators. By sending an "R" in CW, the repeater indicates that the controller has accepted and performed the desired command. Some of the more sophisticated remotely controlled stations use telemetry to report conditions at the remote site, such as inside or outside temperature, wind speed and/or direction, remote station operating frequency, beam heading, transmitter power, the operating condition of different pieces of equipment, and so on. Telemetry can also be used to report the status, or even the activation, of an intrusion alarm.

Such telemetry transmissions are not considered by the FCC to be "codes or ciphers intended to obscure the meaning of communications" [97.217]. However, with the exception of space stations, they must still be properly identified [97.119(a),(b)].

MESSAGE FORWARDING SYSTEMS

The FCC defines a *message forwarding system* as *a group of amateur stations participating in a voluntary, cooperative, interactive arrangement where communications are sent from the control operator of an originating station to the control operator of one or more destination stations by one or more forwarding stations* [97.3(a)(31)].

VHF and UHF, and in some cases HF message forwarding systems, such as digipeaters, can operate under automatic control—a control operator isn't required to be at the control point. The station licensee is, however, still responsible for the operation of the station. When a message is sent, the originating station is primarily accountable for any rules violations contained in the message [97.219(b)].

FIRST FORWARDING STATION RESPONSIBILITIES

The *first forwarding digital station* in the system has additional responsibilities: (1) The first forwarding station must make sure that the originator of the message is authorized to send messages over the system; and (2) The first forwarding station must take responsibility for any messages retransmitted within the system. It acts as a "filter" to protect other forwarding stations down the line.

Consequently, the control operators of the digipeaters or nodes which retransmit such messages, usually done automatically, are not accountable for the violative communications sent over the system. Control operators are, however, responsible for stopping the communications once they become aware of their presence.

DIFFERENCES BETWEEN REPEATERS AND DIGIPEATERS

With the introduction of packet radio technology into the amateur service, another device has seen widespread use—the digipeater, or "digi." A digipeater receives data from one station, processes the data, then relays the digital transmissions to other stations to extend the available range for packet communications.

There is a difference between ordinary voice repeaters and digipeaters: A voice repeater retransmits the incoming signal *in real time* but without changing the incoming signal in any way. A digipeater, on the other hand, takes time to process (this means "change") the incoming data, then retransmits it. Since the incoming signal *is changed* and it is *not* retransmitted in real time, a digipeater does not meet the definition of a "repeater."

As a result, the rules for repeaters *do not* apply to digipeaters. This has several advantages:

1) Any licensee may operate as a digipeater, subject to license class privileges.

2) Digipeaters are not restricted to operation within the frequency subbands where repeater or auxiliary stations must operate.

3) The control operators of only the originating station and the first forwarding station in the system must accept responsibility for the content of any messages transmitted [97.219].

4) Digipeaters may be operated by local, remote or automatic control. There are restrictions on HF automatically controlled digital stations.

5) Digipeaters *may* be operated under automatic control, even when transmitting third-party communications, when they are a part of a RTTY or digital "message forwarding system" [97.109(e)].

AUTOMATICALLY CONTROLLED HF DIGITAL STATIONS

When operating under automatic control below 30 MHz (HF), certain digital stations are restricted to special segments of the HF bands [97.221(b)], unless they are responding to interrogation by another station where there is a control operator present, that is, the station is locally or remotely controlled [97.221(c)]. Earlier in this chapter, we discussed a number of other uses for amateur stations. It is important to note that the rules in this section *do not* apply to auxiliary, beacon, repeater, space or space telecommand stations. These concepts require a bit of explanation.

Unattended digital operation has been allowed on 6 meters and shorter wavelengths since 1986, but *unattended HF digital operation* was much more problematic and required a great deal more study due to the nature of propagation, and international and national band plan considerations. These rules introduce two new concepts:

If a locally or remotely controlled HF digital station accesses an automatically controlled HF digital station, the automatically controlled station and the local or remotely controlled station can operate on *any frequency where digital operation is authorized to US operators.* The rationale is that a real live person can tell whether or not interference is being caused to other stations. The unattended station may occupy a bandwidth of no more than 500 Hz [97.221(c)].

If two or more automatically controlled unattended HF digital stations are connected, the stations *must be within certain band segments* in order to minimize interference to users of other modes [97.221(b)].

As new and more efficient digital technologies, such as PSK 31, continue to evolve, amateurs are challenged to become more efficient by fitting many types of digital modes, in addition to CW which has existed for many years, into a relatively narrow band segment.

SEGMENTS FOR TWO AUTOMATICALLY CONTROLLED UNATTENDED HF DIGITAL STATIONS

Two or more unattended HF digital stations that are connected may be automatically controlled while transmitting a RTTY or data emission, but they are limited to certain segments. Such transmissions may take place on the 6-meter or shorter wavelength bands, and on the following segments: 28.120-28.189 MHz, 24.925-24.930 MHz, 21.090-21.100 MHz, 18.105-18.110 MHz, 14.0950-14.0995 MHz, 14.1005-14.112 MHz, 10.140-10.150 MHz, 7.100-7.105 MHz, or 3.620-3.635 MHz segments [97.221(b)]. Digital stations operated under *manual control* are not limited to these subbands. Confining operation to only certain subbands was the only way to protect real-time communication between live operators from interference from unattended stations. An automatically controlled station may still be placed on a frequency even if it is outside the subbands mentioned above as long as a manually controlled station (a real person) initiates or "turns on" the station. Until this happens, the station will be silent.

CONCLUSION

Part 97 allows unconventional operating modes and techniques. With Part 97, Subpart C—Special Operations in particular, think of Part 97 rules as "pieces." "Plug in" the "pieces" you need to make your system work. Part 97 addresses many different uses of amateur stations with relatively brief regulations. For example, if a link is needed in a system, it is the responsibility of the station operator to make sure that the appropriate rules for links are followed. But just like a puzzle, which doesn't look right if a piece is missing, be sure to consider *all* of the rule "pieces" that pertain to your particular system. You can't just "pick and choose" the rules you want to follow, and ignore others that also apply! Of course, all operators are responsible for understanding the rules that pertain to on-the-air operation. It's an old cliché, but "ignorance of the law is no excuse." Read the appropriate sections of this chapter until you are sure what the rules mean. Refer to Part 97 at the end of this book. Last, enjoy using your station for your desired operation!

[Special thanks to Gary Hendrickson, W3DTN, Chairman of The Middle Atlantic FM and Repeater Council's Open Band Planning Committee, for his assistance. Having served as TMARC repeater coordinator for 25 years, he is a recognized expert in the field of coordination and complex repeater operations.]

4 Technical Standards

The word *standard* implies consistency, conformity and order. This is what Part 97's Subpart D—Technical Standards, is all about. The FCC has made these standards a basic framework so all kinds of amateur operations can exist peacefully together in the same bands and so Amateur Radio can continue to be good sharing partners with other services.

Briefly, Subpart D of Part 97 tells where amateurs may operate as broken down by license class and ITU Region [97.301], what frequency sharing arrangements exist, if any [97.303], and which emission types may be used [97.305]. Emission standards for spectral purity are discussed [97.307]. Due to the nature of emerging technologies, the FCC devotes considerable page space to RTTY and data emission codes as well as for spread spectrum [97.309 and 97.311]. Transmitter power standards are discussed [97.313], as are rules for FCC Certification of external RF power amplifiers and the standards for FCC Certification. All of these will be discussed in this chapter.

This chapter will also outline topics related to technical discussions of the rules, such as amateur band plans and specific emission designators, which aren't part of Part 97.

SUBPART D RULES SUMMARY: TECHNICAL STANDARDS

97.301 Authorized frequency bands.
97.303 Frequency sharing requirements.
97.305 Authorized emission types.
97.307 Emission standards.
97.309 RTTY and data emission codes.
97.311 SS emission types.
97.313 Transmitter power standards.
97.315 Certification of external RF power amplifiers.
97.317 Standards for certification of external RF power amplifiers.

AUTHORIZED FREQUENCY BANDS
AND SHARING REQUIREMENTS

Today, there are numerous other radio services vying for pieces of the spectrum pie, all with legitimate purposes. In years past, the battlegrounds for amateur spectrum for non-amateur uses have centered on the HF bands. As we enter the new millennium, spectrum issues on a national and international basis are and will continue to center on the VHF, UHF and microwave bands. Frequency bands are worth *billions* to commercial services (see March 1998 *QST,* p 15). If it is determined that the needs of a particular new user service are to be accommodated, the international and domestic regulatory agencies often put like services together, taking into consideration priority of importance of each service and compatibility factors. The result is that, in many instances, amateurs share bands with other services. In fact, almost all frequency bands above the 222 MHz band (1.25 m) are shared with other services. Amateurs need to be aware of users in other services that are authorized to be there.

Some amateur allocations are *exclusive*. This means that the Amateur Radio Service is the only authorized service in such a band. Other bands are shared with other services on the basis of priority. In some cases, the Amateur Radio Service is the *primary* or highest status user service in a particular band. Other bands are shared with other *primary* occupants on a *coprimary* basis. In these cases, amateurs operate on a basis of equality: Stations in each service must not cause harmful interference to each other.

In other cases, Amateur Radio is designated a *secondary* service: Amateurs must not cause harmful interference to, and must tolerate interference from, stations in a primary service.

WITH WHOM DO WE SHARE OUR BANDS?

In the discussions of each of the amateur bands in this chapter, descriptions of the sharing arrangements will be provided. To help you understand the nature of these arrangements, and to help you tell what you're hearing, here is a basic set of definitions of some of the other services with which we share our bands:

Fixed Service: A radiocommunication service between specified fixed points.

Fixed-Satellite Service: A radiocommunication service between earth stations at specified fixed points when one or more satellites are used.

Mobile Service: A radiocommunication service between mobile and land stations, or between mobile stations.

Land Mobile Service: A mobile service between base stations and land mobile stations, or between land mobile stations. An example is the communications system for a taxi cab company. The base station at company headquarters dispatches its taxis via radio.

Maritime Mobile Service: A mobile service between coast stations and ship stations, or between ship stations.

Aeronautical Mobile Service: A mobile service between aeronautical stations and aircraft stations, or between aircraft stations.

Broadcasting Service: A radiocommunication service in which the transmissions are intended for direct reception by the general public.

Radionavigation Service: A radiodetermination service for the purpose of navigating a course. LORAN systems, for example, guide ships on their chosen courses.

Radiolocation Service: A radiodetermination service for the purpose of locating objects. Radar, for example, is used for tracking movement of ships and planes.

Amateurs tend to think of amateur bands as 100% amateur, but as we have seen, that isn't always the case. There are other users who, in many cases, have just as much right as amateurs to be on a particular frequency. Because amateurs are good sharing partners with other services, many opportunities for additional spectrum have become available.

BANDS DIFFER REGION TO REGION

The International Telecommunication Union is an international body of the United Nations that has responsibility for organizing frequency allocations for the various radio services on a worldwide basis. The ITU has divided the world into three sections, called ITU Regions: 1, 2 and 3. See **Fig 1**. North and South America and surrounding waters comprise Region 2. Frequency allocations in the Amateur Radio Service and other services can differ internationally between ITU Regions. The same sharing rules as outlined above apply. Where, in adjacent Regions, a band is allocated to different services of the same category, the basic principle is the equality of the right to operate. Stations in a secondary service must not cause harmful interference to, and are not protected from interference from, stations in the primary service.

Why do amateurs care what groups of frequencies are available for possible allocation to services in areas outside the US? While this is less of a concern on frequencies above 50 MHz, on HF there is a good chance you will hear a station operating on amateur frequencies and originating from another country. An example is an international shortwave broadcasting station in ITU Regions 1 and 3 (outside North and South America) in the upper part of the 40-meter band.

Allocations on an international basis can be found in the international Radio Regulations. These have also been codified in §2.106 of the FCC regulations.

Voluntary Band Plans

Another aspect of band sharing is voluntary band plans. Simply stated, band planning is the process that brings together representatives of all parties interested in using a particular frequency band for different purposes. The object of the process is to develop a plan that will accommodate every authorized user's need for spectrum access while minimizing interference.

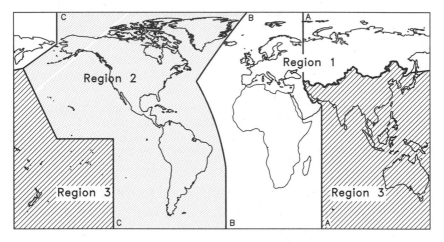

Fig 1—The three ITU regions.

Region 1 includes the area limited on the east by line A (lines A, B and C are defined below) and on the west by line B, excluding any of the territory of Iran which lies between these limits. It also includes that part of the territory of Turkey and the former USSR lying outside of these limits, the territory of the Mongolian People's Republic, and the area to the north of the former USSR which lies between lines A and C.

Region 2 includes the area limited on the east by line B and on the west by line C.

Region 3 includes the area limited on the east by line C and on the west by line A, except the territories of the Mongolian People's Republic, Turkey, the former USSR, and the area to the north of the former USSR. It also includes that part of the territory of Iran lying outside of those limits. Lines A, B and C are defined as follows:

Line A extends from the North Pole along meridian 40° E, to parallel 40° N, thence by great-circle arc to the intersection of meridian 60° E and the Tropic of Cancer; thence along the meridian 60° E to the South Pole.
Line B extends from the North Pole along meridian 10° W to its intersection with parallel 72°N; thence by great-circle arc to the intersection of 50° W and parallel 40° N; thence by great circle arc to the intersection of meridian 20° W and parallel 10°S; thence along meridian 20° W to the South Pole.

Line C extends from the North Pole by great-circle arc to the intersection of parallel 65° 30' N with the international boundary in the Bering Strait; thence by great-circle arc to the intersection of meridian 165° E of Greenwich and parallel 50° N; thence by great-circle arc to the intersection of meridian 170° W and parallel 10° N, thence along parallel 10°N to its intersection with meridian 120° W; thence along meridian 120° W to the South Pole. [2.104]

In the HF bands and in some segments of the VHF and higher bands, band planning must be an international process because our signals propagate internationally, either directly or through satellites. It is conducted through the mechanism of international conferences of the International Amateur Radio Union (IARU), in which the ARRL serves as the representative of amateurs in the US. In other segments of the VHF and higher bands, and especially in the repeater subbands, local needs can be met more efficiently if allowance is made for variations from national or international band plans. It has long been ARRL policy that in such cases, the regional band plans developed by recognized coordination bodies are considered good operating practice in the regions in which they apply. In other words, regional band plans in the VHF and higher bands take precedence over national and international band plans.

Band plans aren't static; they are updated to reflect the ever changing usage of amateur spectrum. As mentioned earlier, although the FCC rules set aside portions of some bands for specific modes, there's still a need to further organize our space among user groups by band plans and "gentlemen's agreements." These agreements usually emerge by consensus of the band occupants and are sanctioned by a national body such as the ARRL. Band plans help amateurs avoid getting in each other's way when using different modes on the same band. For example, a "DX window" segment is set aside on some bands where domestic QSOs are avoided so domestic stations can hear and work weak-signal DX stations. There are others and we will review them on a band-by-band basis in the following discussion. You will see how band plans, in addition to FCC-mandated band/mode requirements, all fit together allowing many amateurs to enjoy many modes on a finite number of frequency bands. What is presented in this chapter is an overview of band allocations broken down by the sharing status in each of the three ITU Regions and by the recognized band plans.

SPECIFIC BAND PARAMETERS

Effective April 15, 2000, the FCC, as part of the 1998 Biennial Regulatory Review of Part 97, restructured the amateur license classes. On that date, the FCC stopped issuing new Novice, Technician Plus and Advanced class licenses. However, existing Novice, Technician Plus and Advanced class licensees may continue to renew their licenses and use their traditional privileges. Technician and Technician Plus licensees will be lumped together in the same class (Technician). Proof of demonstrated Morse code proficiency (Element 1), however, will allow operation on the Novice/Technician Plus HF subbands.

A NOTE ABOUT CW

CW is permitted throughout all the bands allocated to amateurs by the FCC, but check the band plans to find out where CW operation is recommended. The recommended CW segments are generally found at the lower end of each band.

Key To Graphs

In the following discussion, graphs are included to illustrate the band restrictions. Even though the FCC is issuing only *new* Technician, General and Amateur Extra class licenses, all license classes are listed, since they may all be renewed and all retain their privileges. The key:

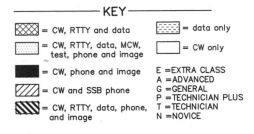

160 METERS: 1800-2000 KHZ

Sharing Arrangements: The Amateur Radio Service in the US enjoys exclusive status on the 1800-1900 kHz segment. Amateur Radio has *secondary* status to the *primary* Radiolocation Service (both government and nongovernment) from 1900 to 2000 kHz [2.106; 97.301; 97.303(b),(c)]. Domestically, Amateur Radio is primary from 1800 to 1900 kHz.

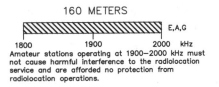

160 METERS

1800   1900   2000 kHz
Amateur stations operating at 1900–2000 kHz must not cause harmful interference to the radiolocation service and are afforded no protection from radiolocation operations.

A possible dark cloud looms over the horizon with respect to 1900-2000 kHz: A future rule-making proceeding in conjunction with expansion of broadcasting into the 1625-1705 kHz band may require some shifting of assignments in this region of the spectrum. For now, amateurs may continue to operate on a secondary basis [2.106, US Footnote 290].

Other Regions: In ITU Region 1, Radiolocation is the exclusive service at 1800-1810 kHz. Amateur Radio is the exclusive service from 1810-1850 kHz. 1850-2000 kHz is allocated to the Fixed and Mobile Services, with no amateur presence [2.106].

In ITU Region 2 (outside the US), the Amateur Radio Service is primary on 1800-1850 kHz. On 1850-2000 kHz, it is coprimary along with the Fixed, Mobile, Radiolocation and Radionavigation Services.

In ITU Region 3, Amateur Radio shares the entire segment 1800-2000 kHz on a *coprimary* basis with Fixed, Mobile (except Aeronautical Mobile) and Radionavigation Services; the radiolocation service is *secondary* [2.106].

License Privileges: General, Advanced and Amateur Extra Class amateurs have access to the entire segment, 1800-2000 kHz [97.301(b),(c),(d)].

Mode Privileges: CW, phone, image, RTTY and data modes are permitted across the entire segment [97.305(c)].

Band Planning: The 160-meter band has traditionally been known as the "gentleman's band" or "top band." A voluntary band plan has developed over time to provide coordination of the various operating activities: ARRL recommends use of 1800-1840 kHz for CW, RTTY and other narrow-band modes. 1840-2000 kHz should be reserved for phone, slow-scan television and other wideband modes.

The "DX window," where only intercontinental QSOs should occur, is 1830-1850 kHz. This allows amateurs to hear DX stations without domestic interference. Were it not for the voluntary cooperation of all operators on the band in keeping this segment clear, DXing would be difficult and frustrating at best.

80 METERS: 3500-4000 KHZ

Sharing Arrangements: 80 meters is a popular night time band, but communications are extremely limited during the daylight hours. In the US, amateurs enjoy *exclusive* status in the entire segment. In the rest of Region 2, Amateur Radio enjoys *exclusive* status from 3500-3750 kHz, and shares the rest of the band with the foreign Fixed and Mobile Services on a *coprimary* basis [2.106].

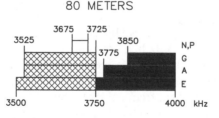

80 METERS

Other Regions: In Region 1, Amateur, Fixed and Mobile Service stations share 3500-3800 kHz on a *coprimary* basis. The rest of the band excludes amateur operation. Fixed, Land Mobile and Aeronautical Mobile Services are the *coprimary* occupants from 3800-3900 kHz. Aeronautical Mobile operations have *exclusive* access to 3900-3950 kHz. Broadcasting and Fixed stations have the segment 3950-4000 kHz on a *coprimary* basis [2.106].

In Region 3, the Amateur Radio Service shares the 3500-3900 kHz segment on a *coprimary* basis with Fixed and Mobile stations. Amateurs are excluded from 3900-4000 kHz. The Aeronautical Mobile and Broadcast Services have access to 3900-3950 kHz on a *coprimary* basis. The

Broadcasting and Fixed services have access to the 3950-4000 kHz segment on a *coprimary* basis.

License privileges: Novice and Technician (for those Technicians who have passed the 5 WPM CW exam) operators can operate at 3675-3725 kHz, CW only [97.301(e); 97.307(f)(9)]. Generals may operate on 3525-3750, and 3850-4000 kHz [97.301(d)]. Advanced licensees have access to 3525-3750 kHz and 3775-4000 kHz [97.301(c)]. Amateur Extra licensees have access to the entire band.

Mode privileges: RTTY and data modes are authorized on the nonphone portion only, 3500-3750 kHz. Phone and image emissions are authorized on the voice segment at 3750-4000 kHz [97.305(c)].

All licensees must observe a 200 W PEP power limit when operating in the Novice/Technician subband [97.313(c)].

Band planning: The ARRL band plan recognizes 3580-3620 kHz for data with packet at 3620-3635 kHz [Region 2 band plan, Curacao, 1992]. The RTTY DX frequency is 3590 kHz. ARRL recommends that CW also be used in the 3635-3750 kHz segment; and that 3790-3800 kHz is the phone DX window. 3845 kHz is the slow scan television (SSTV) frequency. 3885 kHz is the AM calling frequency.

40 METERS: 7000-7300 KHZ

Sharing arrangements: 40 meters is a popular daytime band and worldwide communication is possible at night. Unfortunately, the international Broadcasting Service occupies the 7100-7300 kHz band in many parts of the world (Regions 1 and 3). During the daytime and during periods when sunspot numbers are high, international broadcasting does not cause much interference to US amateurs. At night, however, especially when sunspot numbers are low, the broadcast interference is heavy. Some countries allocate only the 7000-7100 kHz band to amateurs. Others, particularly in Region 2, allocate 7100-7300 kHz as well, which at times is subject to interference from international broadcasters in other Regions. The result is that there is a great demand for frequencies in the 7000-7100 kHz slot.

The effect is that there are two band plans overlaid on each other: The US (and the ITU Region 2 recommendation) allocation, which spreads out over 7000-7300 kHz and the foreign one, which compresses everything into

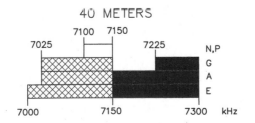

7000-7100 kHz. Foreign stations typically use the upper part of this segment for phone and the 7035-7045 kHz subband for RTTY. The two basic band plans coexist nicely until propagation permits stations in different regions to hear each other. The consolation is that 7000-7035 kHz is fine hunting ground for domestic and DX CW contacts [2.106].

License privileges: The Novice and Technician (for those who have passed the 5 WPM exam) subband on 40 meters is 7100-7150 kHz. Novice and Technician operators can use CW only [97.301(e), 97.307(f)(10)].

General licensees are allowed operation on 7025-7150 kHz and 7225-7300 kHz [97.301(d)]. Advanced operators have privileges at 7025-7300 kHz [97.301(c)]. Amateur Extra amateurs may operate across the entire band. All licensees must limit power output to 200 W PEP on the Novice/Technician subband [97.313(c)].

Mode privileges: RTTY and data modes are allowed on the nonvoice frequencies 7000-7150 kHz [97.305(c)].

The phone segment is 7150-7300 kHz [97.305(c)]. Image modes are also permitted here. Phone and image operation is permitted on 7075 to 7100 kHz for FCC licensed stations in ITU Regions 1 and 3, and by FCC licensed stations in ITU Region 2 west of 130° W longitude or south of 20° N latitude. This applies to stations outside the contiguous 48 states [97.307(f)(11)]. Novice/Technician operators outside of Region 2 may operate CW at 7050-7075 kHz [97.301(e)].

Band planning: Because 40-meter operating patterns in the US are somewhat different than those in the rest of the Region, this band poses a difficult problem. While the US and its possessions in Region 2 are allowed SSB operation only from 7150 kHz and up, the rest of Region 2 uses the band from 7050 (and sometimes even lower) and up for SSB. At the Region 2 meeting in Curacao in 1992, no agreement could be reached that reflected both existing packet activity and the strong desires of other countries for 7050-7100 kHz to be kept free of packet and other digital modes in favor of SSB.

The conference set the range 7035-7050 kHz as the digital zone, with packet priority at 7040-7050 kHz for international communication; 7100-7120 kHz packet priority for communications within Region 2. [Region 2 Band Plan, Curacao, 1992.] In the US, however, 7080-7100 kHz is still recognized as the digital area. 7040 kHz is used as both the RTTY DX channel and as the QRP calling frequency. Slow-scan TV centers around 7171 kHz. 7290 kHz is recognized as the AM calling frequency. 40 meters can be a *very* busy band.

30 METERS: 10.100-10.150 MHZ

Like 40 meters, 30 meters is primarily a night time band and amateurs are limited to CW only.

Sharing arrangements: The Amateur Radio Service is secondary in this band to stations in the Fixed Service outside of the US. Amateurs must avoid causing harmful interference to these foreign fixed stations. If you do, you must be prepared to stop transmitting, if necessary, to eliminate the interference [2.106, 97.303(d)].

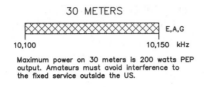

30 METERS

E,A,G

10,100   10,150   kHz

Maximum power on 30 meters is 200 watts PEP output. Amateurs must avoid interference to the fixed service outside the US.

License privileges: General, Advanced and Amateur Extra licensees have access to the entire segment, but are limited to 200 W PEP output using CW, RTTY and data emissions only, with a maximum sending speed of 300 baud [97.301(b),(c),(d); 97.305(c); 97.307(f)(3); 97.313(c)].

Band Planning: RTTY emissions should be restricted to 10.130-10.140 MHz, with packet operation at 10.140-10.150 MHz.

20 METERS: 14.000-14.350 MHZ

20 meters is the most popular HF band and worldwide communications are sometimes possible around the clock. The 20-meter band is allocated on an *exclusive* basis to the Amateur Radio Service throughout the world [2.106].

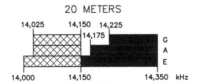

20 METERS

14,025   14,150   14,225

14,175

G
A
E

14,000   14,150   14,350   kHz

License privileges: No Novice, or Technician privileges are afforded at 20 meters. The General segments of the band occur at 14.025-14.150 and 14.225-14.350 MHz [97.301(d)]. Advanced licensees have access to 14.025-14.150 MHz and 14.175-14.350 MHz [97.301(c)]. Amateur Extra amateurs have access to the entire band.

Mode privileges: The phone band is 14.150-14.350 MHz [97.305(c)]. Image emissions are permitted on this voice segment also [97.305(c)]. CW, RTTY and data modes are permitted on the non-phone segment 14.000-14.150 MHz.

Band planning: The ARRL band plan recommends: CW between 14.000-14.070 MHz; RTTY between 14.070 and 14.095 MHz with a packet priority segment at 14.095-14.0995 MHz and a packet shared with foreign SSB segment at 14.1005-14.112 MHz; CW at 14.112-14.150 MHz and phone between 14.150-14.350 MHz. Beacons sponsored by the Northern California

DX Foundation can be found at 14.0995-14.1005 MHz. The SSTV channel centers on 14.230 MHz. The AM calling frequency is 14.286 MHz.

17 METERS: 18.068-18.168 MHZ

Worldwide transmissions are possible on the 17 meter band during the day. The 17-meter band is allocated to the Amateur Radio Service on an *exclusive* basis worldwide [2.106]. The entire segment is available to General, Advanced and Amateur Extra amateurs [97.301(b),(c),(d)]. RTTY and data modes are allowed on 18.068-18.110 MHz [97.305(c)]. RTTY/data modes must be in ASCII, AMTOR or Baudot, 300 baud limit [97.307(f)(3)]. Phone and Image modes are allowed on the rest of the band—18.110-18.168 MHz [97.305(c)].

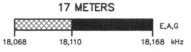

Band planning: The ARRL band plan calls for CW operation at 18.068-18.110 MHz; the Data segment is 18.100-18.105 MHz and the packet segment is at 18.105-18.110 MHz. Phone, CW and image operation occupies the rest of the band at 18.110-18.168 MHz.

15 METERS: 21.000-21.450 MHZ

Another popular daytime DX band, 15 meters is allocated to the Amateur Radio Service on an *exclusive* basis worldwide [2.106].

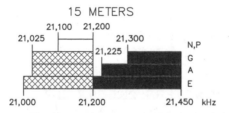

License privileges: The Novice and Technician (with 5 WPM code credit) subband is 21.100-21.200 MHz, CW only [97.301(e); 97.307(f)(9)]. General operators are allowed to use the 21.025-21.200 MHz, and 21.300-21.450 MHz segments [97.301(d)]. Advanced licensees have 21.025-21.200 MHz and 21.225-21.450 MHz [97.301(c)]. Amateur Extra amateurs have access to the entire band. All licensees must limit their power output to no more than 200 W PEP when operating in the Novice/Technician subband (with 5 WPM code credit) [97.313(c)].

Mode privileges: The phone and image segment is 21.200-21.450 MHz [97.305(c)]. Image modes are permitted on this voice segment only [97.305(c)]. RTTY and data modes are permitted on the non-voice segment only, which is 21.000-21.200 MHz [97.305(c)]. Again, RTTY/data emissions must be in Baudot, AMTOR or ASCII, and sent at not more than 300 baud [97.307(f)(3)].

Band planning: The Region 2 band plan allows digital operation at 21.070-21.125 MHz, with packet priority at 21.090-21.125 MHz [Curacao, 1992]. The problem with this arrangement for the US is that it promotes interference to Novice and Technician operators in their subband. The ARRL-suggested band plan is as follows: CW is at 21.000-21.070 MHz; RTTY and data activity is restricted to 21.070-21.090 MHz with packet priority at 21.090-21.100 MHz. The phone and image segment is 21.200-21.450 MHz with an SSTV channel at 21.340 MHz.

12 METERS: 24.890-24.990 MHZ

The 12-meter band is allocated to the Amateur Radio Service on an *exclusive* basis worldwide [2.106].

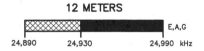

12 METERS

24,890   24,930   24,990 kHz   E,A,G

License privileges: General, Advanced and Amateur Extra licensees have access to the entire segment [97.301(b), (c), (d)].

Mode privileges: CW, RTTY and Data modes are authorized from 24.890-24.930 MHz, AMTOR, ASCII or Baudot, 300 baud limit [97.305(c); 97.307(f)(3)]. The phone and image band is 24.930-24.990 MHz [97.305(c)].

Band planning: The band plan calls for CW only at 24.890-24.920 MHz; RTTY/data modes at 24.920-24.925 MHz; packet priority at 24.925-24.930 MHz; and phone, image and CW at 24.930-24.990 MHz [Region 2 band plan, Curacao, 1992].

10 METERS: 28.0-29.7 MHZ

The entire 10-meter band is allocated to the Amateur Radio Service on an *exclusive* basis worldwide [2.106]. The Novice and Technician (for those Technicians who have passed the 5 WPM code exam) subband is 28.1-28.5 MHz [97.301(e); 97.307(f)(10)]. Novice and Technician licensees must limit their power to no more than 200 W PEP output [97.313(c)(2)]. Amateurs holding a General or higher license may use the full legal limit across the entire band [97.301(b)(c)(d)].

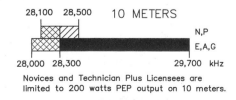

28,100   28,500   10 METERS

N,P

E,A,G

28,000   28,300   29,700 kHz

Novices and Technician Plus Licensees are limited to 200 watts PEP output on 10 meters.

RTTY and data modes are permitted at 28.0-28.3 MHz [97.305(c)]. RTTY/data emissions must be limited to AMTOR, Baudot or ASCII code; the sending speed limit is 1200 bauds. Novice and Technician (and Technician with code) amateurs may use CW, RTTY and data in the 28.1-28.3 MHz segment [97.307(f)(4)].

The phone and image segment is 28.3-29.7 MHz [97.305(c)]. FM voice is effectively limited to frequencies above 29.0 MHz [97.307(f)(1)] and repeaters are permitted from 29.5-29.7 MHz [97.205(b)].

Band planning: The ARRL band plan recognizes CW at 28.000-28.070 MHz and RTTY/data operation at 28.070-28.189 MHz, with packet priority at 28.120-28.189 MHz. SSTV activity centers around 28.680 MHz. Beacons are found between 28.200 and 28.300 MHz. The phone band is 28.300-29.300 MHz. AM operation is found at 29.000-29.200 MHz.

Satellite downlinks exist between 29.30 and 29.510 MHz. Repeater inputs are found from 29.510 to 29.590 MHz and outputs from 29.610-29.690 MHz. The FM simplex calling frequency is 29.600 MHz.

6 METERS: 50-54 MHZ

Six meters is a popular VHF band. In Regions 2 and 3, it is amateur *exclusive*. It is exclusively allocated for Broadcasting in Region 1 (certain Region 1 countries allow limited 6 meter operation) [2.106]. The entire band is available for use by all licensees except Novices [97.301(a)].

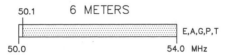

There is a CW exclusive subband from 50.0 to 50.1 MHz. MCW, phone, image, RTTY and data modes are permitted throughout the rest of the band, 50.1-54.0 MHz [97.305(c)].

RTTY and data modes used in sending specified codes may be transmitted at speeds up to 19.6 kilobauds [97.307(f)(5)]. Experimental (unspecified) codes are allowed—the bandwidth must not exceed 20 kHz [97.307(f)(5)].

Band planning: Activities in the 6-meter band are depicted in the following ARRL band plan [ARRL, July 1991].

50.0-50.1	CW, beacons
50.060-50.080	Beacon subband
50.1-50.3	SSB, CW
50.10-50.125	DX window
50.125	SSB calling frequency
50.4	AM calling frequency
50.3-50.6	all modes

50.6-50.8	nonvoice communications
50.62	digital (packet) calling frequency
50.8-51.0	Remote Control (20-kHz channels)
51.0-51.1	Pacific DX window
51.12-51.48	repeater inputs (19 channels)
51.12-51.18	digital repeater inputs
51.5-51.6	simplex (6 channels)
51.62-51.98	repeater outputs (19 channels)
51.62-51.68	digital repeater outputs
52.0-52.48	repeater inputs (except as noted; 23 channels)
52.02, 52.04	FM simplex
52.2	TEST PAIR (input)
52.5-52.98	repeater outputs (except as noted; 23 channels)
52.525	primary FM simplex
52.54	secondary FM simplex
52.7	TEST PAIR (output)
53.0-53.48	repeater inputs (except as noted; 19 channels)
53.0	remote base FM simplex
53.02	simplex
53.1, 53.2, 53.3, 53.4	radio remote control
53.5-53.98	repeater outputs (except as noted; 19 channels)
53.5, 53.6, 53.7, 53.8	radio remote control
53.52, 53.9	simplex

2 METERS: 144-148 MHZ

The most popular amateur VHF band, 2 meters is where much FM repeater activity occurs. The band is amateur *exclusive* in Region 2.

In Region 1, amateurs are limited to 144-146 MHz, but it is an *exclusive* allocation. Fixed and mobile stations occupy 146-148 MHz in this region.

In Region 3, amateurs enjoy 144-146 exclusively and share on a coprimary basis 146-148 MHz with stations operating under the Fixed and Mobile Service [2.106].

There is a CW-only segment from 144.00 to 144.10 MHz. All of the remaining emissions are permitted above 144.10 MHz [97.305(c)].

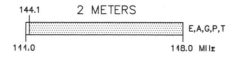

All licensees except Novices are permitted to use the entire segment [97.301(a)]. The following ARRL band plan explains typical operation on the 2-meter band:

144.00-144.05	EME (CW)
144.05-144.10	General CW and weak signals

144.10-144.20	EME and weak-signal SSB
144.200	National calling frequency (CW/SSB)
144.20-144.275	General SSB operation
144.275-144.300	Propagation beacons
144.30-144.50	New OSCAR subband
144.50-144.60	Linear translator inputs
144.60-144.90	FM repeater inputs
144.90-145.10	Weak signal and FM simplex (145.01, 03, 05, 07, 09 are widely used for packet radio)
145.10-145.20	Linear translator outputs
145.20-145.50	FM repeater outputs
145.50-145.80	Miscellaneous and experimental modes
145.80-146.00	OSCAR subband
146.01-146.37	Repeater inputs
146.40-146.58	Simplex
146.52	National Simplex Calling Frequency
146.61-147.39	Repeater outputs
147.42-147.57	Simplex
147.60-147.99	Repeater inputs

1.25 METERS: 222-225 MHZ

Sharing arrangements: In the US, amateurs have *exclusive* use of the 222-225 MHz band. There are no amateur allocations outside Region 2 [2.106].

1.25 METERS

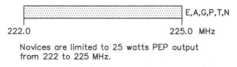

222.0   225.0 MHz

Novices are limited to 25 watts PEP output
from 222 to 225 MHz.

All licensees have access to the entire band 222-225 MHz [97.301(a), (e)]. All modes are permitted [97.305(c)]. A weak signal segment is found at 222.0-222.15 where repeater and auxiliary operation is prohibited [97.201(b); 97.205(b)]. Novice licensees must limit their power to no more than 25 W PEP output [97.313(d)]. Technician and above operators may use the full legal power limit.

Band planning [ARRL, July 1991].
222.0-222.15	Weak-signal modes
222.0-222.025	EME
222.05-222.06	Propagation beacons
222.1	SSB and CW calling frequency
222.10-222.15	Weak-signal CW and SSB

222.15-222.25	Local coordinator's option; weak signal, ACSSB, repeater inputs, control
222.25-223.38	FM repeater inputs only
223.40-223.52	FM simplex
223.5	FM simplex calling frequency
223.52-223.64	Digital, packet
223.64-223.7	Links, control
223.71-223.85	Local coordinator's option, FM simplex, packet, repeater outputs
223.85-224.98	Repeater outputs only

E,A,G,P,T

219.0   220.0 MHz

219-220 MHz: The FCC has allocated 219-220 MHz to amateur use on a *secondary* basis. This allocation is for fixed digital message forwarding systems only and can be operated by all licensees except Novices. *It is not available for other purposes. Amateur operations must not cause interference to, and must accept interference from, primary services in this and adjacent bands.* Amateur stations are limited to 50 W PEP output and 100 kHz bandwidth. Automated Maritime Telecommunications Systems (AMTS) stations are the primary occupants in this band. Amateur stations within 398 miles of an AMTS station must notify the station in writing at least 30 days prior to beginning operations. Amateur stations within 50 miles of an AMTS station must get permission in writing from the AMTS station before beginning operations. ARRL Headquarters maintains a database of AMTS stations. The FCC requires that amateur operators provide written notification including the station's geographic location to the ARRL for inclusion in a database at least 30 days before beginning operations in this segment.

70 CENTIMETERS: 420-450 MHZ

In the US, amateurs share the band with Government Radiolocation (Radar). The Amateur Radio Service is the *secondary* service and therefore must not interfere with the *primary* occupants, which are Government services. Amateurs must also tolerate interference from and can't cause interference to Government Radiolocation stations [97.303(b)].

70 CENTIMETERS

E,A,G,P,T

420.0   450.0 MHz

The 420-430 MHz segment is allocated to the Fixed and Mobile (except Aeronautical Mobile) Services on a *primary* basis worldwide. Amateurs must not cause harmful interference to these stations, nor are amateurs

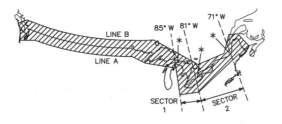

protected from interference from these stations [97.303(f)(2)].

Amateur operation in the 420-430 MHz portion of the band is not permitted north of Line A (see figure) [97.303(f)(1), 2.1].

The FCC has allocated portions of the band 421-430 MHz to the Land Mobile Service on a primary basis within a 50-mile radius centered on Buffalo, Detroit and Cleveland. Amateur stations south of Line A in the vicinities of these cities may continue to operate in the 421-430 MHz spectrum as long as they do not cause interference to and accept interference from Land Mobile or Government Radiolocation users [US Footnote 230, 2.106].

Additionally, 50 W PEP output power limitations apply to amateurs operating within circles centered on designated military installations in the US. Exceptions may be granted when expressly authorized by the FCC after mutual agreement, on a case-by-case basis, with the FCC District Director and the Military Area Frequency Coordinator at the applicable military base. An earth or telecommand station may, however, transmit on the 435-438 MHz segment with a maximum of 611 W ERP without the authorization otherwise required. The transmitting antenna must be pointed above the horizon by at least 10° [97.313(f); US Footnote 7, 2.106].

The affected areas are:

1) Portions of New Mexico and Texas bounded on the south by latitude 31° 45' North, on the east by longitude 104° 00' West, on the north by latitude 34° 30' North, and on the west by longitude 107° 30' West.

2) The entire state of Florida including the Key West area and the areas enclosed within a 200-mile radius of Patrick Air Force Base, Florida (latitude 28° 21' North, longitude 80° 43' West), and within a 200-mile radius of Eglin AFB, Florida (latitude 30° 30' North, longitude 86° 30' West);

3) The entire state of Arizona;

4) Those portions of California and Nevada south of latitude 37° 10' North, and the areas enclosed within a 200-mile radius of the Pacific Missile Test Center, Point Mugu, California (latitude 34° 09' North, longitude 119° 11' West).

5) In the state of Massachusetts within a 160-kilometer (100-mile) radius around locations at Otis AFB, Massachusetts (latitude 41° 45' North, longitude 70° 32' West).

6) In the state of California, within a 240-kilometer (150-mile) radius

around locations at Beale AFB, California (latitude 39° 08' North, longitude 121° 26' West).

7) In the state of Alaska, within a 160-kilometer (100-mile) radius of Clear, Alaska (latitude 64° 17' North, longitude 149° 10' West).

8) In the state of North Dakota, within a 160-kilometer (100-mile) radius of Concrete, North Dakota (latitude 48° 43' North, longitude 97° 54' West).

9) In the states of Alabama, Florida, Georgia and South Carolina within a 200 kilometer (124 mile) radius of Warner Robins AFB, Georgia (latitude 32° 38' North, longitude 83° 35' West).

10) In the state of Texas within a 200 kilometer (124 mile) radius of Goodfellow AFB, Texas (latitude 31° 25' North, longitude 100° 24' West).

The Military Area Frequency Coordinator for items 5 through 10 is located at Peterson AFB, Colorado. [97.313(f); US Footnote 7, 2.106.]

When operating at 449.5-450 MHz, amateurs must not cause interference to, and must accept interference from space operation service and space research service stations or government or non-government space telecommand stations [US Footnote 87, 2.106].

License privileges: All amateurs except Novices have access to the entire segment 420-450 MHz [97.301(a)].

Mode privileges: All mode privileges are authorized across the entire band [97.305(c)]. The RTTY and data mode speed limit is 56 kilobauds [97.307(f)(6)]. Experimental codes are allowed on this segment; the maximum bandwidth allowed is 100 kHz [97.307(f)(6)].

Band planning:

420.00-426.00	ATV repeater or simplex with 421.25 MHz video carrier, control links, and experimental
426.00-432.00	ATV simplex with 427.250-MHz video carrier frequency
432.00-432.070	EME (Earth-Moon-Earth)
432.07-432.10	Weak-signal CW
432.100	Calling frequency
432.10-432.30	Mixed-mode and weak-signal work
432.30-432.40	Propagation beacons
432.40-433.00	Mixed-mode and CW work
433.00-435.00	Auxiliary/repeater links
435.00-438.00	Satellite only (internationally)
438.00-444.00	ATV repeater input with 439.250-MHz video carrier frequency and repeater links
442.00-445.00	Repeater inputs and outputs (local option)
445.00-447.00	Shared by auxiliary and control links, repeaters and simplex (local option);
446.0	National simplex frequency
447.00-450.00	Repeater inputs and outputs

33 CENTIMETERS: 902-928 MHZ

Sharing arrangements: In the US, the Amateur Radio Service is *secondary* to the Government Radiolocation (Radar) Service and amateurs can't cause interference to and must accept interference from those stations [2.106; 97.303(b)].

Amateurs may encounter emissions from Industrial, Scientific and Medical (ISM) equipment. Examples are dialysis machines and manufacturing equipment. Amateurs must not cause interference to, and must accept interference from, these applications [97.303(g)(1)].

33 CENTIMETERS

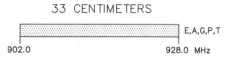

902.0   928.0 MHz   E,A,G,P,T

Amateurs must also accept interference from microwave ovens operating at 915 MHz, manufactured before January 1, 1980 [US Footnote 215, 2.106], and from the Location and Monitoring Service (LMS). Amateurs must not cause interference to LMS systems, which operate across the entire band [US Footnotes 218 and 275; 2.106; 97.303(g)(1)].

Amateurs located in the states of Colorado and Wyoming, bounded on the south by latitude 39° North, on the north by latitude 42° North, on the east by longitude 105° West, and on the west by longitude 108° West may not transmit on this band except in the segments 902.0-902.4, 902.6-904.3, 904.7-925.3, 925.7-927.3, and 927.7-928.0 MHz only [97.303(g)(1); July 2, 1990, waiver, US Footnote 267, 2.106].

Amateurs located in the states of Texas and New Mexico bounded on the south by 31° 41' North, on the north by latitude 34° 30' North, on the east by longitude 104° 11' West, and on the west by longitude 107° 30' West may not transmit on this band [US Footnote 275, 2.106; 97.303(g)(2)]. In addition, amateurs outside these boundaries but within 150 miles of the White Sands Missile Range must limit their peak envelope power to 50 watts [97.313(g)].

License privileges: All licensees except Novices have full access to the segment [97.301(a)].

Mode privileges: All modes may be used on the entire band [97.305(c)].

Band planning [ARRL, July 1989]:

902.0-903.0	Weak signal
902.1	Calling frequency
903.0-906.0	Digital
903.1	Alternate calling frequency
906.0-909.0	FM repeater outputs
909.0-915.0	ATV

915.0-918.0	Digital
918.0-921.0	FM repeater inputs
921.0-927.0	ATV
927.0-928.0	FM simplex and links

23 CENTIMETERS: 1240-1300 MHZ

The Amateur Radio Service is *secondary* to the Government Radiolocation Service. Amateurs must not cause interference to the primary occupants. All emission privileges are allowed on this band, and are available to all licensees except Novices [97.305(c); 97.301(a), (f)]. Novice operators may use the 1270-1295 MHz subband and are limited to 5 watts PEP [97.301(f); 97.313(e)]. This band, as are virtually all amateur bands between 222 MHz and 24.250 GHz (24.00-24.05 GHz is an exception), is allocated to amateurs on a secondary, non-interference basis, to the primary Government Radiolocation Services [2.106; 97.303(b)].

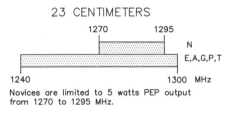

Novices are limited to 5 watts PEP output
from 1270 to 1295 MHz.

Band planning [ARRL, January 1985]:

1240-1246	ATV #1
1246-1248	Narrow-bandwidth FM point-to-point links and digital, duplexed with 1258-1260.
1248-1252	Digital Communications
1252-1258	ATV #2
1258-1260	Narrow-bandwidth FM point-to-point links and digital, duplexed with 1246-1252
1260-1270	Satellite uplinks
1260-1270	Wide-bandwidth experimental, simplex ATV
1270-1276	Repeater inputs, FM and linear, paired with 1282-1288. (239 pairs, every 25 kHz, e.g., 1270.025, 050, etc)
1271/1283	Non-coordinated test pair
1276-1282	ATV #3
1282-1288	Repeater outputs, paired with 1270-1276
1288-1294	Wide-bandwidth experimental, simplex ATV
1294-1295	Narrow-bandwidth FM simplex services, 25-kHz channels

1294.5	National FM simplex calling frequency
1295-1297	Narrow bandwidth weak-signal communications (no FM)
1295.0-1295.8	SSTV, FAX, ACSSB experimental
1295.8-1296.0	Reserved for EME, CW expansion
1296.0-1296.05	EME-exclusive
1296.07-1296.08	CW beacons
1296.1	CW, SSB calling frequency
1296.4-1296.6	Crossband linear translator input
1296.6-1296.8	Crossband linear translator output
1296.8-1297.0	Experimental beacons (exclusive)
1297-1300	Digital communications

13 CENTIMETERS: 2300-2310 AND 2390-2450 MHZ

The 13 cm band is broken into two separate pieces. The Amateur Radio Service is *secondary* to stations operating in the Government Radiolocation Service. Amateurs can't cause interference to and must accept interference from stations in this service. ARRL is currently seeking a change from *secondary* to *primary* status in the 2300-2305 MHz and 2400-2402 MHz segments.

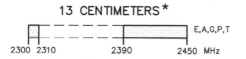

13 CENTIMETERS*

*Amateurs are primary on the 2390-2400 MHz and 2402-2417 MHz subbands.

The ARRL Board of Directors adopted the following band plan in January, 1991.
2300-2310 and 2390-2450 MHz

2300-2303	High-rate data
2303-2303.5	Packet radio
2303.5-2303.8	TTY, packet
2303.8-2303.9	Packet, TTY, CW, EME
2303.9-2304.1	CW, EME
2304.1-2304.2	CW, EME, SSB
2304.2-2304.3	SSB, SSTV, FAX, Packet, AM, AMTOR
2304.3-2304.32	Propagation beacon network
2304.32-2304.4	General propagation beacons
2304.4	Calling frequency
2304.4-2304.5	SSB, SSTV, ACSSB, FAX, Packet, AM, AMTOR, Experimental

2304.5-2304.7	Crossband linear translator input
2304.7-2304.9	Crossband linear translator output
2304.9-2305	Experimental beacons
2305-2305.2	FM simplex (25-kHz spacing)
2305.2	FM simplex calling frequency
2305.2-2306	FM simplex (25-kHz spacing)
2306-2309	FM repeaters (25-kHz) input
2309-2310	Control and auxiliary links
**********	
2390-2396	Fast-scan TV
2396-2399	High-rate data
2399-2399.5	Packet
2399.5-2400	Control and auxiliary links
2400-2403	Satellite
2403-2408	Satellite high-rate data
2408-2410	Satellite
2410-2413	FM repeaters (25-kHz spacing) output
2413-2418	High-rate data
2418-2430	Fast-scan TV
2430-2433	Satellite
2433-2438	Satellite high-rate data
2438-2450	Wideband FM, FSTV, FMTV, SS experimental

ABOVE AND BEYOND

All modes and licensees (except Novices) are authorized on the following bands [97.301(a)]:

3300-3500 MHz
5650-5925 MHz
10.0-10.5 GHz
24.0-24.25 GHz
47.0-47.2 GHz
75.5-81.0 GHz*
119.98-120.02 GHz
142-149 GHz
241-250.0 GHz
All above 300 GHz

*Amateur operation in the 76-77 GHz band has been temporarily suspended in exchange for an upgrade to coprimary status in the 75.5-76 and 77-78 GHz segments.

AUTHORIZED EMISSION TYPES

Once upon a time, if it sounded like a duck, you had to call it J3E. Thankfully the FCC now just calls it "phone." This approach is used in Part

97 with a cross-reference to the alphanumeric ITU emission designators. For those who are at loose ends unless they know which specific emission they're emitting, the appropriate designators have been implemented into the following discussions of each mode type. The complete list is in §2.201 of the FCC Rules, which can be found in Appendix 2 of this book. Even more detailed information about international emission standards can be found at **http://www.itu.int/radioclub/rr/aps01.htm**.

To find out what is permitted under the emission designators, start by looking up the definitions [97.3(c)]. For CW and test emissions, check §97.305(a) and (b), respectively. For other emission designators, check §97.305(c) to find the bands where these emissions are permitted, along with any restrictions and/or additional modes authorized for specific bands, which are located in §97.307(f). The rules provide latitude for the experimenter, while preserving the traditional demarcation between RTTY/data and phone/FAX/SSTV operation in the HF bands.

The FCC defines nine different types of emissions in §97.3(c): CW, MCW, Phone, Image, RTTY, Data, Pulse, Spread Spectrum and Test. Differences between these emissions can be confusing at times. The same equipment can be used to transmit Phone, SSTV or RTTY. The type of information transmitted, as well as how it's transmitted, determines how an emission is classified. Let's look at each one.

CW

The term *CW* (Continuous Wave) is used by hams to denote the oldest radio modulation system, telegraphy by on-off keying of a carrier. CW emission can be used on any frequency in the amateur bands [97.305(a)]. The term continuous wave came about to differentiate a carrier generated by sources that produce a clean, steady signal (such as oscillators) from *damped waves*, the rough, broad signals generated by a spark gap transmitter (damped wave transmissions were outlawed in the 1930s). Some parts of the electronics industry use the term CW to signify a steady unmodulated carrier.

In the past, the FCC only used the designator A1A to designate CW (on/off keying of the main carrier), but wouldn't have minded if you produced the same result by keying a tone and feeding it into a single sideband transmitter. Technically that would have been J2A, which the old rules did not specifically say was permissible. However, the current rules explicitly permit on/off keying of a tone modulating a single-sideband transmitter. As with any CW signal, you need to use a beat-frequency oscillator (BFO) to hear the Morse code keyed tone.

The FCC uses these ITU designators for CW: International Morse code telegraphy emissions having designators with A, C, H, J or R as the first symbol; 1 as the second symbol; A or B as the third symbol; J2A or J2B [97.3(c)(1)].

First symbol: Type of modulation of the main carrier:

A Double sideband
C Vestigial sideband
H Single sideband, full carrier
J Single sideband, suppressed carrier
R Single sideband, reduced carrier

Second symbol: Nature of signal(s) modulating the main carrier:

1 A single channel containing quantized or digital information without the use of a modulating subcarrier

Third symbol: Type of information to be transmitted:

A Telegraphy—for aural reception
B Telegraphy—for automatic reception

And J2A and J2B:

J Single sideband, suppressed carrier
2 A single channel containing quantized or digital information with the use of a modulating subcarrier
A Telegraphy—for aural reception
B Telegraphy—for automatic reception

MCW

MCW (Modulated CW) is produced by modulating a carrier with a tone, then keying the tone or both the tone and the carrier. Most ham rigs don't have this mode built in, in which case you supply the tone with an external tone generator. Unlike CW, you don't need a beat-frequency oscillator (BFO) to hear the tone. This makes it particularly useful for repeater IDs.

For many years, MCW was the modulation of choice for emergency transmitters used in aircraft and vessels. MCW occupies a bandwidth wider than that of ordinary CW. With hard keying and square-wave tone modulation, MCW creates such a splatter that it is hard to miss, even with a mistuned receiver, with or without a BFO. MCW, even with soft keying and a clean sine-wave modulating tone, is not permitted in the crowded HF ham bands for general communications, for example as a substitute for CW. There is a special provision in the rules allowing MCW to be used on the HF phone bands for code practice transmissions when interspersed with speech [97.3(c)(4)]. It isn't MCW, however, unless a carrier is transmitted, as in the case of tone keying an FM or AM transmitter. If a keyed tone is transmitted over an SSB transmitter, there is no carrier, so the Morse transmission is CW, not MCW, and a BFO is needed in the receiver.

This is what the rules permit as MCW emission: Tone-modulated international Morse code telegraphy emissions having designators with A, C, D, F, G or R as the first symbol; 2 as the second symbol; A or B as the third symbol [97.3(c)(4)].

First symbol: Type of modulation of the main carrier:

A Double sideband
C Vestigial sideband
D Emission in which the main carrier is amplitude and angle modulated either simultaneously or in a pre-established pattern
F Frequency modulation
G Phase modulation
R Single sideband, reduced carrier

Second symbol: Nature of signal(s) modulating the main carrier:

2 A single channel containing quantized or digital information with the use of a modulating subcarrier

Third symbol: Type of information to be transmitted:

A Telegraphy—for aural reception
B Telegraphy—for automatic reception

IMAGE

The word *image* encompasses both television and facsimile. Basically, the rules permit you to transmit image information using essentially any modulation method. Because image operation on HF is within the phone bands, you can alternate image modulation with phone modulation. You can also transmit image and phone on the same carrier by using independent-sideband modulation. The bandwidth limitation in this case is essentially the same as that for transmitting a single channel of communications quality speech, or 3 kHz for single sideband, 6 kHz for double sideband or for two channels of information [97.305(c), 97.307(f)(2)]. If you can fit it into this bandwidth, you can transmit it. Both slow scan television (SSTV) and facsimile (FAX) can be transmitted here.

The rule limiting bandwidth of an image emission to that of a communications quality phone signal of the same modulation type applies to all amateur bands from 160 to 1.25 meters. Thus fast scan television, with its wide bandwidth requirement, is permitted only in and above the 70 cm (440 MHz) band.

Image transmissions may be either analog or digital, as long as they meet the bandwidth limitations for the frequencies to be used. Station identification may be done by image as long as all or part of the communications on the frequency are in the same image emission, and it conforms to the applicable standards of §73.682(a) (NTSC transmissions).

The FCC uses these ITU designators for Image: Facsimile and television emissions having designators with A, C, D, F, G, H, J or R as the first symbol; 1, 2 or 3 as the second symbol; C or F as the third symbol; and emissions having B as the first symbol; 7, 8 or 9 as the second symbol; W as the third symbol [97.3(c)(3)].

First symbol: Type of modulation of the main carrier:

A Double sideband

C Vestigial sideband

D Emission in which the main carrier is amplitude and angle modulated either frequency modulation

G Phase modulation

H Single sideband, full carrier

J Single sideband, suppressed carrier

R Single sideband, reduced carrier

Second symbol: Nature of signal(s) modulating the main carrier:

1 A single channel containing quantized or digital information without the use of a modulating subcarrier

2 A single channel containing quantized or digital information with the use of a modulating subcarrier

3 A single channel containing analog information

Third symbol: Type of information to be transmitted:

C Facsimile

F Television (video)

Also emissions with:

First symbol: Type of modulation of the main carrier:

B Independent sidebands

Second symbol: Nature of signal(s) modulating the main carrier:

7 Two or more channels containing quantized or digital information

8 Two or more channels containing analog information

9 Composite system with one or more channels containing quantized or digital information, together with one or more channels containing analog information

Third symbol: Type of information to be transmitted:

W Combination of the above

"W Combination of the Above" covers a combination of facsimile or television and telephony by means of independent-sideband (ISB) modulation. ISB modulation with image on one sideband and phone on another is permitted in the MF and HF bands. Literally, the designator means a combination of any of the following types of information:

N No information transmitted

A Telegraphy—for aural reception

B Telegraphy—for automatic reception

C Facsimile

D Data transmission, telemetry, telecommand

E Telephony

F Video

However, when transmitting ISB, it would be prudent to limit the information content of the two independent sidebands to the types of information permitted in that band segment. As phone and image are usually permitted in the same segments and CW is allowed in all bands, it would seem that these are the only emissions permitted for ISB modulation in such segments.

PHONE

Phone (short for telephony) used to mean speech only. Now it includes speech and other sounds. No, that doesn't mean rock music with 100% distortion, but it does include almost any sound hams might need to transmit. *Amplitude Modulation* (AM, designator A3E), *Frequency Modulation* (FM, designator F3E) and *Single Sideband Suppressed Carrier* (SSB, designator J3E) emissions are all included under phone, as long as sounds are transmitted.

Tone alerting and selective calling are explicitly permitted on frequencies authorized for phone [97.3(c)(5)]. The rules permit subcarrier tones that are incidental to the operation of the telephone channel. For example, a subcarrier to control the level of the demodulated signal (compandoring) is permitted—so you can add a pilot tone for *amplitude-compandored single sideband* (ACSSB) if desired [97.3(c)(5)].

You can also send your station identification by Morse code or other digital means on any frequency where phone operation is permitted. The key word here is *incidental*: Speech is the main thing, and the tones are supplemental [97.3(c)(5)].

You can choose virtually any phone modulation method that can convey speech: double-sideband full carrier, single-sideband full carrier, single-sideband reduced or variable-level carrier, single-sideband suppressed carrier, vestigial sideband, or independent sidebands with one sideband carrying speech and the other having slow-scan TV or facsimile. The last is a form of multiplexing—carrying two or more channels of information on one signal.

You are no longer restricted to analog modulation—digitized signals are also permitted, as long as the intelligence being transmitted is telephony. Thus, digital voice is permitted wherever phone operation is authorized.

Is there any bandwidth limitation to phone transmissions? None according to the rules, except for the general requirement of "good engineering practice" [97.101(a)]. On the other hand, using excessive bandwidth will get you in immediate trouble with other hams who are trying to share the band with you. So it's wise to limit phone bandwidth on the HF bands to that of a single-sideband transmission of a single analog audio channel (roughly 3 kHz) if possible. There are exceptions to that: bandwidths on the order of 6 kHz are needed for double-sideband AM phone, for FM phone and for independent-sideband transmissions, where each sideband is roughly 3 kHz wide. Good engineering practice in these cases boils down to "reasonable and proper bandwidth"—don't use more than you need.

Above 902 MHz, the rules permit multiplexing (MUXing) FM phone modulation (designated F8E) [97.305(c); 97.307(f)(12)]. This permits more than one analog channel to be transmitted on the main carrier. Good engineering practice for multiplexing again amounts to using no more bandwidth than you need. When in doubt, check with the frequency coordinator in your area to see what sort of protection adjacent-channel users need.

The following is the ITU definition of Phone emission: Speech and other sound emissions having designators with A, C, D, F, G, H, J or R as the first symbol; 1, 2 or 3 as the second symbol; E as the third symbol. Also speech emissions having B as the first symbol; 7, 8 or 9 as the second symbol; E as the third symbol [97.3(c)(5)].

First symbol: Type of modulation of the main carrier:
A Double sideband
C Vestigial sideband
D Emission in which the main carrier is amplitude and angle modulated either simultaneously or in a pre-established pattern
F Frequency modulation
G Phase modulation
H Single sideband, full carrier
J Single sideband, suppressed carrier
R Single sideband, reduced carrier

Second symbol: Nature of signal(s) modulating the main carrier:
1 A single channel containing quantized or digital information without the use of a modulating subcarrier
2 A single channel containing quantized or digital information with the use of a modulating subcarrier
3 A single channel containing analog information

Third symbol: Type of information to be transmitted:
E Telephony

The following are also permitted:

First symbol: Type of modulation of the main carrier:
B Independent sidebands

Second symbol: Nature of signal(s) modulating the main carrier:
7 Two or more channels containing quantized or digital information
8 Two or more channels containing analog information
9 Composite system with one or more channels containing quantized or digital information, together with one or more channels containing analog information

Third symbol: Type of information to be transmitted:
E Telephony

And F8E above 902 MHz:
F Frequency modulation
8 Two or more channels containing analog information
E Telephony

RTTY

RTTY is narrow band, direct printing telegraphy communications received by automatic techniques. RTTY (as well as data) is commonly referred to as a digital mode even though the FCC differentiates the two.

Is PSK31 Legal?

Some armchair lawyers have questioned the legality of PSK31 since its Varicode is not specifically mentioned as a "legal" digital code in Part 97. Some confusion is understandable, given the wording of 97.309(a).

However, the FCC clarified the meaning of the rules in an Order released October 11, 1995 (December 1995 *QST*, p 84). The Order (DA 95-2106) reads in part: "This Order amends Section 97.309(a) of the Commission's Rules . . . to clarify that amateur stations may use any digital code that has its technical characteristics publicly documented. This action was initiated by a letter from the American Radio Relay League, Inc. (ARRL)."

The Order goes on to note that "The technical characteristics of CLOVER, G-TOR, and PACTOR have been documented publicly for use by amateur operators, and commercial products are readily available that facilitate the transmission and reception of communications incorporating these codes. Including CLOVER, G-TOR, and PACTOR in the rules will not conflict with our objective of preventing the use of codes or ciphers intended to obscure the meaning of the communication. We agree, therefore, that it would be helpful to the amateur service community for the rules to specifically authorize amateur stations to transmit messages and data using these and similar digital codes."

Given that PSK31 is in the public domain for amateur use, that software is readily and freely available, and that its emission characteristics clearly meet the standards of Section 97.307 for RTTY/data, there is little doubt that its use by FCC-licensed amateur stations is legal.

However, just to complete the documentation, in a letter to the FCC dated January 27, 1999, ARRL General Counsel Christopher D. Imlay, W3KD, documented the technical characteristics of PSK31 in a manner similar to how CLOVER, G-TOR, and PACTOR were previously documented. There is no need for PSK31 to be mentioned specifically in the rules, because CLOVER, G-TOR, and PACTOR are simply given as examples.

Only a digital code of a type specifically authorized for RTTY in Part 97 may be transmitted, as well as any other technique that has had its technical characteristics documented publicly, such as CLOVER, G-TOR or PacTOR. PSK31 is also permitted (see sidebar).

RTTY is keyboard sending, hard copy or screen presentation, possibly with computer buffering. There is little or no manipulation or reformatting of text prior to presentation (what is sent is what you get). Text is sent in Baudot or ASCII and there is generally no error control (except when using AMTOR or some other techniques). Asynchronous transmission is used (in other words, start and stop pulses are used, except when using AMTOR).

Here's what the rules permit under the RTTY emission: Narrow-band direct-printing telegraphy emissions having designators with A, C, D, F, G, H, J or R as the first symbol; 1 as the second symbol; B as the third symbol; and emission J2B [97.3(c)(7)]. In terms of ITU emission designator definitions, that means:

First symbol: Type of modulation of the main carrier:

A Double sideband

C Vestigial sideband

D Emission in which the main carrier is amplitude and angle modulated either simultaneously or in a pre-established pattern

F Frequency modulation

G Phase modulation

H Single sideband, full carrier

J Single sideband, suppressed carrier

R Single sideband, reduced carrier

Second symbol: Nature of signal(s) modulating the main carrier:

1 A single channel containing quantized or digital information without the use of a modulating subcarrier

Third symbol: Type of information to be transmitted:

B Telegraphy—for automatic reception and J2B:

J Single sideband, suppressed carrier

2 A single channel containing quantized or digital information with the use of a modulating subcarrier

B Telegraphy—for automatic reception

DATA

Data is a computer mode in which files are sent and received. There may be some reorganization of the information prior to transmission and probably before presentation. Data transmissions use error detection and/or error correction as well as packetized transmission. Synchronous transmission is also used which means there are no start and stop pulses.

First, you can transmit specified digital codes of Baudot, AMTOR, ASCII, as well as any other technique that has had its technical characteristics documented publicly, such as CLOVER, G-TOR or PacTOR. PSK31 is also permitted (see sidebar). [97.309(a)]. It is important to note that Baudot does not use error detection and correction and it isn't packetized. A station may also use an "unspecified digital code, except to a station in a country with which the United States does not have an agreement permitting the code to be used" [97.309(b)]. "Unspecified digital codes must not be transmitted for the purpose of obscuring the meaning of any communication" [97.309(b)]. The rules permit unspecified digital codes as well as the previously mentioned "specified" codes to be used above 50.1 MHz, but only Baudot, AMTOR or ASCII as well as any other technique that has had its technical characteristics documented publicly (such as CLOVER, G-TOR, PacTOR, PSK31) may be used below that frequency [97.305(c) and 97.307(f)(3),(4)]. RTTY and data multiplexing is allowed on frequencies above 50.1 MHz within the bandwidth limitations [97.307(f)(5)-(8)].

In terms of ITU emission designators, the following types of emission are permitted for data emission: Telemetry, telecommand and computer communications emissions having designators with A, C, D, F, G, H, J or R as the first symbol; 1 as the second symbol; D as the third symbol; and emission J2D. That expands to:

Q&A—Data, RTTY Modulation Methods

Q. Is it permissible to modulate an FM voice transmitter with data or RTTY?

A. It depends on the frequency. It is permissible only where data or RTTY emissions are authorized above 50 MHz. This type of transmission is commonly used in the VHF bands because of the ready availability of FM transceivers.

Some amateurs have expressed a desire to operate using this mode in the 10-meter band above 29.0 MHz. Although FM voice is specifically authorized as a mode, neither data nor RTTY is permitted on 10 meters, except in the 28.0-28.3 MHz segment [97.305(c); 97.307(f)(1)].

Q. Are there any speed limits or bandwidth constraints for data or RTTY?

A. Yes, at least below 450 MHz. The limits break down as follows [97.307(f)]

Frequency Range	Speed Limit for Specified Codes	Maximum Bandwidth for Unspecified Codes
1.80 - 24.93 MHz	300 bauds	Not permitted
28.0 - 28.3 MHz	1200 bauds	Not permitted
50.1 - 148 MHz	19.6 kilobauds	20 kHz
222 - 450 MHz	56 kilobauds	100 kHz
Above 902 MHz	No speed limit	No bandwidth limit

Even though there is no bandwidth limit on amateur bands on and above the 902 MHz band, all amateur transmissions must fit inside the band.

The maximum bandwidth is, in this case, the "width of a frequency band outside of which the mean power of the transmitted signal is attenuated at least 26 dB below the mean power of the transmitted signal within the band" [97.3(a)(8)]. Where no speed or bandwidth limits are listed, the basic rule is to stay within the ham band. There are, however, some operational considerations. The HF RTTY/data bands are crowded, and it wouldn't set too well with other hams if you were to use excessive bandwidth. The practical limitation at HF is imposed by the audio characteristics of the SSB transceivers generally used. Typically, they may have –6 dB audio bandwidths of 2.1 to 2.7 kHz. Most RTTY operators use 500 Hz (or narrower) filters. So packet radio bandwidths on the HF bands have been limited to about 2 kHz. For example, the packet frequencies just above 14.100 MHz are spaced every 2 kHz. In all cases, check the band plan, and where appropriate, contact your frequency coordinator to determine the appropriate bandwidth for your operation.

Q. Can I use a parallel modem on HF?

A. This refers to a modem that uses several tones, rather than switching between two, and keys them at a slower rate to avoid the effects of multipath (intersymbol) distortion. The emission J2D does not limit the number of tones; it simply limits the transmission to a single channel of information. So, the answer is yes, if you use J2D emission.

First symbol: Type of modulation of the main carrier:
A Double sideband
C Vestigial sideband
D Emission in which the main carrier is amplitude and angle modulated either simultaneously or in a pre-established pattern
F Frequency modulation
G Phase modulation
H Single sideband, full carrier
J Single sideband, suppressed carrier
R Single sideband, reduced carrier

Second symbol: Nature of signal(s) modulating the main carrier:
1 A single channel containing quantized or digital information without the use of a modulating subcarrier

Third symbol: Type of information to be transmitted:
D Data transmission, telemetry, telecommand and J2D:
J Single sideband, suppressed carrier
2 A single channel containing quantized or digital information with the use of a modulating subcarrier
D Data transmission, telemetry, telecommand

PULSE

Pulse is a sequence of controlled signal variations. It is a type of modulation of the main carrier—on a par with amplitude modulation (AM) and angle modulation (a category covering both frequency modulation and phase modulation) [97.3(c)(6)]. Pulses may be modulated in the following ways:

- unmodulated pulses
- pulses modulated in amplitude
- pulses modulated in width/duration
- pulses modulated in position/phase
- pulses in which the carrier is angle modulated during the period of the pulse

Pulse emission also permits transmission of any type of information, namely:

- no information
- telegraphy
- facsimile
- data transmission, telemetry, telecommand
- telephony
- television
- combination of the above (3rd symbol W)
- cases not otherwise covered (3rd symbol X)

Pulse is permitted in bands above 902 MHz excluding 1240-1300 MHz and 10.0-10.5 GHz [97.305(c)].

In terms of ITU emission designators, the following types of emission are permitted for pulse emissions: Emissions having designators with K, L, M, P, Q, V or W as the first symbol; 0, 1, 2, 3, 7, 8, 9 or X as the second symbol; A, B, C, D, E, F, N, W or X as the third symbol [97.3(c)(6)].

First symbol: Type of modulation of the main carrier:
Emission of pulses
P Sequence of unmodulated

A sequence of pulses:

K —Modulated in amplitude
L —Modulated in width/duration
M —Modulated in position/phase
Q —In which the carrier is angle-modulated during the period of the pulse
V —Which is a combination of the foregoing or is produced by other means
W —Cases not covered above, in which an emission consists of the main carrier modulated, either simultaneously or in a pre-established sequence in a combination of two or more of the following modes: amplitude, angle, pulse

Second symbol: Nature of signal(s) modulating the main carrier:
0 No modulating signal

Third symbol: Type of information to be transmitted:
N No information transmitted
A Telegraphy, for aural
B Telegraphy, for automatic
C Facsimile
D Data transmission, telemetry, telecommand
E Telephony (including sound broadcasting)
F Television (video)
W Combination of the above
X Cases not otherwise covered

SPREAD SPECTRUM

Spread spectrum (SS) is a departure from the normal rule of keeping radio-frequency bandwidth as narrow as possible for a given information rate. Spread spectrum deliberately spreads the signal energy over a wide bandwidth instead of concentrating all the transmitted energy in a tight bandwidth. The bandwidth expansion amounts to at least 10 times the information bandwidth and may be as much as several hundred times. Checking the ITU designators shows that you can use any type of modulation of the carrier (except for no modulation or pulse modulation) and can transmit any type of signal and information permitted in the Amateur Radio Service when using spread spectrum.

There are some restrictions. Code, modulation and transmitter power limitations are detailed in 97.311. The maximum power is 100 watts PEP, and it can only be used on frequencies on and above the 70 cm band. In 1999, the FCC relaxed rules governing the use of spread spectrum techniques by radio amateurs making international SS communication possible. The FCC now allows Amateur Radio stations to transmit additional spread spectrum emission types. The new rules, effective November 1, 1999, allow amateurs to use techniques other than frequency hopping and direct sequence spreading. The new rules require that spread spectrum stations running more than 1 W incorporate automatic transmitter power control. Amateur stations using SS are restricted to a maximum power of 100 W.

In 1999, the FCC also amended the rules to eliminate what is called "now-unnecessary record keeping and station identification requirements" that apply only to stations using spread spectrum. The FCC agreed to let SS stations identify themselves using conventions developed by the Amateur Radio community. A copy of the FCC's complete Report and Order is available at **http://www.arrl.org/announce/regulatory/wt97-12**.

The rules [97.3(c)(8)] permit the following types of modulation, according to ITU emission designators: A, C, D, F, G, H, J or R as the first symbol, X as the second symbol, and X as the third symbol.

First symbol: Type of modulation of the main carrier:
A Double sideband
C Vestigial sideband
D Emission in which the main carrier is amplitude and angle modulated either simultaneously or in a pre-established pattern
F Frequency modulation
G Phase modulation
H Single sideband, full carrier
J Single sideband, suppressed carrier
R Single sideband, reduced carrier

Second symbol: Nature of signal(s) modulating the main carrier:
X Cases not otherwise covered

Third symbol: Type of information to be transmitted:
X Cases not otherwise covered

TEST

Test transmissions contain no information. "No information" is not necessarily the same as "no modulation," as it is possible to frequency modulate a transmitter with a steady tone that carries no intelligence. We're talking about transmissions like unmodulated tones or key-down carriers to tune transmitters or to measure antenna patterns, for example. One of the most common uses of test transmissions above 51 MHz is for alignment of high gain antennas.

The FCC decided to use the emission designator test as a catch all category. Technically, test is defined as "Emissions containing no information having the designators with N as the third symbol" [97.3(c)(9)].

There are two basic rules of the road for test emissions. Test emissions are authorized for all amateur bands above 51.0 MHz [97.305(c)], and there is no limit to the length of your test signals. It's uncertain how other amateurs would welcome your transmitter being key down 24 hours a day, however.

It may take quite a long time to align antennas on a 10-GHz circuit, but it's not a good idea to do so on your local repeater. Below 51.0 MHz, however, §97.305(b) applies, and the key word is *brief*.

RTTY AND DATA EMISSION CODES

Digital communications are an entire class of emissions that use discrete (quantized) levels, rather than continuously variable quantities as in analog communications. Although digital communications are associated with computers and machine information transfers, there will be a tendency for some of the older analog modulation techniques to give way to digital techniques for reasons of noise and error reduction. The rules permit a new class of digital emissions for speech and image transmissions. We will not discuss them further in this chapter because we need to wait and see how digital speech and image transmissions develop among amateurs. As these new modes evolve, it will be increasingly difficult to tell them apart from packet radio used to transfer computer data. Computers can, after all, be used to generate speech and images.

RTTY

RTTY is an abbreviation for radioteletype. In §97.3(c)(7) the FCC defines RTTY as "narrow-band direct-printing telegraphy." Direct printing means that the originating station formats the message to print out on a page of paper (hard copy). The receiving operator could elect to display the incoming message on a computer screen. Or, the receiving station computer could store the information in memory and never print it out. Nevertheless, the original intent was to produce page copy at the receiving end.

The bandwidth of a RTTY signal is normally narrower than that of an SSB signal on the MF and HF bands (160-10 meters). The necessary bandwidth for a typical 45-baud (*baud* is a unit of signaling speed equal to one pulse per second) RTTY signal using frequency-shift keying with a shift of 170 Hz is 249 Hz. For information on calculating bandwidth, see the *ARRL Handbook for Radio Amateurs* or *ARRL's HF Digital Handbook*.

DATA

The rules define *data* as "Telemetry, telecommand and computer communications emissions" [97.3(c)(2)]. That agrees closely with the ITU definition, which is: "Data transmission, telemetry, telecommand" [2.201(e)]. The term "computer communications" is simply another way of saying "data transmission." You are using data transmissions when you exchange computer files, programs and messages not intended for direct paper printout.

Telemetry refers to one-way transmissions of measurements at a distance from the measuring instrument [97.3(a)(45)]. The best-known kind is space telemetry, which is a one-way transmission from a space station (an amateur satellite, for example) made from the measuring instruments aboard a spacecraft, including those related to its functioning. An increasing use is gathering weather data. Hams have been remotely controlling repeaters for years with an indication back from the repeater station that it understood the command. After all, if you're going to control something remotely, you better know about its health and welfare before you command it. Once you command it, you'd like to know whether it did what you told it to do. That feedback channel is telemetry. Telemetry is also just measuring anything at a distance, even when you can't remotely control the function. An example of this might be an indication of voltage on a battery charged by solar cells.

Telecommand is the use of telecommunication for the transmission of signals to initiate, modify or terminate functions of equipment at a distance (in other words: remote control) [97.3(a)(43)]. One way to send tele-command or remote-control signals without getting into the realm of unspecified codes would be to use the control characters in ASCII or those positions in Baudot/AMTOR codes not assigned to letters, numerals or fraction bar (/).

DIGITAL CODES

In Part 97, the FCC specifies the following codes for RTTY or data emissions.

BAUDOT

Baudot is the familiar name for a 5-bit code known worldwide as International Telegraph Alphabet No. 2 (ITA2) [97.309(a)(1)]. Its formal definition is found in International Telegraph and Telephone Consultative Committee (CCITT) Recommendation F.1, Division C. Combinations of ones and zeros in 5 bits can produce 32 positions. Each position is assigned a graphic character or a machine control function. By having two cases (letters and figures), the letters of the Latin alphabet, numerals and commonly used punctuation marks can be accommodated. For a table showing the bit patterns and their assignments, see the *ARRL Handbook*.

AMTOR

AMTOR is an acronym for *AMateur Teleprinting Over Radio*. It is an adaptation of *SITOR (Simplex Teleprinting Over Radio)*, a teletype mode used in the maritime service. The term *TOR* has caught on as a generic reference to these kinds of systems. Its formal definition may be found in International Radio Consultative Committee (CCIR) Recommendations 476-2 (1978), 476-3 (1982), 476-4 (1986) or 625 (1986) [97.309(a)(2)]. The bit patterns and their assignments are given in the *ARRL Handbook*. One important ingredient in TOR is its 7-bit code. For example, the bit sequences for the letter A (and hyphen in figures case) is 1000111, and for B (? in figures case) is 1110010. Both bit sequences have four 1s and three 0s; this is true for all TOR code combinations.

This is done to provide a method of error detection at the receiving station. If anything but the correct four 1s-three 0s combination is received, the receiving station knows there was an error in reception.

Another feature is a mode called Automatic Repeat reQuest (ARQ), also called Mode A. This is a protocol that calls for the sending station to transmit three characters, wait for an ACKnowledgment, then three more characters, and so forth. If the four 1s-three 0s combination is not received, an ACK is not given, and the sending station repeats the three characters until an ACK is received.

There is also a Mode B, which uses Forward Error Correction (FEC). Mode B is used for transmissions from one point to more than one receiving station—situations where it would be impractical to wait for an ACK from each receiving station. In the FEC mode, each block of three characters is sent twice in a one-way transmission. The theory is that the receiving station equipment will accept characters having the correct 4/3 ratio and reject the others, and each character gets two chances to be received. Mode B is useful for bulletin transmissions and roundtables where ACKs are not feasible. For example, W1AW transmits its AMTOR bulletins using Mode B.

ASCII

Officially, *ASCII* is called the American Standard Code for Information Interchange by the American National Standards Institute (ANSI) X3.4-1977 [97.309(a)(3)]. The rules also permit International Telegraph and Telephone Consultative Committee (CCITT) Recommendation T.50, International Alphabet No. 5 (IA5), or International Organization for Standardization, International Standard ISO 646 (1983), which are international forms of ASCII [97.309(a)(3)].

ASCII is a 7-unit coded character set having 128 code combinations. A table showing the character set is given in the *ARRL Handbook*.

The rules permit ASCII code extensions as provided for in CCITT Recommendation T.61 (Malaga-Torremolinos, 1984) [97.309(a)]. These extensions provide for additional graphic symbols and diacritical marks used for foreign languages. None of these special characters would come up in everyday English-language text, but they're there if you need them. Permission to use code extensions does not relieve a station of identifying properly using the basic character set. That's the same idea as for phone, in which you can chat in a foreign language, but you must identify in English or international phonetics so others on the band can understand.

OTHER TECHNIQUES

The FCC has clarified that amateur stations may also use any digital code that has its technical characteristics publicly documented. The technical characteristics of CLOVER, G-TOR, PACTOR and now PSK31 have been documented publicly for use by amateur operators, and commercial products are readily available that facilitate the transmission and reception of communications incorporating these codes. Although these codes are not "specified" in the rules, they have been publicly documented and hence are legal. They are not considered to be "unspecified" codes as discussed below.

UNSPECIFIED DIGITAL CODES

Above 50 MHz where data and RTTY emissions are permitted, unspecified digital codes may be used in communication between stations licensed by the FCC [97.307(f); 97.309(b)]. Baudot, AMTOR and ASCII are specified in the rules, along with those codes that are publicly documented (see discussion above), so "unspecified" includes everything else. There is a provision for using unspecified codes when communicating with stations in other countries that have an agreement with the US to that effect. However, there are no such agreements in effect as of this writing. Unspecified digital codes must not be used to obscure the meaning of any communication [97.309(b)].

PACKET RADIO

Packet radio is simply a packaging method for data transmission using the ASCII digital code. The basic idea is to break up a message into small transmission blocks, called packets. Depending on the speed of transmission, a packet may last only a fraction of a second or several seconds. The length may vary, but a typical packet might contain a line of text, a header showing who it came from and where it's going, and a trailer with error-control bits.

Packet radio is one of the most popular modes of digital communications because it is very efficient and provides error-free data transfer. Packet networks can be created using one of several different protocols, allowing long distance communications with limited resources. The *ARRL Handbook* gives a technical description of packet radio and *The ARRL Operating Manual* contains operating information. The ARRL publication *Practical Packet Radio* is also very helpful.

SPREAD SPECTRUM EMISSION TYPES

As mentioned earlier, spread spectrum deliberately spreads the signal energy over a wide bandwidth instead of concentrating all the transmitted energy in a tight bandwidth. The bandwidth expansion amounts to at least 10 times the information bandwidth and may be as much as several hundred times. Prior to November 1, 1999, spread spectrum was more tightly regulated than other modes, but these restrictions were relaxed effective that date.

If it important to keep in mind the following points concerning Spread Spectrum operation:

• It is allowed only on and above 70 cm [97.305] using no more than 100 watts PEP [97.305 and 97.311(d)];

• SS is only possible between points regulated by the FCC and with points regulated by the FCC and other countries in which SS is permitted [97.311(a)];

• SS emission transmissions must not be used for the purpose of obscuring the meaning of any communication [97.311(a)];

• A station transmitting SS emissions must not cause harmful interference to stations employing other authorized emissions, and must accept all interference caused by stations employing other authorized emissions [97.311(b)];

• When contacted by the FCC, amateurs must follow any instructions given by the FCC [97.311(c)];

• If more than 1 W is used, automatic transmitter control shall limit output power to that which is required for the communication. This shall be determined by the use of the ratio, measured at the receiver, of the received energy per user data bit (Eb) to the sum of the received power spectral densities of noise (N0) and co-channel interference (I0). Average transmitter power over 1 W shall be automatically adjusted to maintain an Eb/(N0 + I0) ratio of no more than 23 dB at the intended receiver [97.311(d)].

EMISSION STANDARDS

To help minimize interference between hams and other radio services, the FCC has written rules about the spectral purity. The most important rule as far as RFI is concerned are the absolute limits on spurious emissions that fall outside the amateur bands. These are described in detail in §97.307 and shown in graph form in **Figs 3** and **4**. The level of spurious signals varies from band to band and with power level, but here are some examples that cover typical amateur operation: For typical HF QRP operation, all spurious emissions must be at least 30 dB less than the fundamental signal; for HF

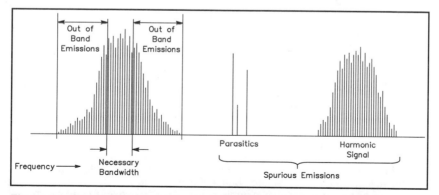

Fig 2—An illustration of spurious emissions. Some of the keying sidebands are outside the necessary bandwidth. These are considered out-of-band emissions, not spurs. The harmonic and parasitic emissions shown here are considered spurious emissions; these must be reduced in accordance with §97.307.

Q&A— Band Edges

"How close can I set my dial to the band edge?" is a question asked not only by the beginner, but by experienced amateurs as well. We'll tell you how close you can go to get that rare DX QSL card—and avoid that rare FCC "QSL" card.

Phone

Q. I'm an active HF phone DXer. How close to the band edge can I set my VFO?

A. Many factors are involved. Amateurs commonly consider full-carrier, double-sideband AM signals to be about 6 kHz wide and single-sideband, suppressed-carrier signals to be about 3 kHz wide. Those bandwidths, however, are usually only 6 dB down, and that isn't what the FCC worries about. Thus, to determine where you may set your VFO in relation to the band or subband edge for your class of license, you'll have to figure out where your signal is attenuated by 40 dB. Don't assume that if your SSB transmitter bandwidth is 3 kHz, that you can just add a few hundred Hz to be safe. That's fine only if the shape of the band-limiting filter is sharp enough to attenuate the signal to –40 dB at 3 kHz. If you're going to operate as near as possible to a band edge, then do so only after carefully reviewing your equipment specifications to see if such information is included. Another alternative is to carefully measure the attenuation if you have access to top-notch lab equipment. If you can't do either, then allow a larger margin of safety for possible inaccuracy of your frequency readout.

Remember, your carrier and all of your sidebands must be confined within the amateur bands and subbands as applicable.

Morse Code

Q. When I operate CW, how close to the band edge can I go?

A. Your transmitter keying envelope rise and fall times determine both the bandwidth of your CW signal and the maximum speed at which you can send and still be received properly. Once set, the rise and fall times (not the keying speed) determine the bandwidth. If your rise and fall times are 5 ms, your signal will have a bandwidth of about 150 Hz, in which case you would have to stay at least 75 Hz from a band edge. If the rise and fall times are 2 ms (fairly typical of commercial transceivers), the bandwidth would be 375 Hz.

TV and Facsimile

Q. Why is fast-scan television not found on the HF bands?

A. Fast-scan television, a mode in which images appear in the same manner as a home broadcast TV, is not found at HF because of bandwidth limitations. §97.307(f)(2) states that on any band below 420 MHz "No non-phone emission shall exceed the bandwidth of a communications quality phone emission of the same modulation type" [97.307(f)(2)]. To get across all the information necessary for a fast-moving TV picture, a great deal of spectrum is required; so much, in fact, that one fast-scan TV signal could occupy one fifth of the entire HF spectrum! Bandwidth limits restrict HF TV operation to the slow-scan variety, where images appear as a photograph, or "stop action," and do not require oodles of band space.

No special bandwidth limits apply above 420 MHz, so you'll find wider bandwidth modes, such as fast-scan television, there. But remember, in all cases not specifically covered by the rules, the various signals must be used in accordance with good engineering practice. Use modern equipment that is properly adjusted. Conserve spectrum!

"barefoot" operation, spurious emissions must be attenuated at 40 dB; for HF 1500-W operation, spurious signals must be attenuated 44 dB; and for VHF operation, the required attenuation ranges from 46 dB for 1-W transmitters to 60 dB for 25-W operation.

The levels defined in §97.307 are absolute-maximum levels of spurious emissions. This means that your spurious emissions must not exceed these levels, *whether the spurious emissions are causing interference or not.* Nearly all modern amateur manufactured equipment meets the requirements spelled out in the rules. Test results for many amateur transmitters are published in *QST* product reviews. However, it is possible to generate excessive harmonics by mistuning HF amplifiers when pushing the matching range in an effort to use non-50 Ω antennas without an external transmatch.

In addition, FCC regulations state that if a spurious emission from a transmitter causes interference to another radio service, the operator of the transmitter must take whatever steps are necessary to reduce or eliminate the interference. At the edge of a TV station's range, you might need 70 or 80 dB of attenuation of your spurious emissions to ensure that a harmonic doesn't cause interference with a relatively weak TV signal. (This doesn't apply to "fringe" reception. If your neighbor is trying to receive a TV signal

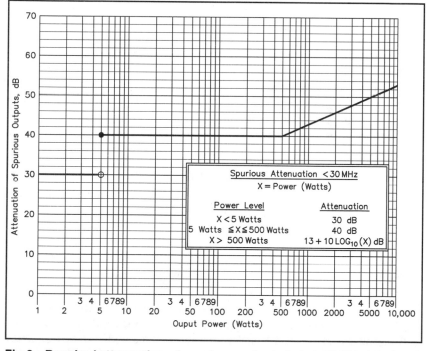

Fig 3—Required attenuation of spurious outputs below 30 MHz is related to output power.

from 200 miles away, the FCC does not offer any protection to a TV signal that is that weak.)

Meeting these regulations is all that Part 97 *requires* you to do. If interference to consumer equipment is caused by fundamental overload, it cannot be fixed at your transmitter; it *must* be fixed by adding filtering or shielding to the affected equipment. In cases involving non-radio equipment, the FCC's opinion is that these devices should not pick up radio signals at all.

Like most of Part 97, the technical standards exist to promote operating techniques that make efficient use of spectrum and minimize interference. No one wants to transmit a "dirty" signal, and the standards in Part 97 can help you identify problems that should be solved.

GOOD SIGNALS 99-44/100% PURE

§97.307 spells out the standards the FCC expects amateur transmissions to meet. The first paragraph is the most important: "No amateur station transmission shall occupy more bandwidth than necessary for the information rate and emission type being transmitted, in accordance with good amateur practice" [97.307(a)]. Simply stated, don't transmit a wide signal when a narrow one will do.

The next paragraph states that "Emissions resulting from modulation must be confined to the band or segment available to the control operator." Every modulated signal produces sidebands. You must not operate so close to the band edge that your sidebands extend out of the subband, even if your dial says that your carrier is inside the band. Further: "Emissions outside the necessary bandwidth must not cause splatter or key-click interference to operations on adjacent frequencies" [97.307(b)]. Seems like common sense, doesn't it? The rules simply codify good operating practice. If your signal is causing key clicks or splatter interference up and down the band, clean them up! Sideband splatter is often caused by excessive mic gain settings. A 1/10th to 1/3rd indication of PEP power is a perfectly normal indication on an analog meter because it is not designed to register voice peaks.

SPURIOUS EMISSIONS

The rules address *spurious emission* standards [97.307(c)]. Just what are spurious emissions anyway? The FCC defines them this way: "An emission, on frequencies outside the necessary bandwidth of a transmission, the level of which may be reduced without affecting the information being transmitted" [97.3(a)(42)]. In addition, Part 2 of the FCC Rules adds the following (from the international Radio Regulations): "Spurious emissions include harmonic emissions, parasitic emissions, intermodulation products and frequency conversion products, but exclude out-of-band emissions" [2.1(c)].

To fully understand this, we must again consult Part 2 for more definitions. *Necessary bandwidth* is defined as: "the width of the frequency band which is just sufficient to ensure the transmission of information at the rate and with the quality required under specified conditions." An *out-of-*

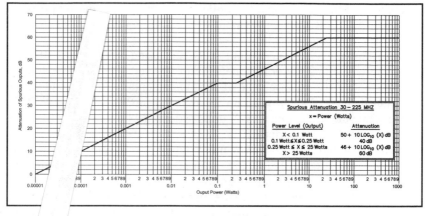

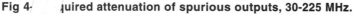

Fig 4- ⌐uired attenuation of spurious outputs, 30-225 MHz.

ban⌐ ⌐ission is: "Emission on a frequency or frequencies immediately out⌐ ⌐he necessary bandwidth which results from the modulation process, but excluding spurious emissions." Out-of-band emissions are not necessarily outside an amateur "band" [2.1(c)].

Refer to Fig 2. Some of the keying sidebands are outside the "necessary bandwidth." These are out-of-band emissions, but they are not considered spurious emissions. On the other hand, we have already seen [97.307(b)] that these sidebands must not interfere with other stations. The harmonics and parasitics shown in Fig 2 are spurs, and they must be reduced to the levels specified in Part 97. The FCC states that all spurious emissions must be reduced "to the greatest extent practicable." Further, "if any spurious emission, including chassis or power line radiation, causes harmful interference to the reception of another radio station, the licensee of the interfering amateur station is required to take steps to eliminate the interference." If your spurs are causing interference, it's your job to clean them up [97.307(c)]. Make sure your transmitter is clean!

HOW FAR IS FAR ENOUGH?

Now that we know what the spurs are, what do we do with them? The FCC is very specific [97.307(d)]. If your transmitter or RF power amplifier was built after April 14, 1977, or first marketed after December 31, 1977, and transmits on frequencies below 30 MHz the mean power of any spurious emissions must:

• never be more than 50 mW;

• be at least 30 dB below the mean power of the fundamental emission, if the mean power output is less than 5 W; and

• be at least 40 dB below the mean power of the fundamental emission, if the mean power output is 5 W or more. The requirement that no spurious emission exceed 50 milliwatts means that above 500 watts, the suppression must be greater than 40 dB. At 1500 watts, the suppression must be 44.77 dB. The requirements for transmitters operating below 30 MHz are shown graphically in Fig 3.

The following requirements apply between 30 and 225 MHz [97.307(e)]:

- Transmitters with 25 W or less mean output power: spurs must be at least 40 dB below the mean power of the fundamental emission and never greater than 25 μW, but need not be reduced further than 10 μW. This means that the spurs from a 25 W transmitter must be at least 60 dB down to meet the 25 μW restriction.

- Transmitters with more than 25 W mean output power: spurious emissions must be at least 60 dB below the mean power of fundamental emission. The situation for transmitters operating between 30 and 225 MHz is more complex. The combination of the requirement that spurious emissions be less than 25 μW and the stipulation that they don't need to be reduced below 10 μW makes the requirements vary significantly with power level, ranging from 0 dB suppression required for a transmitter whose power is 10 μW to 60 dB of suppression required for power levels above 25 watts. The requirements for transmitters operating between 30 and 225 MHz are shown graphically in Fig 4. There are no absolute limits for transmitters operating above 225 MHz, although the general requirements for good engineering practice would still apply.

TRANSMITTER POWER STANDARDS

"An amateur station must use the minimum transmitter power necessary to carry out the desired communication" [97.313(a)].

In other words, don't run more power than you need.

How closely do radio amateurs adhere to this principle? We all know that in some cases the answer is, not as closely as we should.

We know there are times when we could get along with reduced power. Even for moonbounce you don't always need to run the legal limit. Most hams don't own legal limit equipment and have no interest in doing so. Many enjoy the challenge of QRP operating, and some can boast of making intercontinental contacts at milliwatt levels. Others must run low power for economic or other reasons, but still gain a full measure of enjoyment from Amateur Radio.

When you reduce power, you reduce the impact your operating has on others. Nearby amateurs can use the same band; distant amateurs can use the same or adjacent frequencies. Your electric bill goes down. If the person you're talking to was receiving you well to begin with, all that happens when you reduce power is that his S meter doesn't bounce quite as high.

PEP AND POWER MEASUREMENT

Peak envelope power (PEP) is the "average power supplied to the antenna transmission line by a transmitter during one radio frequency cycle at the crest of the modulation envelope taken under normal operating conditions" [2.1(c)]. Amateur transmitters may never be operated with a peak envelope power (PEP) output of more than 1500 W [97.313(b)]. There are further limitations on operation in certain bands, or by holders of certain classes of license.

The FCC has published the following standards of measurement:

(1) Read an in-line peak-reading RF wattmeter that is properly matched to the transmission line (commercial units are available), or

(2) calculate the power using the peak RF voltage as indicated by an oscilloscope or other peak-reading device. Multiply the peak RF voltage by 0.707, square the result and divide by the load resistance. The SWR must be 1:1.

The FCC requires that you meet the power output regulations, but does not require that you make such measurements or possess measurement equipment. The methods listed simply indicate how the Commission would measure your transmitter's output during a station inspection.

As a practical matter, most hams don't have to worry about special equipment to check their transmitter's output because they never approach the 1500-W PEP output limit. Many common amateur amplifiers aren't capable of generating this much power. However, if you do have a planet-destroyer amplifier and do operate close to the limit (only on those rare occasions when you need the extra power, of course) you should be prepared to measure your output along the lines detailed above.

It is not acceptable to measure power by looking at the voice peaks on an ordinary power meter. The ratio between PEP and the meter reading can vary tremendously, depending on voice characteristics and meter damping. Similarly, it is possible for an amplifier to put out significantly more power on peaks than on CW, particularly if the power supply sags a lot under load.

NOVICE AND TECHNICIAN SUBBANDS

All licensees operating in the Novice and Technician (if the licensee has passed the 5 WPM code element) subbands on 80, 40 and 15 meters must never operate with a peak envelope power output in excess of 200 W [97.313(c)(1)]. In addition, Novice and Technician (with 5 WPM credit) licensees are limited to 200 W PEP output in their 28-MHz subband (28.1-28.5 MHz) [97.313(c)(2)]; Novices are limited to 25 W PEP in the 222 MHz band [97.313(d)] and to 5 W PEP in the 1270 MHz band [97.313(e)]. Other amateurs may use up to 1500 W PEP in these subbands [97.313(c)(2)]. All amateurs are limited to 200 W PEP when operating on the 7.050-7.075 MHz segment in FCC regulated areas of ITU Regions 1 and 3 [97.313(c)(3)].

WHAT'S A PART 15 DEVICE?

Hams are very familiar with Part 97 of Title 47 of the Code of Federal Regulations, the rules that govern ham radio, but other parts in Title 47 govern other radio services, some of which affect the Amateur Radio service either directly or indirectly. As was discussed earlier in this chapter, many amateur bands are shared with other services. Part 15 is important to amateurs because it regulates low power, unlicensed devices that could cause interference to the Amatewur Radio Service and vice versa. Part 15 covers an assortment of electronic equipment that generates RF energy whether it's **intentional, unintentional** or **incidental**. Amateurs will need to consider Part 15 as it relates to digital devices, computers, low-powered, unlicensed transmitters, electrical devices and any other "generic" device that might generate RF in the normal course of its operation.

Part 15 devices can operate on almost any frequency provided that they do not cause harmful interference to other radio services, but if they do, the owner of the device is required to take steps to eliminate the interference. Amateurs are sometimes very concerned to see a Part 15 device, such as a remote wireless thermometer operating on 443.92 MHz or a cordless telephone operating in the 902 MHz band, but in most cases, they are properly authorized by the FCC and are legal provided that they do not cause harmful interference. The FCC requires that the manufacturers of these devices have them tested to ensure that they do not exceed the absolute maximum limits, which vary depending on the frequency on which the device is operated and its purpose. For more information, see *The ARRL RFI Book* and the *ARRLWeb* site at **www.arrl.org/tis/info/part15.html**.

SPECIAL RESTRICTIONS

- All amateurs are limited to 200 W PEP on the 30-meter band (10.1-10.15 MHz) [97.313(c)(1)].
- Beacon stations are limited to 100 W power output [97.203(c)].
- 70 cm and 33 cm bands: Special 50 W PEP output limits apply to stations operating in these bands when they are located near certain military installations in the US [97.313(f), (g)].
- A station being used to control a model craft is limited to 1 W power output (yes, that's one watt) [97.215(c)].
- Spread Spectrum stations may not exceed 100 W power output [97.311(d)].

EQUIPMENT CERTIFICATION AND STANDARDS OF EXTERNAL HF POWER AMPLIFIERS

Like other radio services, amateur equipment must meet certain standards. Unlike other services, however, most amateur equipment does not have to be certificated. Certification is an equipment authorization granted by the FCC, based on equipment-measurement data submitted by the applicant, usually the manufacturer. It's used to ensure that the equipment will function properly in the service for which it's been accepted. Certification is usually required for equipment operating in commercial services, such as the Maritime, Public Safety or Land Mobile services. Even though amateur equipment can often be modified to operate in these services, it is not certified and thus may not be used in them. Standards for certification are usually higher than those for the amateur service; ham equipment that easily meets amateur standards often cannot meet the more stringent certification requirements.

USING FCC CERTIFCATED EQUIPMENT ON AMATEUR FREQUENCIES

Equipment which is certified for use in another service may be used on amateur frequencies by a licensed amateur as long as it meets all appropriate standards. Modification of certificated equipment for use on amateur frequencies is likely to void its FCC Certification (formerly called Type acceptance), however, which means that it cannot then be used back in its original service.

AMATEUR EQUIPMENT THAT REQUIRES FCC CERTIFICATION

There is one type of amateur equipment that does require certification, formerly known as FCC Type Acceptance.

In 1978, the FCC banned the manufacture and marketing of any external radio-frequency power amplifier or amplifier kit that is capable of operation on any frequency below 144 MHz unless the FCC has issued a grant of certification for that model amplifier. This was done to stem the flow of amplifiers being distributed for illegal use on frequencies in and around the Citizen's Band Radio Service. The requirements for type acceptance of a commercial amplifier specify that it cannot be able to operate between 24 and 35 MHz, nor can it have accessible wiring, circuitry, internal or external controls, or instructions that will allow it to be operated in a manner contrary to the FCC Rules. It must also meet the emission standards of Part 97 [97.317].

An external RF power amplifier does not need to be certified when
• The device isn't capable of operation below 144 MHz.
• The amplifier was purchased before April 28, 1978.
• The amplifier was constructed (but not from a kit) or modified by an amateur for use at that amateur's own station.
• The amplifier is sold to another amateur or to a dealer.
• The amplifier is purchased in used condition by an equipment dealer from an amateur operator and the amplifier is further sold to another amateur operator for use at that operator's station.

An amateur may not construct or modify more than one unit of the same model amplifier capable of operation below 144 MHz in any calendar year without a grant of type acceptance [97.315].

CONCLUSION

The technical rules and standards as outlined in Subpart D are significantly less comprehensive than in most other FCC rule Parts. This gives amateurs the flexibility to experiment by building "homebrew" equipment to help develop new technologies—a Basis and Purpose of the Amateur Radio Service. Amateurs must, however, make sure that their transceivers meet the spectral purity standards as specified in Subpart D. The FCC entrusts amateurs with this freedom to experiment because they know that amateurs have knowledge of what is and isn't legal and that they will comply with Part 97.

Providing Emergency Communications

5

S ubpart E, "Providing Emergency Communications," is a brief, but important section of Part 97. It addresses disaster communications, stations in distress, communications for the safety of life and protection of property, and the Radio Amateur Civil Emergency Service (RACES). "Providing emergency communications" is also a basis and purpose of the Amateur Radio Service. Many amateurs report that one of their main reasons for obtaining an amateur license is to provide public service and emergency communications. Congress has even recognized the value of Amateur Radio in times of emergency.

When it comes to supplying emergency communications, that is, communications related to the *immediate* safety of life and/or the *immediate* protection of property, in the absence of other communications facilities, the rules permit amateurs wide latitude [97.403]. The rules permit the FCC to specify conditions and rules for amateur operation during an emergency. The FCC can set aside specific frequencies for emergency use only [97.401(c)]. Actually a service within a service, RACES uses amateurs for civil preparedness (sometimes called civil defense, or emergency management) communications during local, regional or national civil emergencies. To participate, you must be enrolled as a member of a local civil defense agency [97.407].

In this chapter, we'll discuss these issues and give specific examples to help understand the rules concerning emergency communications.

SUBPART E RULES SUMMARY: PROVIDING EMERGENCY COMMUNICATIONS

97.401 Operation during a disaster.
97.403 Safety of life and protection of property.
97.405 Station in distress.
97.407 Radio Amateur Civil Emergency Service.

EMERGENCY COMMUNICATIONS
AND AMATEUR RADIO

Amateur Radio means different things to different people. Some think of it as just a hobby while others recognize its true value as also a *service*. Your nonamateur neighbor probably doesn't know or care how many DXCC entities you've worked and the general public often doesn't hear about Amateur Radio until disaster strikes. Amateurs have a responsibility to perform communications in the public interest, convenience and necessity. In fact, the FCC believes that the public and emergency communications aspect is so important that it's dedicated an entire subpart of its rules to it!

There are major emergencies and there are smaller, more localized emergencies. An example of the latter is a car stalled on the highway with its occupants in distress. You may summon assistance via 2 meters. Larger emergencies require whole armies of amateurs, such as the Oklahoma City bombing in 1995. In 1999, Hurricane Floyd involved emergency operators up and down the entire east coast. Amateurs are organized for emergency communication preparedness in networks and membership groups.

Two major organizations exist: ARES and RACES. ARES, the Amateur Radio Emergency Service, begun in 1935, is the emergency communications and disaster preparedness program sponsored by the ARRL. There are approximately 80,000 ARES members in the US. RACES, the Radio Amateur Civil Emergency Service, founded in 1952, is the emergency communications and disaster preparedness program of the US government. It was originally intended to be a temporary service to ensure that in serious national emergencies, amateurs would be put to immediate use without delays in selecting frequencies and processing security clearances.

ARES and RACES are similar in some ways and different in others. Both are made up of amateurs and both provide emergency communications, but the similarities end there. ARES serves numerous served agencies, such as the Red Cross, the Salvation Army and the National Weather Service. RACES is restricted to serving local, state and federal government emergency management agencies.

OPERATION DURING A DISASTER

This is what Part 97 says about operation during a disaster:

"When normal communication systems are overloaded, damaged or disrupted because a disaster has occurred, or is likely to occur, in an area where the amateur service is regulated by the FCC, an amateur station may make transmissions necessary to meet essential communication needs and facilitate relief actions [97.401(a)]."

If an emergency strikes a widespread area, disrupting the normal lines of communication, the District Director of the FCC field office for the area may designate certain frequencies for use by stations assisting the stricken area only [97.401(c)]. All amateur transmissions with, or within, the designated area conducted on the FCC-designated emergency frequencies must pertain directly to relief work, emergency service or the establishment and maintenance of efficient networks for handling emergency traffic. If warranted, the FCC will declare a communications emergency. This usually happens several times each year, generally in connection with a severe hurricane, earthquake or other major disaster. The FCC may also set forth further special conditions and rules during the communications emergency [97.401(c)]. The emergency conditions imposed by the FCC can be lifted only by the FCC or its authorized representative. Authorized amateurs desiring a declaration of a communication emergency should contact the FCC District Director of the area concerned [97.401(c)].

Amateurs can transmit emergency communications on any *amateur* frequency. In addition, amateurs in Alaska, because of the rural nature of that state, may transmit emergency communications using SSB or RTTY on 5.1675 MHz using no more than 150 watts. *This does not apply to stations outside Alaska.*

EMERGENCY COMMUNICATIONS—ARE THEY LEGAL?

As mentioned above, the FCC, ARRL and amateurs all across the country believe strongly in the communications capabilities of amateurs during emergencies. The US Congress does, too! See the sidebar "Congress and Amateur Radio." In most cases, the emergency communications amateurs provide are legal and strongly encouraged. Yet, because of folklore and second-hand anecdotes, many amateurs have become confused about emergency and public-service communications. Much of this confusion can be traced to the FCC's rules (in effect from 1971 until 1993) banning any form of "business communications." During those years, a "talk-in" station to a hamfest was technically illegal!

When the Need is There, Amateur Radio Comes Through

Public service communications have had a traditional responsibility since 1913, when amateurs at the University of Michigan and Ohio State University, in conjunction with numerous amateurs in and around the region, successfully bridged the communications gap surrounding a large area left isolated by a severe windstorm in the Midwest. In the early days, emergency communications were individual efforts, conducted on an ad hoc basis. Now, Amateur Radio emergency communications are highly organized, disciplined and planned. Notwithstanding modern commercial infrastructure, including cellular telephones and the like, the first and only operational communications facilities at major natural disaster sites, and for some time thereafter, are almost inevitably Amateur Radio.—*ARRL General Counsel Chris Imlay, W3KD*

SOME EXAMPLES

Example 1: When nearly *700 square miles* of California forest lands were destroyed by wildfire, causing the evacuation of tens of thousands of mountain residents, hundreds of ham operators provided support communications for the US Forest Service, the California Department of Forestry, the American Red Cross and other relief agencies. This was a widespread emergency and normal fire and rescue channels were overloaded. Amateurs were called to provide communications assistance. Once the fires were out, several hams were heard asking, "Were we legal?"

Example 2: At a 200-mile bike ride, a "sag wagon" with Amateur Radio communications arrived on the scene of a serious accident at a rural site surrounded by mountains. A volunteer paramedic was already present and administering first aid. Because of the extent of the injuries, the paramedic asked to confer with a physician who happened to be in the vicinity of the amateur net control station. Strangely, the net control operator refused to allow the physician to speak directly over the radio. In spite of complicated medical terminology and the potential for mistakes, the net control operator insisted on verbally relaying each message. The control operator questioned whether it was be legal for the paramedic to speak directly with the physician.

The fact that these questions were asked at all, under the circumstances,

The Boston Marathon: When a seriously injured runner was on the way for needed medical attention, Kevin Erickson, N1ERS, in the communication trailer in downtown Boston helped relay messages from the "sweep" bus team to the medical facility at the finish line. Some runners picked up by the buses experienced heat illness, dehydration, hypothermia and foot injuries. *(Photo courtesy NQ1R)*

Good Amateur Practice in Disasters: A Case Study

When a hurricane devastated the Caribbean island of Jamaica and wiped out its communications infrastructure, amateurs were the first to get word out and performed heroically providing essential communications. We also learned a number of lessons that should help us provide better communications in future disaster situations:

• Communications channels in support of damage assessment and disaster relief agencies were slow to be established, and in some cases had to be established outside the amateur bands. (Incredibly, some stations even followed these officially designated stations outside the bands, without authorization!)

• Preoccupation with welfare inquiry traffic got in the way of higher priority communication. The Red Cross placed a moratorium on inquiries to Jamaica for several days; this provided time for outbound welfare messages to be sent, each of which could potentially head off at least one, and perhaps many, inquiries. Accepting inquiry traffic before there is any way to handle it raises false hopes and clogs the system.

• In a disaster, control belongs in the affected area; people there are in the best position to know the priorities. Those of us fortunate enough to be outside the disaster area are there to support them, not the other way around.

• In providing information to the media, amateurs must make sure what is being passed along is authentic, and not unsubstantiated hearsay.

General Considerations in Emergencies

• Use your receiver more, your transmitter less. The tendency to transmit rather than listen causes excessive QRM.

• Monitor emergency net frequencies.

• Listen to W1AW and watch the ARRL Web page at **www.arrl.org** for the latest bulletins and news.

---

illustrates the confusing interpretations of the FCC rules within the amateur fraternity. Amateur communications in both of these examples is quite legal and encouraged.

Big Emergencies

Obvious examples of major emergencies include natural disasters—such as tornadoes, hurricanes, blizzards, floods—and other forms of severe weather, forest fires, landslides and earthquakes. These typically cause immediate danger to life and property and outages or degradations of normal communication systems (telephones and public-safety radio systems).

During an emergency, you may use your amateur station to meet essential communication needs and facilitate relief actions. [97.401(a); 97.403]. Even though putting out fires or providing disaster assistance may be the *regular* business of your fire department or of the American Red Cross, in these situations an emergency affecting the immediate safety of life and property has occurred. Your Amateur Radio participation is not only allowed, but encouraged. Under these guidelines, assisting the Forest Service during a

Congress and Amateur Radio

In 1994, Congress approved legislation which recognized the value of Amateur Radio, particularly the public service and emergency communications aspect:

Public Law 103-408—Oct. 22, 1994
Public Law 103-408
103rd Congress
Joint Resolution
To recognize the achievements of radio amateurs, and to establish support for such amateurs as national policy.

Whereas Congress has expressed its determination in section 1 of the Communications Act of 1934 (47 U.S.C. 151) to promote safety of life and property through the use of radio communication;

Whereas Congress, in Section 7 of the Communications Act of 1934 (47 U.S.C. 157), established a policy to encourage the provision of new technologies and services;

Whereas Congress, in Section 3 of the Communications Act of 1934, defined radio stations to include amateur stations operated by persons interested in radio technique without pecuniary interest;

Whereas the Federal Communications Commission has created an effective regulatory framework through which the amateur radio service has been able to achieve the goals of the service;

Whereas these regulations, set forth in Part 97 of title 47 of the Code of Federal Regulations clarify and extend the purposes of the amateur radio service as a—

(1) voluntary noncommercial communication service, particularly with respect to providing emergency communications;

(2) contributing service to the advancement of the telecommunications infrastructure;

(3) service which encourages improvement of an individual's technical and operating skills;

(4) service providing a national reservoir of trained operators, technicians and electronics experts; and

---

wildfire, allowing a physician to use your radio or performing Red Cross disaster assessment are all legitimate Amateur Radio operations provided that a control operator of the appropriate license class is present.

Little Emergencies

Other situations, however, are less clear cut. For example, you spot a motorist stranded along a suburban highway. Can you call for a tow truck on the repeater autopatch? Under the pre-1993 rules this could have been construed as "business communications;" under the current rules it's perfectly okay. Amateurs are now even permitted to conduct their own personal business over Amateur Radio as mentioned in the Report and Order authorizing the reordered business rules in 1993. Requesting police assistance for a stranded motorist would have been legal at any time. While this example may hardly seem like an emergency, it represents a real danger to the stranded motorist. A San Francisco Bay Area mother and daughter

(5) service enhancing international good will;
Whereas Congress finds that members of the amateur radio service community has provided invaluable emergency communications services following such disasters as Hurricanes Hugo, Andrew, and Iniki, the Mt. St. Helens Eruption, the Loma Prieta earthquake, tornadoes, floods, wild fires, and industrial accidents in great number and variety across the Nation; and

Whereas Congress finds that the amateur radio service has made a contribution to our Nation's communications by its crafting, in 1961, of the first Earth satellite licensed by the Federal Communications Commission, by its proof-of-concept for search rescue satellites, by its continued exploration of the low Earth orbit in particular pointing the way to commercial use thereof in the 1990s, by its pioneering of communications using reflections from meteor trails, a technique now used for certain government and commercial communications, and by its leading role in development of low-cost, practical data transmission by radio which increasingly is being put to extensive use in, for instance, the land mobile service: Now, therefore, be it

Resolved by the Senate and House of Representatives of the United States of America in Congress assembled,

SECTION 1. FINDINGS AND DECLARATIONS OF CONGRESS

Congress finds and declares that—

(1) radio amateurs are hereby commended for their contributions to technical progress in electronics, and for their emergency radio communications in times of disaster;

(2) the Federal Communications Commission is urged to continue and enhance the development of the amateur radio service as a public benefit by adopting rules and regulations which encourage the use of new technologies within the amateur radio service; and

(3) reasonable accommodation should be made for the effective operation of amateur radio from residences, private vehicles and public areas, and that regulation at all levels of government should facilitate and encourage amateur radio operation as a public benefit.

Approved October 22, 1994

---

were killed when their disabled automobile was struck from behind. They were parked well off the right side of the freeway, emergency flashers on, hood up, in broad daylight. So pick up your H-T and call!

At the scene of an accident, can you hand your radio to an unlicensed person, such as a fire chief? Yes, as long as you remain the control operator, this is merely standard third-party operation [97.115(b)(1)]. In fact, this is usually the most efficient way to provide emergency communications to an agency. Instead of relaying the message yourself, why not put the sender and the recipient on the radio? This eliminates errors and is much more efficient.

SAFETY OF LIFE AND PROTECTION OF PROPERTY

Part 97 states:

"No provision of these rules prevents the use by an amateur station of any means of radiocommunication at its disposal to provide essential communication needs in connection with the immediate safety of human life and immediate protection of property when normal communication systems are not available" [97.403].

In the examples above, there were no other means of communications other than amateur. If other means of communications are available, they should be used first.

EXTRAORDINARY EMERGENCY COMMUNICATIONS

If you have equipment capable of operating beyond your own amateur license privileges, and you are present when an emergency occurs or find yourself in extreme distress, can you use that ability to call for help? Under §§97.403 and 97.405, the answer is a qualified "yes." As stated above, Part 97 doesn't prevent "the use by an amateur station of any means of radiocommunication at its disposal to provide essential communication needs in connection with the immediate safety of human life and immediate protection of property when normal communications systems are not available."

Note the words "essential" and "immediate," and the phrase "when normal communications systems are not available." If you can possibly communicate by any other method, including nonradio means, do so. If the situation doesn't involve an immediate threat to life or property, or if the communications are not essential to relieve the situation, keep quiet! Remember that Part 97 rules apply only to the Amateur Radio Service. Operate on frequencies assigned to another service only in an *extreme* emergency. Remember that you must keep any communications to the absolute minimum to pass the information. Once the information is passed, stay off the channel. Public service agencies do not appreciate unauthorized people operating on their frequencies, so don't be surprised if you encounter resistance. Be prepared to justify your actions afterward to the FCC and to authorized users of that particular service. Remember also that if you modify amateur transceiver for use outside the amateur bands in a service that requires FCC Certification (formerly known as Type Acceptance) and if you use such a transceiver, you've violated the FCC rules.

STATIONS IN DISTRESS

It shouldn't surprise anyone that FCC rules state "an amateur station in distress [isn't prohibited from using] any means at its disposal to attract attention, make known its condition and location, and obtain assistance". [97.405(a)]. The rules don't prohibit the operator of an amateur station "in the exceptional circumstances described in paragraph (a), [from using] any means of radiocommunications at its disposal to assist a station in distress." Note the word *exceptional* circumstances. If you think it's an extreme emergency, it probably is! If no other means of communications are available, including nonradio means, and it is an *extreme* emergency as detailed above, take whatever steps necessary to provide vital, life saving communications.

THE NEW AND IMPROVED "BUSINESS" RULES

The opening of this chapter discussed concerns about the appropriateness of some public service communications. FCC licensees, amateur or otherwise, are supposed to serve "the public interest, convenience, and necessity." In §97.1 of the Commission's Rules, the basis and purpose of the Amateur Radio Service, is spelled out clearly. Obviously, public service and educational activities are to be actively encouraged; how could there be any question about their being legal?

Around 1970 there were concerns about possible abuses of Amateur Radio by non-amateur and business interests. These concerns led the FCC to prohibit amateur communications "to facilitate the business or commercial affairs of any party" or "as an alternative to other authorized radio services." Over time, the interpretations of these rules became progressively more literal until they had a chilling effect even on meritorious public service activities. Something had to be done to put things back on track.

On September 13, 1993, following a rulemaking proceeding, the FCC dropped the old "no business" language, and replaced it with a prohibition on communications for compensation, on behalf of one's employer, or in which the amateur has a pecuniary interest [97.113(a)(2),(3)]. In place of the flat prohibition on providing an alternative to other radio services is a less restrictive one against doing so on a regular basis [97.113(a)(5)].

These changes mean a lot to public service-oriented amateurs. They removed the ambiguities that have plagued amateur public-service communications, and have curtailed the endless hair-splitting discussions about whether particular communications were permitted.

The focus now is on whether the amateur, or his or her employer, stands to benefit financially, rather than on the content of the communication [97.113(a)(2),(3)]. If so, then the communication is still prohibited. If not, then the remaining question is whether the communications need is one that ought to be met by some other radio service. Here, the rule of reason applies. A need that arises on a regular basis, and for which other communications services are reasonably available, should not be met by Amateur Radio. The FCC declined to define "regular," but this shouldn't pose much of a problem for us since abuses will tend to be self-limiting; volunteers don't like being taken advantage of, and if they are they should just say no. One popular activity for which there is no practical communications alternative available, collecting data for the National Weather Service, was singled out by the FCC as an example of what is permitted under the new rules [Report and Order to PR Docket 92-136, 97.113(a)(5)].

The new rules do not represent a philosophical departure from our "roots." In fact, they are almost identical with the regulations in effect prior to the "no business communications" rule. They provide latitude in our operating and especially in our public service communications, just as we had for decades before the onset of over-regulation in the early '70s. This is one of those rare times when we get to return to the "good old days." For a more general discussion of the business rules, see Chapter 2.

TACTICAL CALL SIGNS

Tactical (self-assigned) call signs are often used when working with other agencies during an emergency, or during large public-service activities. For example, during a running race, names like "Finish line," "Mile 1," "Mile 2," "First Aid 1" and "Water Truck" quickly identify each function and eliminate confusion when working with other agencies, such as a fire department, where amateur call signs are meaningless. They also help prevent confusion when several operators may take turns at a position.

The use of tactical call signs is a good idea, but it in no way relieves you of the obligation to identify your operation under the FCC's Rules for normal station identification. You must still give your FCC-assigned call sign at the end of your communication, and at least every 10 minutes during the contact [97.119].

RADIO AMATEUR CIVIL EMERGENCY SERVICE

Founded in 1952 with the help of the ARRL, the *Radio Amateur Civil Emergency Service* is sponsored by local and state civil defense organi-

---

Table 1
RACES Frequencies

All of the authorized frequencies and emissions allocated to the Amateur Radio Service are also available to RACES on a shared basis [97.407(b)]. If Amateur Radio operation is suspended by a Presidential proclamation of national emergency, RACES, if activated, may operate only on these frequencies. There are specific operating limitations with respect to these frequencies, and in all cases not specifically covered by the RACES rules, amateurs engaging in RACES operation are governed by the provisions of the rules governing Amateur Radio stations and operators.

RACES Frequencies

kHz	MHz	MHz
1800-1825	10.10-10.15	52-54
1975-2000	14.047-14.053	50.350-50.750
3500-3550	14.220-14.230	144.50-145.71
3930-3980	14.331-14.350	146-148
3984-4000	21.047-21.053	222-225
7079-7125	21.228-21.267	420-450
7245-7255	28.550-28.750	1240-1300
	29.237-29.273	2390-2450
	29.450-29.650	

---

zations and supported by the Federal Emergency Management Administration (FEMA) and it operates under the jurisdiction of the FCC. It is one of the three services addressed in Part 97. The other two are the Amateur Radio Service and the Amateur-Satellite Service. RACES works principally at the local level, through local (and state) civil defense agencies organized by state governments, to provide emergency communications when activated by the appropriate civil defense authority.

RACES is intended to provide government-to-government communications for civil defense purposes *only*, during periods of local, regional or national civil emergencies. These emergencies can include war-related activities, but are more likely to involve natural disasters such as fires, floods and earthquakes. RACES operation is authorized only by the appropriate local, state, or federal official, and is strictly limited to official civil defense activities in an emergency communications situation. RACES is defined by the FCC as:

"A radio service using amateur stations for civil defense communications during periods of local, regional or national civil emergencies" [97.3(a)(37)].

One important aspect of RACES is that, when activated, it can continue in operation on certain frequencies even if normal amateur operation is suspended during a national emergency that necessitates the invoking of the President's War Emergency Powers, such as a declaration of war. See Table 1 for a list of these frequencies. Before 1990, a war or national emergency proclamation by the President automatically mandated the closing of all Amateur Radio stations [97.407(b)]. This is highly improbable now. Part of Section 214 of Title 47 of the *Code of Federal Regulations* (which deals with the National Security Council) was changed on December 11, 1990

Michael Goodman, KD5FAQ, in front of the newly built Beebe Junior High School building, destroyed in the January 21, 1999 tornado in Beebe, Arkansas, assists with health and welfare traffic.

eliminating the requirement that the Amateur Radio Service be automatically shut down during such an emergency. Instead, when a national emergency is declared, amateurs are obligated to observe whatever orders the FCC may issue in the interests of national security.

OPERATION IN RACES

The FCC rules permit two types of stations to operate as part of RACES. These are FCC licensed RACES stations, and amateur stations that have been properly registered with a civil defense organization. Any station may operate under RACES provided that it has been registered with a civil defense organization [97.407(a)].

The FCC stopped issuing new RACES station licenses in 1978, and effective April 15, 2000, the FCC will not to renew existing RACES licenses. The FCC believed that RACES stations are redundant, because any station can operate in RACES under the auspices of its own license. A special license is not needed. RACES may operate *only* during declared emergencies or during drills ordered by the served civil defense organization. The control operator of a station engaged in RACES operation must hold an FCC-granted amateur operator license and is bound by the privileges authorized by their license.

Operation in RACES is highly regulated. Amateur stations operating in RACES must be registered with a specific civil defense organization and may only communicate with other stations registered with the same body unless specifically authorized to communicate with other stations by the local civil defense authority. No station operating in RACES may communicate with a station that is not operating in RACES except, when authorized, another US Government station or an FCC licensed station in another service.

RACES COMMUNICATIONS

The types of communications permitted are similarly restricted. RACES operators are restricted concerning which stations they can contact, how long they can participate in drills and what the communications can be about. See the sidebar "ARES and RACES: Two Flavors of Amateur Radio Emergency Communication" for a complete discussion. Of particular interest is the fact that RACES drills and tests "may not exceed a total time of 1 hour per week. With the approval of the chief officer for emergency planning the applicable State, Commonwealth, District or territory, however, such tests and drills may be conducted for a period not to exceed 72 hours no more than twice in any calendar year [97.407(e)(4)]."

Aside from drills, communications in RACES may consist only of civil defense messages concerning:

1) Public safety or national defense during times of local, regional, or national emergencies;

2) Immediate safety of life or immediate protection of property, the

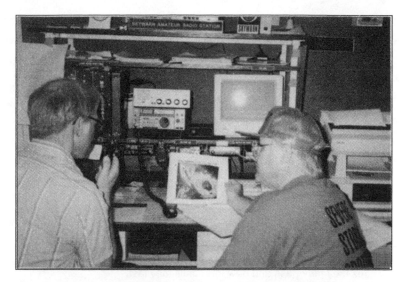

Jan Jubon, K2HJ (l), and Joe Peters, WB4WZZ, cover the night shift at the SKYWARN Amateur Radio station in the Washington, DC, forecast office of the National Weather Service. The time is early Monday morning, August 24, 1992, and Peters holds the latest printout of a GOES satellite image showing Hurricane Andrew as it begins to touch land in Florida. SKYWARN in Washington was activated to provide a backup radio link, if needed, between the National Hurricane Center in Coral Gables, Florida, and the backup hurricane center at the National Meteorological Center in Camp Springs, Maryland. The amateur HF transceiver was used to monitor hurricane nets, and 2 meters was used to coordinate local amateur staffing for the SKYWARN backup station. *(photo courtesy of SKYWARN Net Manager Dan Gropper, KC4OCG)*

maintenance of law and order, alleviation of human suffering and need, and the combating of armed attack or sabotage;

3) The accumulation and dissemination of public information or instructions to the civilian population as required by the civil defense organization or other government agencies or relief agencies [97.407(e)].

WHAT'S ARES?

The Amateur Radio Emergency Service (ARES) is the emergency and disaster preparedness program of the ARRL. It consists of licensed amateurs who have voluntarily registered with ARRL their personal qualifications, commitment and equipment capabilities for communications duty to public service when disaster strikes. An all volunteer service, it is open to any amateur regardless of ARRL membership. The only qualification is that the amateur have a sincere desire to serve.

There are four levels of ARES organization: national, section, district and local. National emergency coordination at ARRL Headquarters is under

Q&A—ARES and RACES: Two Flavors of Amateur Radio Emergency Operation

Q. During an emergency, when is ARES activated? How about RACES?

A. ARES is activated before, during and after an emergency. Generally, ARES handles all emergency messages, including those between government emergency management officials. RACES, on the other hand, almost never starts before an emergency and is active only during the emergency and during the immediate aftermath if government emergency management offices need communications support. RACES is normally shut down shortly after the emergency has cleared.

Q. I don't see ARES mentioned in Part 97? What's the story?

A. True, there's nothing in Part 97 about ARES specifically. ARES operators are, of course, bound by all applicable Part 97 rules, but they aren't bound by the specific emergency rules as specified in §97.407, as stations operating under RACES are. ARES operators have greater flexibility. RACES stations are limited by Part 97 as to who they can communicate with, which messages they may pass and how long drills may last.

Q. Can any licensed amateur volunteer for RACES? How about ARES?

A. Yes on both counts. You can volunteer for RACES by enrolling with a civil defense organization locally. To volunteer for ARES, register with your local ARRL Emergency Coordinator.

Q. I've heard that the FCC has in the past issued RACES licenses that can be used only for RACES activities. What's the status of RACES licenses?

A. There are fewer than 250 RACES station licenses and calls have been issued from the WC#$$$ call sign block such as WC1AAA. They've been assigned to certain civil defense organizations, not to individual amateurs. The FCC stopped issuing new RACES licenses in 1978, and it will not renew existing ones.

Q. If I am enrolled in a local civil defense organization and if it declares a RACES drill, what call sign do I use since the FCC isn't issuing RACES licenses? How about ARES?

A. RACES operation is conducted by amateurs using their own primary license call sign and by existing RACES licensees who hold RACES licenses. Club and military recreation stations are also eligible if authorized by a civil defense organization locally with the appropriate control operator [97.407(a)].

If you are operating under ARES, you can also use your own primary license and call sign or any other call sign authorized by a given control operator.

Q. Which stations may a RACES station communicate with? How about ARES stations?

A. A station operating under RACES may only communicate with:
　　1) A RACES station licensed to the local civil defense organization;
　　2) Other RACES licensees;
　　3) Certain amateur stations registered with civil defense organizations;
　　4) Certain US government stations authorized by the responsible agency to communicate with RACES stations and;

5) Stations in a service regulated by the FCC when authorized by the FCC [97.407(d)].

A station operating in ARES may communicate with any station.

Q. What type of communications may be transmitted by stations operating under RACES?

A. RACES members may transmit only messages related to:

1) Impending danger to the public or affecting national defense during emergencies;

2) The immediate safety of individuals, the immediate protection of property, maintenance of law and order, alleviation of human suffering and need, and combating armed attach and sabotage;

3) The dissemination of information to the public from a local civil defense organization or other government or relief organization and;

4) Communications during RACES drills [97.407(e)].

Q. How long may RACES drills and tests be held? What about ARES?

A. RACES drills and tests can't exceed a total time of one hour per week. With proper authorization, such drills and tests may be conducted for a period not to exceed 72 hours and such drills can occur no more than twice in a calendar year [97.407(e)].

There are no specific limits on ARES drills and tests.

Q. Why are there limits on RACES drills?

A. These rules aren't there to restrict amateurs unduly, but to protect the Amateur Radio Service from nonamateur abusers. The drill time limits were implemented in 1976 because, among other things, local government land mobile communications operators were using the amateur service improperly.

Q. Our weekly RACES net is in operation for more than an hour per week. How can we be in compliance with §97.407(e) and still practice our emergency preparedness skills?

A. The easiest way is to make your RACES net an ARES net with the approval of your local EC so that your group isn't bound by the specific time constraints, yet volunteers still get emergency preparedness training. If participating amateurs are registered in ARES and RACES, they can switch hats as conditions dictate. ARRL and FEMA both recommend dual membership.

Stations operating under ARES have much more flexibility because the main purpose of ARES is to serve the emergency communications needs of many agencies, not just the government. RACES is structured and rigid and must be activated by a local civil defense official; ARES can be activated by an ARRL official such as the local ARRL Emergency Coordinator (EC).

Q. How can I register for RACES? How about ARES?

A. RACES and ARES are both vital organizations and need your participation to make them effective. To register for RACES, contact your local civil defense office.

To register with ARES, complete an ARRL Form FSD-98 and send it to your local EC. You can obtain this ARRL form and others from ARRL HQ and, if you have access to the World Wide Web, from: **http://www.arrl.org/field/forms/#fsd-98**. If you don't know who your EC is, contact your ARRL Section Manager. For the name of your SM, see page 12 of a current issue of *QST*. An updated list also appears on ARRLWeb at: **http://www.arrl.org/field/org/smlist.html**.

David Nailing, KF4JYP, and Ricky Brown, KE4CES, of the West Tennessee Amateur Radio Society, handle ARES and Red Cross net control duties in Jackson, Tennessee.

the supervision of the ARRL Field and Educational Services Manager. This person is responsible for advising all ARES officials regarding their problems, maintaining contact with federal government and other national officials concerned with amateur emergency communications potential, and in general with carrying out the ARRL's policies regarding emergency communications.

The structure at the section level is as follows: Section Manager (SM); Section Emergency Coordinator (SEC); District Emergency Coordinator (DEC); Emergency Coordinator (EC) and ARES members. Most organizing is done on a local level between ECs and ARES members. For more information on ARES, see the *ARRL Public Service Communications Manual* and the *ARRL Operating Manual*. Information on ARES and other emergency services such as SKYWARN can be obtained from ARRL HQ. For those with Web access, see: **http://www.arrl.org/field/pscm/sec1-ch1.html** and **http://www.skywarn.org/**.

CONCLUSION

Some say that there is less of a need for Amateur Radio during small roadside emergencies, for example, but during widescale emergencies in particular, amateurs are skilled at communicating and working with others. Many amateurs participate in club events providing communications for walk-a-thons and other public service events and this is another way hams can prepare themselves for possible future emergencies. Let's hope you'll never need to use the emergency preparedness skills learned as an amateur during a real emergency. If you can help save one life or assist in at least one emergency, then all of your hours of preparation are worth it!

Qualifying Examination Systems

6

The final subpart of the rules, Subpart F, deals with the examination system. It covers such things as the requirements for qualifying for a license, exam elements and standards. It defines examination procedures, the requirements to be a Volunteer Examiner and a VE Sessions Manager.

In December 1983, the FCC delegated much of the exam administration program to amateurs themselves through national or regional Volunteer Examiner Coordinators. The rules provide a system of checks and balances on VEs who administer exams at the local and regional levels. This protects against fraud and provides integrity for the exam process.

SUBPART F RULES SUMMARY: QUALIFYING EXAMINATION SYSTEMS

97.501 Qualifying for an amateur operator license.
97.503 Element standards.
97.505 Element credit.
97.507 Preparing an examination.
97.509 Administering VE requirements.
97.511 Examinee conduct.
97.513 VE session manager requirements.
97.515 [Reserved]
97.517 [Reserved]
97.519 Coordinating examination sessions.
97.521 VEC qualifications.
97.523 Question pools.
97.525 Accrediting VEs.
97.527 Reimbursement for expenses.

Under international agreements, the FCC is obligated to ensure that you have a license before you operate on amateur frequencies and that you can operate your station safely while limiting interference to others. It must also make sure you can copy Morse code if you want to operate on the HF bands.

To meet these ends, the FCC manages a licensing program that was restructured as a result of the 1998 Biennial Regulatory Review of Part 97 (WT Docket 98-143). The long awaited restructuring rules, effective April 15, 2000, reduced the number of license classes for new and upgrading licensees to Technician, General and Amateur Extra. Each of these license classes dangles a bigger carrot of increased operating privileges.

There is now only one code speed requirement—5 wpm—and three written elements, one each for Technician, General and Amateur Extra. For amateurs who only want to operate on VHF and above, the entry level class of license is the Technician in which code is not required. The entry level class of license for those who want to operate on VHF and above and HF is the Technician, but amateurs must have passed the 5 wpm code requirement (Element 1). As mentioned earlier, this is an international requirement.

Amateurs licensed under the pre-April 15, 2000 licensing structure may continue to operate on their traditional subbands and renew their licenses indefinitely. Prior to April 15, 2000, the licenses offered were Novice, Technician, Technician Plus, General, Advanced and Amateur Extra. On or after April 15, 2000, the FCC will only issue *new* Technician, General and Amateur Extra class licenses. No *new* Novice or Advanced class licenses will be issued.

An examination (or exam credit) is always required for a new amateur license and for each change in license class. The FCC makes no exceptions [97.501].

CLASSES OF LICENSE

TECHNICIAN CLASS

The entry level class of license is the Technician. There are two entry level license possibilities—one with frequency privileges of 30 MHz and above, which requires no CW requirement and one for amateurs who also want limited HF privileges, which requires passing Element 1, the 5 wpm code requirement. **Table 1** shows the operating privileges for each class of license.

One of the attractions of the Technician class license is that there is no Morse code requirement. Candidates for Technician must merely pass a written examination for Element 2 [97.501(c)]. There are 35 questions on the Element 2 exam, at least 26 of which must be answered correctly to pass [97.503(b)(1)].

The Technician class candidate can also gain limited HF privileges by passing the 5 wpm code exam (Element 1) in addition to the Technician class written (Element 2) [97.501(c), 97.503(a); (b)(1)]. In addition to the Technician's privileges above 30 MHz, a Technician who has passed

Element 1 is granted Technician HF privileges. All Technicians or current Technician Plus licensees who were licensed before February 14, 1991 and who have passed a code test have automatic credit for Element 1. There is no difference on the FCC database between an amateur who has passed the 5 WPM exam and one who has not. The amateur must retain the CSCE as proof of limited HF privileges.

GENERAL CLASS

This class of license conveys most HF privileges where you can participate in Amateur Radio activities such as DXing, net operation, RTTY and contesting. Because of the extensive privileges on the "low bands," the written exam (Element 3) focuses on the regulatory, operating and technical aspects of HF operation [97.501(b)]. The exam has 35 questions concerning

---

Table 1

Amateur Operator Licenses†

Effective April 15, 2000, only the following *new* licenses will be issued. Novice, Technician Plus, General, Advanced and Amateur Extra class licenses may be renewed and licensees operate using their pre-April 15, 2000 privileges:

Class	Code Test	Written Examination	Privileges
Technician	None	Technician class written (Element 2)	All amateur privileges above 30.0 MHz.
Technician*	5 WPM (Element 1)	Technician class written (Element 2)	All Technician or Technician Plus HF privileges** and all privileges above 30.0 MHz
General	5 WPM (Element 1)	General class written (Element 3)	All amateur privileges except those reserved for Advanced and Amateur Extra class.
Amateur Extra	5 WPM (Element 1)	All lower exam elements plus Amateur Extra theory (Element 4)	All amateur privileges

†A licensed radio amateur will be required to pass only those elements that are not included in the examination for the amateur license currently held.

*If you hold a valid Technician class license issued before March 21,1987, you also have credit for Elements 1 and 3. You must be able to prove your Technician license was issued before March 21,1987 to claim this credit. If your pre-March 1987 Technician license is expired, you may claim credit for Elements 1 and 3. You must pass Element 2 again, however.

**CW on 3.675-3.725, 7.100-7.150 and 21.100-21.200 MHz with 200 W PEP output maximum;

**CW, RTTY and data on 28.100-28.300 MHz with 200 W PEP output maximum;

**CW and SSB voice on 28.300-28.500 MHz with 200 W PEP output maximum

these additional privileges, at least 26 of which must be answered correctly to pass [97.503(b)(2)]. No additional Morse code is required other than Element 1 [97.503(a)].

AMATEUR EXTRA CLASS

At the top is the Amateur Extra license, conveying all amateur privileges, and, accordingly, the right to operate on segments reserved exclusively for Amateur Extra class operators, away from the crowds on the rest of the band. The written examination (Element 4) contains 50 questions on advanced techniques, at least 37 of which must be answered correctly to pass [97.503(b)(3)]. No additional Morse code requirement is needed once the applicant has passed Element 1.

ELEMENT STANDARDS

THE MORSE CODE ELEMENT

Prior to April 15, 2000, there were three levels of Morse code proficiency: 5, 13 and 20 wpm. Effective on that date, only one code speed was required for any class of license: 5 wpm (Element 1). A code exam must be sufficient to prove that the examinee has the ability to send correctly by hand and to receive correctly by ear texts in the international Morse code at not less than 5 wpm using all the letters of the alphabet, numerals 0-9, period, comma, question mark, slant mark and prosigns AR, BT and SK [97.503(a)]. Element 1 is required of Technician (version with HF privileges), General and Amateur Extra class licensees. The only class which does not require the Morse code element is the Technician class license that does not carry any HF privileges. The FCC rules concede that passing a Morse code receiving test is adequate proof of an examinee's ability to *both send and receive* telegraphy. The administering VEs, however, may also include a sending segment in a telegraphy examination if they so choose, but it is not a requirement that they do so [97.509(g)].

THE WRITTEN ELEMENTS

The FCC requires that an amateur possess the operational and technical qualifications required to perform properly the duties of an amateur service licensee. The written elements prove that the applicant possesses these qualifications.

The FCC has set standards for the various written examination elements. Each written examination must be comprised of a question set as follows [97.503]:

Element	Class of License	Examination Questions	Minimum to Pass
2	Technician	35	26
3	General	35	26
4	Amateur Extra	50	37

See **Table 2** for a list of the required elements for the classes of license.

ELEMENT CREDIT

When you upgrade, you will be required to pass only the test elements for the new license that are not included in the exam for the amateur license

---

Table 2
Required Exam Elements

Each applicant must pass an examination for a new amateur operator license and for each change in operator class. Each applicant for the class of operator license specified below must pass, or otherwise receive examination credit for, the following examination elements:

1) Technician Class: Element 2;*
2) General Class: Elements 1, 2, and 3;
3) Amateur Extra Class: Elements 1, 2, 3 and 4 [97.501].

*Limited HF privileges if Element 1 is passed or credit is obtained.

Table 3
Element Credit

The administering VEs must give credit as specified below to an examinee holding any of the following license grants or license documents:

License Document	Credit granted for	Rule cite
1) An unexpired FCC-granted Advanced Class license (or within the grace period)	Elements 1, 2 and 3	[97.505(a)(1)]
2) An unexpired FCC-granted General Class license (or within the grace period)	Elements 1, 2 and 3	[97.505(a)(2)]
3) An unexpired Technician Plus Class (including a Technician Class operator license granted before February 14, 1991)	Elements 1 and 2	[97.505(a)(3)]
4) An unexpired Technician Class license (or within the grace period for renewal)	Element 2	[97.505(a)(4)]
5) An expired or unexpired Novice Class license	Element 1	[97.505(a)(5)]
6) A valid Certificate of Successful Completion of Examination (valid for 365 days)	Element 1, 2, 3 or 4	[97.505(a)(6)]
7) An unexpired (or expired less than 5 years) FCC commercial radiotelegraph operator license or permit.	Element 1	[97.505(a)(7)]
8) An expired FCC-issued Technician Class operator license document granted before March 21, 1987.	Element 3	[97.505(a)(8)]
9) An expired or unexpired FCC-issued Technician Class license granted before February 14, 1991.	Element 1	[97.505(a)(9)]

you currently hold [97.501]. For example, when you upgrade from General to Amateur Extra, you will be required to pass only Element 4; you don't have to take Element 3 again. Your license must be unexpired (or expired less than two years) to qualify for credit. For a list of the license documents that are valid for element credit, see **Table 3.**

Most of the reasons for granting element credit are clear; if you've already obtained a license, you don't need to pass its test elements again. Credit for any element is given to applicants who produce a valid *Certificate of Successful Completion of Examination* (CSCE). For example, if you take the General exam, pass the code, but fail the written test, you will receive a CSCE for the code element. Because CSCEs are valid for 365 days, you've got a year to use it for credit at other exam sessions [97.505(a)(6)].

The FCC grants credit for Elements 1 and 2 for amateurs who hold an unexpired Technician Plus class or a Technician class operator license granted before February 14, 1991. The significance of that date is that's when the FCC began issuing codeless Technician licenses. All holders of Technician licenses issued before that date *had* to have passed the 5 wpm code requirement. Consequently, a Technician class license issued on or *after* February 14, 1991 is not proof that the code element has been passed, but credit is given for having passed Element 2, the Technician written element. Since no new Novice licenses are issued, there is no equivalent element credit for the theory examination; however, credit is granted for the 5 wpm CW requirement for an unexpired Novice license (or, if expired, within the two year grace period) [97.505(a)(5)].

A valid Certificate of Successful Completion of Examination is good for the element passed, and can be issued for Elements 1, 2, 3 or 4 [97.505(a)(6)]. A CSCE is valid for 365 days.

An unexpired (or expired less than 5 years) FCC-issued commercial radiotelegraph operator license or permit is valid for Element 1 credit. No other commercial operator licenses are valid, however [97.505(a)(7)].

An expired FCC-issued Technician Class operator license granted before March 21, 1987 is valid for Element 3. Prior to that date the Technician class written examination was the same as for the General class license. (The only difference in the requirements for the two licenses was the Morse code speed: Generals had to pass the 13 wpm test.) On March 21, 1987, the question pool was split in half, with two separate written elements emerging, one for Technician applicants and the other for General applicants.

Since a Technician licensed prior to March 21, 1987 has already passed the code element, to upgrade to General after April 15, 2000, the amateur needs only to provide documentary proof of this [97.505(a)(8)].

Prior to the creation of the codeless Technician license on February 14, 1991, all amateurs were required to pass the 5 wpm code element. With the creation of the codeless Technician, amateurs were not required to do so. If amateurs can provide proof that they were licensed as a Technician before February 14, 1991, they are granted credit for having passed Element 1. This proof can include an expired or unexpired license granted before February

14, 1991 [97.505(a)(9)]. It can also include a Letter of Verification that they were licensed as a Technician class before February 14, 1991 (available from the FCC's Gettysburg office). Proof can also be obtained from the FCC's archiver, the International Transcription Service (ITS) by contacting them at 717-337-1433 or **www.itsdocs.com/**.

SPECIAL ACCOMMODATIVE PROCEDURES
FOR INDIVIDUALS WITH DISABILITIES

The administering VEs must accommodate an examinee whose physical disabilities require a special examination procedure. The administering VEs may require a physician's certification indicating the nature of the disability before determining which, if any, special procedures must be used [97.509(k)]. Such special accommodations can be substituting a sending CW examination in place of a receiving test for someone who is deaf or reading the written examination verbally to someone who is blind.

Before the FCC amended the rules for the license restructuring effective April 15, 2000, the FCC granted exemptions of the 13 and 20 wpm code elements in cases where a physician has certified an applicant's inability to pass the exam because of a severe physical handicap or disability. Since there is now only one code speed—5 wpm—the exemptions pass into history. There have never been any exemptions for the basic 5 wpm code test other than the exception for commercial radio*telegraph* license holders, described above [97.505(a)(7)].

LICENSE EXAMINATION STANDARDS

PREPARING AN EXAMINATION

Teams of three accredited amateur **Volunteer Examiners (VE)**, under the supervision of umbrella organizations known as **Volunteer Examiner Coordinators (VEC)**, administer exams for all license applicants. Exams are given at locations across the country at convenient times specified by the VEs, following advance public notice [97.509(a); 97.519(a)]. Exams are typically given in public halls and schools, and at conventions, hamfests, flea markets and club meetings. The number of examinees may be limited by the VEs [97.509(a)].

The FCC has specific standards for administering examinations. The code and theory elements must be prepared by a VE holding an Amateur Extra Class operator license, except that an Advanced class VE may also prepare Element 3 question sets and an Advanced, General or Technician (including Technician Plus) class operator may also prepare Elements 1 and 2 [97.507(a)]. When VEs develop the various examinations, each question must be taken from the applicable question pool for the element administered [97.507(b)]. Each Morse code message and each written question set administered to an examinee must be prepared, or obtained from a supplier, by the administering VEs according to instructions from the coordinating VEC [97.507(c)]. The code examination must consist of a message sent in the international Morse code at no less than 5 wpm for a minimum of 5 minutes. The message must contain each required telegraphy character at least once. No message known to the examinee may be administered in a telegraphy examination. Each 5 letters of the alphabet must be counted as 1 word. Each numeral, punctuation mark and prosign must be counted as 2 letters of the alphabet [97.507(d)].

ADMINISTERING VE REQUIREMENTS

Three or more VEs must be present and observe candidates throughout the entire exam process. They are responsible for its proper conduct and supervision under instructions from the VEC. VEs check examinee identification, verify license information and previously earned exam credit as issued within 365 days, grade test papers, report results and handle all paperwork with their VEC. The VEC, in turn, serves as the interface between the Volunteer Examiners and the FCC.

A VE session manager may be selected by the VE team for each examination session. The VE session manager must be accredited as a VE by the same VEC that coordinates the examination session. The VE session manager may serve concurrently as an administering VE. The VE session manager may carry on liaison between the VE team and the coordinating VEC. The VE session manager may organize activities at an examination session [97.513)].

CHECKS AND BALANCES

The administering VEs must immediately terminate the examination upon failure of the examinee to comply with their instructions [97.509(c)]. The FCC doesn't let just any person administer examinations and this is part of the system of checks and balances to insure that the VE Program works effectively.

An administering VE *must*:

1) Be accredited by the coordinating VEC;

2) Be at least 18 years of age;

3) Hold the appropriate class of license to administer the exam to the candidate. To administer a Technician exam, the VE must hold an Amateur Extra, Advanced or General Class. To administer a General class exam, the examining VE must hold an Amateur Extra or Advanced Class operator license and a VE must hold an Amateur Extra class license in order to administer an Amateur Extra class operator license examination.

4) Not be a person whose grant of an amateur station license or amateur operator license has ever been revoked or suspended [97.509(b)].

An administering VE *can not* be related to the applicant. This means that a VE can't administer an examination to his or her spouse, children, grandchildren, stepchildren, parents, grandparents, stepparents, brothers, sisters, stepbrothers, stepsisters, aunts, uncles, nieces, nephews and in-laws [97.509(d)].

Another of the FCC's system of checks and balances in the VEC system is that no VE may administer or certify any examination by fraudulent means or for monetary or other consideration including reimbursement in any amount in excess of that permitted. Violation of this provision may even result in the revocation of the VE's amateur station license and the suspension of the grant of the VE's amateur operator license! [97.509(e)]. The FCC means business! The FCC also states that no examination that has been compromised shall be administered to any examinee. Neither the same code message nor the same question set may be re-administered to the same examinee [97.509(f)].

In addition, when the examinee is credited for all examination elements required for the operator license sought, three VEs must certify that the examinee is qualified for the license grant and that the VEs have complied with these administering VE requirements. The certifying VEs are jointly and individually accountable for the proper administration of each examination element reported. The certifying VEs may delegate to other qualified VEs their authority, but not their accountability, to administer individual elements of an examination [97.509(i)].

When an applicant does not pass a particular element, the administering VEs must return the application form to the applicant and inform the person of the score [97.509(j)]

As discussed earlier, administering VEs must accommodate an examinee whose physical disabilities require special accommodations. The administering VEs may require a physician's certification indicating the nature of the disability which can be used in deciding which, if any, special accommodative procedures should be used [97.509(k)].

The administering VE Team must also issue a CSCE to an applicant who successfully passes the examination [97.509(l)].

Within 10 days of the administration of a successful examination for an amateur operator license, the administering VEs must submit the application document to the coordinating VEC [97.509(m)].

APPLICATION

On test day, each candidate must present the examiners with an NCVEC Form 605 prior to the beginning of the exam. Most VE teams have an adequate supply of NCVEC Form 605 applications on hand for all the candidates who may not have them. With the implementation of the Universal Licensing System, the FCC no longer accepts FCC Forms 610.

The NCVEC Form 605 is provided to candidates at all VE sessions, but it can only be presented to the VE team, not directly to the FCC. This form was designed by the National Conference of VECs. It can be found at **http: //www.arrl.org/arrlvec/605ins.html**.

Candidates are required by the FCC to bring two identification documents, including their original (not a photocopy) license documents and original Certificates of Successful Completion of Examination (CSCE). (You may, however, attach a photocopy of your license to Form 605.) It is recommended that you bring an additional copy of your FCC license (if you are licensed) and an additional copy of any valid CSCEs (issued to you within the previous 365 days) that you present for exam credit.

FOLLOWING INSTRUCTIONS

Candidates must follow the instructions given by the examiners [97.511]. The examiners will immediately terminate the exam if the candidate doesn't follow directions [97.509(c)].

CODE TEST

The 5 wpm code test element (1) can be prepared by the examiners, or a qualified supplier or obtained from the VEC, according to the VEC's instructions [97.507(c)]. The person preparing the code test must hold an Amateur Extra, Advanced, General or Technician class license [97.507(a)]. The test must prove the applicant's ability to send and receive the code at 5 wpm, using all the letters of the alphabet, numerals 0-9, period, comma, question mark, slant mark and prosigns AR, BT and SK.

The sending test is no longer required, as the FCC stated that those who can receive the code can typically send it as well. At their discretion, however, VEs may also administer a sending test [97.509(g)] in addition to a receiving test.

The style of test—fill-in-the-blank, multiple-choice, straight-copy—is chosen by the VEC or in some cases, the VEs themselves. In cases where "straight copy" testing is used, each five letters of the alphabet count as one word; each numeral, punctuation mark and prosign counts as two letters of the alphabet.

WRITTEN TEST

The VEC or VEs select questions for each test from the appropriate pool of questions approved by the majority of VECs (see "Question Pools" later in this chapter) [97.507(b); 97.523]. The VEC or VEs keep the exact exam designs secret, but the general question pools are available to the public (copies of each element's pool are available from ARRL HQ and appear on *ARRLWeb* at **http://www.arrl.org/arrlvec/pools.html**) and they are also available from the ARRL VEC for a 9×12 envelope with $1.50 postage [97.523].

VEs receive test papers from their VEC, or in some cases create their own and administer them to the candidates in accordance with the VEC's instructions [97.507(c)].

IF YOU PASS...

Upon completion of each examination element, the administering VEs must immediately grade the examinee's answers. The administering VEs are responsible for determining the correctness of the examinee's answers

[97.509(h)]. When an applicant passes an exam element, the examiners issue a *Certificate of Successful Completion of Examination* (CSCE) [97.509(l)]. This certificate is required for already-licensed applicants operating with newly acquired privileges of a class higher than that of their permanent license. With a CSCE showing a successful license upgrade, the applicant can (with appropriate identification—see "Interim Identification," later in this chapter) operate with the new privileges prior to the FCC granting the upgraded ticket. The certificate also carries with it a 365-day credit for elements passed when taking subsequent exams.

When the candidate passes all of the exam elements for a license, the examiners indicate that fact on Form 605. Within 10 days following the exam, the examiners must send the application of a successful candidate to their coordinating VEC [97.509(m)]. The VEC screens the application data and test results before sending the data on, within 10 days of receipt, to the FCC Licensing Division in Gettysburg [97.519(b)]. Each VEC must make any examination records available to the FCC upon request. Since January 1995, VECs have been able to file examination data with the FCC electronically. Today all VECs file electronically, which has sped up the licensing process dramatically (what used to take several weeks when VECs mailed the applications to the FCC now takes an average of 10 days or less). VECs are now required to file electronically and must keep the Form 605 documents available for FCC inspection for 15 months [97.519(b),(c)].

IF YOU DON'T PASS...

If the examinee does not score a passing grade on an examination element, the administering VEs must return the application document to the examinee and inform the examinee of the grade [97.509(j)]. There is no waiting period before reexamination after failing an exam element. The FCC requires, however, that VECs not use the same set of exam questions in successive exam sessions to ensure that "retest" doesn't mean "remembering" [97.509(f)].

At the discretion of the VEs, many applicants will retest immediately if more than one version of the failed elements(s) is available at the session. If the VE team charges a test fee (some VECs don't require a fee), another test fee may be charged in order to be retested.

SPECIAL FCC EXAMS

At any time, the FCC may readminister any exam given by a VEC, itself or under the supervision of VEs it designates. The FCC can cancel the license of a licensee who doesn't show up for, or fails to pass, an FCC directed reexamination. This allows the FCC to spot check and maintain integrity in the exam process [97.519(d)].

VOLUNTEER EXAMINER COORDINATORS

Some amateurs confuse VECs and VEs and think that they are one and the same. VECs are umbrella organizations that serve as interfaces between the FCC and the Volunteer Examiners in the field. The ARRL-VEC and the W5YI-VEC process the vast majority of the new applications in the US. VECs coordinate the efforts of VEs, print and distribute exam papers to VEs and forward successful applicants' Form 605 data to the FCC's licensing division [97.519]. All VEs must be accredited by a VEC. VEs are the amateurs at a VE session who actually administer the examinations to candidates.

All VECs have entered into special agreements with the FCC after having met certain qualifications: A VEC must be an organization that exists for the purpose of furthering the interests of Amateur Radio [97.521(a)]. It must be able to serve at least one of the VEC regions [listed in Appendix 2 of the Rules] and agree to coordinate test sessions for all classes of license [97.521(b),(c)].

It is the VEC's legal responsibility to accredit a broad range of hams to be Volunteer Examiners, regardless of race, sex, religion or national origin. A VEC may not refuse to accredit a volunteer on the basis of membership (or lack thereof) in an Amateur Radio organization, nor on the basis of the person accepting or declining to accept reimbursement [97.525(b)].

A VEC must not accredit a volunteer to be an examiner, however, if (1) he or she does not meet the VE qualifications; (2) the FCC refuses to accept the services of the volunteer; (3) the VEC refuses to accept the services of the volunteer; (4) the VEC determines that the volunteer is not competent to perform the function of a VE; or (5) the VEC determines that questions of the volunteer's integrity or honesty could compromise the exam [97.525(a)].

It is the responsibility of the VEs themselves to follow all of the policies of the VEC and to make sure that they are all carried out.

CONFLICT OF INTEREST

The FCC Rules formerly prohibited amateurs from holding a significant interest in, or being an employee of, a company that made or distributed amateur equipment, or published or distributed amateur licensing study materials, unless that amateur could show he or she wasn't engaged in making, publishing or distributing such equipment or materials. Similar conflict of interest requirements applied to VECs. The Telecommunications Act of 1996 dropped all conflict of interest requirements, and the FCC modified its rules accordingly on April 11, 1996.

INTERIM IDENTIFICATION

If you already hold a license, and qualify for a new higher-class license, you may use your new privileges immediately [97.9(b)]. The FCC has established temporary identifier codes for license upgrades. This code is a slant bar (/) followed by a two-letter group: KT for Technician or Technician with HF privileges, AG for General and AE for Amateur Extra. The ID code is usually shown on the certificate issued to you when you successfully complete your exam. It must be added as a suffix to your call sign when you operate with your new privileges [97.119(f)]. For example, a Technician who passes the General test may operate on 20 meters immediately after receiving the CSCE, but would have to give his or her call sign as "WA4XXX/Temporary AG" until the FCC grants the upgrade and it appears on the FCC database. If the amateur operates on the Technician frequencies, he or she does not have to add the special suffix. Since VECs process applications promptly and the FCC acts on the application within a few days, the interim ID is used less today than it was years ago.

QUESTION POOLS

In addition to reducing the number of license classes and exam elements in its December 1999 action, the FCC also revised its rules to provide VEs and VECs with additional flexibility in determining the specific content of written exams. Specifically, the FCC eliminated the question pool topics and the algorithm that was found in 97.503, saying that the Question Pool Committee (QPC) of the National Conference of VECs (NCVECs) has a better ability to ensure that the question pools reflect current technology than it [the FCC] does by specifying general topics in the rules. The FCC said the QPC "is capable of both specifying topics and organizing questions by topic, *if this function is necessary* [emphasis added], as part of its maintenance of the question pools for amateur radio operator examinations."

The FCC also said "that the general standard suggested by the ARRL— i.e., testing should be related to privileges, should place greater emphasis on operating practices and current technologies, and should support and encourage experimentation—is a reasonable standard for the Question Pool Committee of the NCVECs to use in reorganizing the current question pools and revising the written examination elements."

Question pools are large numbers of exam questions from which specific question sets for tests are extracted [97.3(a)(34),(35)]. Pools for each written test element are developed by all VECs working together at regular annual question-pool review sessions [97.523].

All VECs cooperate in maintaining one question pool set for each written exam element. Each question pool must have at least 10 times the number of questions required for a single exam. The question pools must be published and made available to the public prior to their use in making a question set. Each question on each VEC question pool must be prepared by a VE holding the required FCC-issued operator license [97.523].

EXAMINATION EXPENSE REIMBURSEMENT

The FCC allows VEs and VECs to charge exam fees to recover their out-of-pocket expenses incurred in preparing, processing and administering exams [97.527(a)]. Some VECs do still require their VEs to maintain such records for ready reference.

7 Amateur Service Regulation

The electromagnetic spectrum is a limited resource; each kilohertz is precious to the competing interests that lay claim to it. Fortunately, unlike natural resources, the spectrum is a limited but nondepletable resource that, if misused, can be restored to normal as soon as the misuse stops. Each day gives us a new opportunity to use the spectrum efficiently and intelligently.

Who decides where Amateur Radio frequencies will be, or, for that matter, where your favorite AM or FM broadcast station will be? With the proliferation of competing services within the physical confines of the radio spectrum comes the need for controls. Without such controls, chaos would reign with radio services colliding with each other. Not surprisingly, controls have developed over the years, implemented at the international and domestic levels. The International Telecommunication Union (ITU) has the vital role of dividing up the range of communications frequencies for the entire world. Based on the demonstrated or perceived needs of different services, which include commercial broadcast, land mobile and private radio (including Amateur Radio), member-nations of the ITU decide which radio services will be given which band of frequencies. Once that's done, the government regulators for each particular country take over.

INTERNATIONAL REGULATION OF THE SPECTRUM

Nations sign all sorts of treaties and agreements (international communications, nuclear arms, ozone depletion and so on) to bring some order to international relationships. Without these agreements, anarchy would prevail. Those affecting Amateur Radio have proved quite effective over the years. These must be *inter*-national in scope because radio waves know no geographical or political boundaries—they don't stop for customs inspections.

Amateur Radio frequency band allocations don't just happen. Band allocation proposals must survive a maze of national agencies, the ITU and the gauntlet of other spectrum users. The ITU allocates portions of the radio spectrum to each service vying for its own slice of the pie. The ITU develops regulations designed to reduce potential interference problems.

The process occurs at the international conference table. Member-nations' delegates bring their countries' official positions to the table. They debate the merits of these positions, taking into consideration changes in technologies since the previous conference and the needs of each administration. They finally arrive at an International Table of Allocations and Radio Regulations. Amateur Radio is provided for in Article S25 of those regulations.

The international Radio Regulations of the ITU affect all radio amateurs. The US has a responsibility to make rules that are consistent with these international agreements. Once the international allocations have been decided, it's up to the Federal Communications Commission (FCC) to decide the best way to allocate frequency bands to those services using them in the US. The FCC is the governing body in the US when it comes to Amateur Radio. The Communications Act of 1934, as amended, is the chief tool by which the US carries out its obligations to the world's telecommunications community. Through the authority delegated to the FCC by Congress in the Communications Act, the FCC adopted a body of rules to deal with communications. Part 97 (officially cited as 47 CFR Part 97) of the FCC Rules governs Amateur Radio. This stands for Title 47 (Telecom-munications) of the Code of Federal Regulations.

FEDERAL COMMUNICATIONS COMMISSION

What is the FCC? It's the outfit that issues your license, for one thing! The FCC is the US government agency charged with regulating interstate and foreign communication involving radio, television, wire cable and satellites. The FCC does not function like any other government department; it is a sovereign federal agency created by Congress and, as such, reports directly to Congress.

The FCC allocates bands of frequencies to nongovernment commu-nications services and assigns frequencies to individual stations. It licenses and regulates stations and operators, and regulates common carriers in interstate and foreign communications by telegraph, telephone and satellite. One job it does not do is regulate federal government radio operations; this is done by the National Telecommunications and Information Administration (NTIA), under delegated authority of the President.

The FCC consists of five commissioners appointed by the President with the approval of the Senate. No commissioner can have a financial interest in any FCC-regulated business. Appointments are for five years, except when filling an unexpired term. One of the commissioners is appointed to be chairman by the President, and his tenure as chairman runs with the

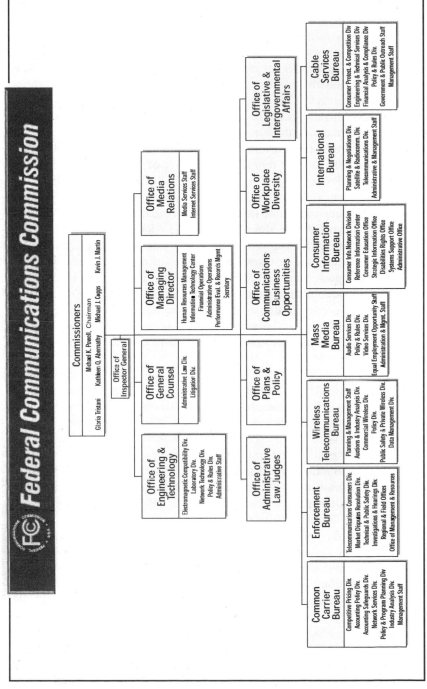

Fig 1—FCC Organization Chart.

President's term of office. The chairman may revert to commissioner if the President leaves office before the end of the chairman's term as commissioner. As with many federal agencies, the commissioners function "collegially" (that is, one person-one vote), supervising all FCC activities, with substantial delegation of responsibilities to FCC staff members. The chairman is responsible for the overall administration of the internal affairs of the FCC and sets the basic agenda for the agency. Otherwise, as noted above, he, like his fellow commissioners, has only one vote in formal policy decisions. The internal structure of the FCC is shown in **Fig 1**.

Policy determinations are made by the commission as a whole. FCC practices conform to the Communications Act of 1934, as amended, the Administrative Procedure Act, as amended, and other applicable laws.

The FCC cooperates with other agencies, such as those involved with radio and wire communication in international and domestic matters. It also cooperates with radio-user groups, such as the ARRL.

FCC regulation of radio includes consideration of applications for construction permits and licenses for all classes of nongovernment stations, and frequency, power and call sign assignments. The FCC is involved in authorization of communications circuits, modification and renewal of licenses, and inspection of transmitting equipment and regulation of its use. The FCC has enforcement powers and may levy fines in cases of noncompliance with its rules. In sum, the FCC carries out the Communications Act.

Although the FCC has authority over the Amateur Radio Service, it mainly concerns itself with a number of other services. These include aviation (aircraft and ground); marine (ship and coastal); public safety (police, fire, forestry conservation, highway maintenance, local government, special emergency and state guard). The FCC holds jurisdiction over industrial services including business, forest products, manufacturers, motion pictures, petroleum, power, relay press, special industrial and telephone maintenance. The land transportation services cover railroad, passenger and truck, taxicab and automobile emergency communications. Other services include the General Mobile Radio Service (including the CB radio service), disaster, experimental and common carrier. The latter service covers a wide range of communications, including paging, land mobile, microwave relay, broadcast relay, and international radiotelephone and telegraph.

The FCC is charged with taking care of communications provisions of treaties and international agreements to which the US is a party. Under Department of State auspices, the FCC participates in related international conferences. The FCC licenses radio and cable circuits from the US to foreign ports and regulates the operating companies. It also licenses the radio stations on American planes and ships in international service and, under international agreements and upon request, inspects the radio equipment of foreign vessels touching US ports. In addition, it is the medium for resolving cases of interference between domestic and foreign radio stations.

The FCC is required "to study new uses for radio, provide for experimental uses of frequencies, and generally encourage the larger and more effective use of radio in the public interest." Cooperation is maintained with government and commercial research activities. The FCC also carries out studies to provide information on complex questions facing the FCC and the telecommunications industry as a whole.

Wire and radio communications facilities that are used to aid national defense form one of the basic requirements of the Communications Act. Congress has delegated some of these functions to the FCC.

The functions relating to assignment of frequencies to radio stations belonging to, and operated by, the US government were assigned to the Assistant Secretary of Commerce for Communications and Information (who also holds the title of NTIA Administrator).

Internal Structure of the FCC

In the fall of 1994, the FCC underwent a major reorganization. The Wireless Telecommunications Bureau (WTB) included functions of the old Private Radio Bureau. An International Bureau and a Cable Services Bureau were also created. According to the FCC, personal communications systems and other emerging technologies made the WTB necessary, and the new International Bureau "will better meet the challenges ahead as the FCC continues its role in international telecommunications."

FCC reorganization in 1999 resulted in the dissolution of the Compliance and Information Bureau, and creation of new Enforcement and Consumer Information Bureaus.

There are now seven operating bureaus in the FCC: Mass Media, Common Carrier, Consumer Information, Enforcement, International, Cable Services, and Wireless Telecommunications. In addition there are 11 staff offices: Managing Director, Engineering and Technology, Plans and Policy, General Counsel, Administrative Law Judges, Legislative and Intergovernmental Affairs, Media Relations, Secretary, Inspector General, Communication Business Opportunities, and Workplace Diversity. FCC headquarters are located in Washington, DC.

The FCC field staff is in field offices throughout the country. The field staff engages for the most part in engineering work. This includes monitoring the radio spectrum to see that station operations meet technical requirements, inspecting stations of all types and issuing permits or licenses to those found qualified. It locates and closes unauthorized transmitters, furnishes radio bearings for aircraft or ships in distress, locates sources of interference and suggests remedial measures. The field staff performs special engineering work for other government agencies, and obtains and analyzes technical data for FCC use.

Where does Amateur Radio fit into the FCC's scheme of things? Amateur

Radio is administered by the Wireless Telecommunications Bureau, specifically the WTB's Private Wireless Division. Amateur Radio is considered private because it is a two-way service for individuals to use for private, strictly noncommercial communications. In contrast, broadcasting serves a mass audience and common-carrier services (such as the telephone system) provide a communications service for hire.

Included under the Wireless Telecommunications Bureau heading is the Licensing Division in Gettysburg. Other components of the FCC hierarchy of concern to Amateur Radio are the Office of Engineering and Technology and the Enforcement Bureau.

The FCC's Enforcement Bureau, established in November 1999, enhances the FCC's ability to serve the public by improving the effectiveness of the agency's enforcement program. The new Enforcement Bureau is the primary FCC organization responsible for enforcement of the Communications Act, as well as Commission rules, orders and author-izations. It consolidates enforcement functions and personnel from the Commission's existing Common Carrier, Mass Media, Wireless Telecommunications and former Compliance and Information Bureaus.

Taking advantage of technology advances, the FCC upgraded all nine of its monitoring stations around the country by installing new High Frequency Direction Finding (HFDF) equipment, which covers the frequency range of 100 kHz through 30 MHz. All nine sites, which are now referred to as the National Automated Monitoring Network, are remotely controlled from a central control office located in Columbia, Maryland.

Additionally, the FCC closed nine of its 25 field offices, replacing them with two "resident agents" per office and consolidated its six Regional Offices into three (Chicago, Kansas City and San Francisco). A central, toll free calling line provides an improved level of customer service. This telephone number, 1-888 CALL FCC (1-888-225-5322), should now be used for all contacts with the FCC.

Deregulation

In the 1980s, a mandate was passed down to regulatory agencies that there should be less intrusion into people's lives by the federal government, with the understanding that a marketplace philosophy—based on individual initiative and free enterprise—should prevail whenever possible. The enactment of the Communications Amendments Act of 1982 (Public Law 97-259) opened the door to sweeping changes in the amateur service and placed the primary responsibility for protecting the future of Amateur Radio where it belongs: On amateurs themselves. Signed into law by President Reagan on September 14, 1982, Public Law 97-259 amended the Communications Act in several critical areas (all of which have been incorporated into Part 97), as follows:

• Authority was vested in the FCC to regulate the susceptibility of electronic equipment to RFI.

• The amateur service was exempted from the "secrecy of communications" provisions of §705 of the Communications Act. This cleared the way for a more active role on the part of amateurs to help regulate their own bands.

• Because of this exemption, the FCC was legally authorized to use volunteers to monitor the bands for rules violations and convey information to FCC personnel. This formed the basis for the creation of the League's Amateur Auxiliary to the FCC's Compliance and Information Bureau.

• The FCC was authorized to use volunteers in preparing and administering exams, which led the ARRL (and others) to become Volunteer Examiner Coordinators and coordinate exams throughout the US and overseas.

• The term of an amateur license was increased from 5 to 10 years to reduce the administrative burden on the FCC and amateur licensees.

The most recent example of deregulation has been the dramatic license restructuring, which became effective April 15, 2000. Most observers agree that telecommunications deregulation has generally been positive.

HOW FCC RULES ARE MADE

The FCC Rules are not just handed down to us from the Commission; amateurs have a right to directly participate in the rule-making procedure. As American citizens, we can and do have a profound effect on what rules are added, dropped or modified. See **Fig 2**.

The Administrative Procedure Act

The Administrative Procedure Act and certain sections of the Communications Act set forth specific procedures that all administrative agencies must follow in adopting and amending their rules. The Act also sets forth the procedures to be followed in adjudicatory (that is, trial-like) hearings.

Where rule making is concerned, the essential provisions of the Act are (1) Public notice of the proposal in the *Federal Register*, and (2) The right of interested persons to submit written comments. This is "notice-and-comment" rule making. Prior notice need not be given if an agency, for good cause, finds that the notice and comments are impractical, unnecessary or contrary to the public interest. Overall, rules may be adopted, amended or repealed by an agency on its own initiative, or may be requested by any interested person who files a petition for rule making. If the FCC feels a petition has merit, a rule making (RM) file number (such as RM-9815) is assigned.

Some petitions that plainly do not warrant FCC consideration are not given RM file numbers and are usually dismissed by an FCC bureau chief under delegated authority. Any interested person may file a statement in support of or in opposition to a Petition for Rule Making not later than 30 days from issuance of the Public Notice. Replies to supporting or opposing statements are due not later than 15 days after the filing of such statements. All FCC filings must be sent to the FCC, 445 12th St, SW, Washington, DC 20554, or filed electronically. See the sidebar, "Hints on Filing Comments with the FCC," later in this chapter.

Notice of Proposed Rule Making

Rule making involving Amateur Radio matters usually falls under the jurisdiction of the FCC's Wireless Telecommunications Bureau. Petitions

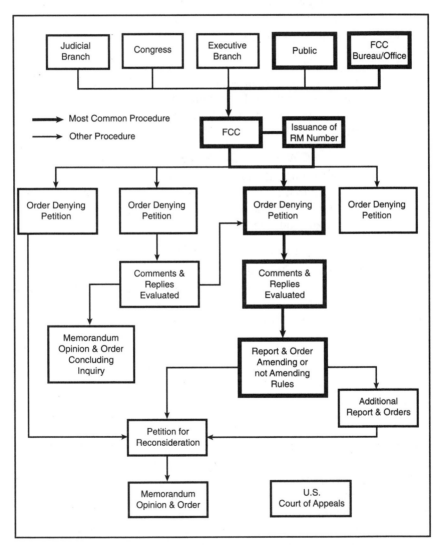

Fig 2—How FCC Rules are made.

Format to be Used for Petition or Formal Comments

Before the
FEDERAL COMMUNICATIONS COMMISSION
Washington, DC 20554

In the Matter of)	
)	
Amendment of Section 97. –)	
(Insert rule number if an)	RM- (*or docket number*)
amendment is)	
proposed, and the)	
subject matter of the)	
Amateur Radio Service Rule(s).))	

involving amateur matters are processed by the Private Wireless Division of the WTB. If a petition has merit, a draft Notice of Proposed Rule Making (NPRM) may be submitted by the WTB Chief to the Commissioners for their consideration. If adopted for release—which requires a majority vote by the Commissioners—a docket number is assigned (WT Docket 98-143, for example). The entire NPRM is then released to the public and published in the *Federal Register* for comments.

Depending on the FCC's workload, its priorities and the amount of interest shown by concerned parties, several months or even years may elapse between the release of an NPRM and when the FCC reaches a final decision, if at all.

The Administrative Procedure Act requires that the NPRM set forth the terms or substance of the proposed rule or a description of the issues involved, and a reference to the legal authority for the rule making. It also requires a statement of the time, place and nature of public rule making proceedings. Deadlines for filing comments and reply comments are given (reply comments are those filed in response *not* to the underlying NPRM but to the *comments that were filed* in response to the underlying NPRM which are available to the public at the FCC's public reference room in Washington). The NPRM must be published in the *Federal Register*. Interested persons have an opportunity to participate in the proceedings through the submission of written data, views or arguments.

If you are filing comments in an NPRM, use the caption format shown above, making sure that you put the appropriate docket number at the top.

When you write your comments, list your credentials, be fact-specific and to the point. When you comment on an active NPRM, the FCC wants you to send in an original and four copies, for a total of five documents (make an additional copy for your own records). If you want to be sure that each FCC commissioner gets a personal copy, send five additional copies. So, if you want to have all bases covered, your envelope to the FCC must contain 10 documents—the original and nine copies. To be considered formally, comments must have type at least 12 points in height, be double spaced and be printed on $8\frac{1}{2}\times11$-inch paper with the printed material not exceeding $6\frac{1}{2}\times9\frac{1}{2}$ inches. The same rules apply for filing reply comments. See the accompanying sidebar, "Hints on Filing Comments with the FCC."

All comments are reviewed by the FCC staff and play a role in the ultimate decision made by the FCC. Therefore, it's important to get them in by deadline. Comments not filed on time may not be considered by the FCC in its deliberations. Occasionally, a Notice of Inquiry (NOI) may be issued or combined with an NPRM. An NOI will set forth the FCC's concern over a particular matter and solicit comments and suggestions for the world at large as to whether adoption, amendment or repeal of a rule may be desirable. The same notice and comment procedures are followed with NOIs as with NPRMs.

Copies of FCC NPRMs concerning Amateur Radio are available from ARRL HQ. Summaries or the word-for-word text of NPRMs are printed in the *Federal Register*, which is available in most local libraries and on the Internet at this address: **http://www.access.gpo.gov/su_docs/index.html**. Listen to W1AW and watch *QST, The ARRL Letter, ARRLWeb* and other ham publications for information on the latest FCC happenings concerning Amateur Radio. Copies of FCC documents may be obtained, for a fee, from the FCC's contractor for records duplication: The International Transcription Service, 1231 20th St, NW, Washington, DC 20036, phone 202-857-3800. ITS may also be contacted at: ITS, 1270 Fairfield Rd, Gettysburg, PA 17325, phone 717-337-1433. FCC NPRMs are usually posted on the FCC Internet sites; see Appendix 13.

The Report and Order

Once all the comments are reviewed (for amateur matters, this is usually done by the Private Wireless Division of the WTB), a draft Report and Order will be prepared by that branch and submitted to the Chief of the WTB. Then the document must work its way up the hierarchy, surviving checkpoints along the way. A draft Report and Order must be approved at each level within the bureau and then coordinated with other interested bureaus or offices within the FCC before formally being presented to the commissioners for their consideration and approval. A Report and Order is just what it sounds like—the Commission issues a detailed report of its findings and an order is issued based on the judgment of the commissioners (as recommended by the staff).

Specific rules changes are listed. Revisions of the Report and Order take place right up to the moment it is adopted by the FCC commissioners, usually after due consideration by the commissioners at an "Open Meeting," a regular meeting of the commissioners that has a published agenda and is open to the public. During these open meetings, FCC staff members most familiar with the subject at hand make the presentation. The Commissioners may decide to adopt the Report and Order as presented to them by the staff, order the staff to make specific revisions in the document and then adopt it, or terminate the NPRM without amending any rule or taking any action.

The rule or rules finally adopted need not be identical to the original proposal. The courts have held that there must merely be some relationship between the proposal and the rule finally adopted, and that the FCC must have considered all the relevant comments that were submitted. The Administrative Procedure Act requires that there must be a concise general statement of the basis and purpose incorporated in the rules. Sometimes these "concise" statements of why the FCC did what it did are anything but, going on and on in excruciating detail. What the FCC is doing is putting all its cards on the table to show it made a rational decision—this is done to avoid problems with Congress (which can exert pressure on the FCC because Congress controls the FCC's appropriations, that is, the purse strings) and judicial review of its decision (see "Court Appeals," below). The FCC tends to be sensitive to Congress and the courts, so it carefully frames its Reports and Orders and the like to ensure that it has stated its case as persuasively as possible.

Generally, a Report and Order is the end of the line for a particular rules change. The rules become law under the Administrative Procedure Act 30 days after publication in the *Federal Register*.

Due Process

You might wonder why this process takes so long and if it's worth it. As has been said many times, this is the price we pay for democracy. We are saddled with these elaborate and often slow procedures because we have a free society. All interested persons have an opportunity to hear and to be heard on a given issue—it's called due process of law, which is embodied in the US Constitution. These tedious procedures that allow for public participation at the expense of speedy decision-making are desirable in our system. It's one of the things that distinguishes us from the totalitarian regimes around the world, and makes the US the world leader in freedom.

Petitions for Reconsideration

§405 of the Communications Act, as amended, affords "a person aggrieved or whose interests are adversely affected" by an order (a new or amended rule, etc) the right to petition the FCC for reconsideration. The petitioner must state specifically why the FCC's action should be changed. A Petition for Reconsideration must be filed within 30 days of the date of the public notice of the final FCC action, which generally means within 30 days of its publication in the *Federal Register*.

A Petition for Reconsideration usually is referred to the same bureau that prepared the original Report and Order. It is virtually impossible to obtain a favorable action on a Petition for Reconsideration if no new facts are presented.

Occasionally, however, if the petitioner shows good cause, the FCC may grant the Petition for Reconsideration and modify the earlier order.

Comments in opposition to a Petition for Reconsideration must be filed within 15 days of the date of public notice of the petition's filing, again usually the date of publication in the *Federal Register*. Replies to an opposition must be filed within 10 days after the time for filing oppositions has expired.

The format and number of copies required for reconsideration petitions are the same as described above, although they may not exceed 25 double-spaced typewritten pages. Oppositions to Petitions for Reconsideration are

---

Hints on Filing Comments with the FCC

The FCC is interested in any experiences, knowledge or insights that outside parties may have to shed light on issues and questions raised in the rule-making process. The public and industry have the opportunity to comment on Petitions for Rule Making, NOIs, NPRMs, Further NPRMs, Report and Orders, and others' comments on the aforementioned documents. It is a common misconception that one must be a lawyer to be able to file comments with the FCC. All that is necessary is an interest in an issue and the ability to read and follow directions.

Prior to drafting comments, it is crucial to read and understand fully the item you wish to comment on. Usually, the NPRM, NOI, or other item will specify and invite comment on the issue(s) that the Commission is interested in studying further. Examination of the issue(s) and relevant documents is the most important part of the comment process. Comments may take any form, but below are some hints to assist you in writing them.

Format: There is no required format for informal comments, although if you plan to file formally, it is required that they be typed, double-spaced, and on 8.5 ×11 paper. Additional requirements for formal filings are set forth in §§1.49 and 1.419 of the FCC Rules. The Docket Number or Rule Making Number of the item at hand should be included on your comments, and can be found on the front page of the Commission document or public notice. You should also include your name and complete mailing address.

Content: Your comments should state who you are and what your specific interest is. (You do not need to represent yourself in an official capacity. You may, for example, express your opinion as a concerned consumer, concerned parent, etc, and sign your name.) State your position and the facts directly, as thoroughly but as briefly as possible. Explain your position as it relates to your experience and be explicit. Make clear if the details of a proposed rule or only one of several provisions of the rule are objectionable. If the rule would be acceptable with certain safeguards, explain them and why they are necessary.

Support: Statements of agreement or dissent in comments should be oupportod to tho boot oxtont poooiblo by faotual (otudioo, otatiotioo, oto), logioal and/or legal information. Support should illustrate why your position is in the public interest. The more support made, the more persuasive the comments will be.

Length: Comments may be any length, although it is preferred that they be succinct and direct. If formal comments are longer than 10 pages, it is required that they include a summary sheet.

Time Frame: Your comments should be submitted well within the time

---

also limited to 25 double-spaced typewritten pages, while replies to an opposition are limited to 10 double-spaced typewritten pages.

The effective date of a new or amended rule is not automatically postponed by the filing of a Petition for Reconsideration. If a stay of the effective date of the rule or amendment is desired, the petitioner must specifically request it in a "Motion to Stay" and must show good cause (such as irreparable harm) why the rule should not go into effect.

Court Appeals

Judicial review of an FCC decision may be sought under §402(a) of the

---

frame designated on the original document or public notice. It is almost always included on the first page of an NPRM or NOI. However if the deadline has passed, you can still submit your views informally in a permissible *ex parte* presentation.

Filing: Send your written comments to Secretary, Federal Communications Commission, 445 12th St, SW, Washington DC 20554. If you wish your comments to be received as an informal filing, submit the original and one copy. If you want your comments to be received as a formal filing, you should submit an original and four copies. For more specific filing information, please refer to the FCC Public Notice "Guidelines for Uniform Filings" available from the same address. Comments (and Reply Comments) may be submitted electronically on the FCC Web page as specified below.

Reply Comments: As the name implies, reply comments are used to respond to comments filed by other parties. You may file reply comments even if you did not submit comments initially. When drafting reply comments, use the same guidelines expressed above regarding content and be careful not to raise additional or irrelevant issues.

Tracking your Comments: After you have properly filed your comments with the FCC, they will be part of the official Commission record. To track the progress of proceedings in which you have filed comments, you may check the Daily Digest or Federal Register for releases and notices. The Daily Digest can be obtained from the FCC Web site, **http://www.fcc.gov/**.

For Further Information: For further information, you may directly contact the Secretary's office at the FCC, 445 12th St, SW, Washington DC 20554. Explicit information about filings in rule-making proceedings can be found In §§1.49 and 1.419 of the FCC Rules. Copies of any FCC documents can be obtained through the FCC's duplicating contractor, ITS, 1231 20th St NW, Washington, DC 20036, tel 202-857-3800 or from ITS, 1270 Fairfield Rd, Gettysburg, PA 17325, tel 717-337-1433. Most FCC dockets may be downloaded from the FCC Web site at **www.fcc.gov**.

Filing Comments Electronically

The Electronic Comment Filing System (ECFS) is designed to give access to Commission rulemakings and docketed proceedings via the World Wide Web. ECFS will: accept electronic comments in FCC rulemakings and docketed proceedings; scan in paper documents; and research, retrieve and print any documents in the system. ECFS includes data and images from 1992 onward. See **http://www.fcc.gov/e-file/**.

Communications Act and §§701-706 of the Administrative Procedure Act, as long as review is sought over a final decision. Appeals from decisions and orders of the Commission are, in cases listed in §402(b) of the Communications Act, to be taken to the United States Court of Appeals for the District of Columbia. The court may either affirm (approve) the action of the FCC, reverse it, or send it back to the FCC for further consideration.

Generally, the court will be quite deferential to an agency such as the FCC, because of the technical nature of the communications world, so the chances of the aggrieved person prevailing on appeal are remote. The standard the court uses is whether the agency action is "arbitrary, capricious or an abuse of discretion." If the court can find a reasonable or rational basis for an agency action (which is, again, why FCC Report and Orders try to address every conceivable issue), no abuse of discretion will be found. A court might set aside a rule-making action if, for example, the FCC exceeded the authority delegated to it by Congress or under the Constitution, if it failed to properly follow its notice-and-comment procedures, on the record (that is, the agency's fact-finding was unreasonable), or in the event there was a prejudicial error.

As mentioned, the court generally follows a policy of not substituting its judgment for that of the agency because of the agency's presumed expertise in that field. Moreover, courts are much more comfortable with issues of law (procedure, applicability of statutes, and so on) and are reluctant to address the facts and details of a particular controversy. The standard for evaluating a question of fact would be whether the FCC's action was supported by substantial evidence on the record; in questions of law, the court would be much more inclined to substitute its own judgment for that of the FCC or other agency. As such, in a factual determination, the court will rarely go beyond the facts and evidence already put on the record during the agency rule making.

In the relatively rare event that the court remands a rule-making matter back to the FCC for further consideration, it will usually be sent back to the same bureau that handled it originally.

It is clear from this discussion that Petitions for Reconsideration and appeals to the courts are not guaranteed to bring about changes in rules adopted in the rule-making process. Often the most practical course is to file a new petition for rule making after experience has been gained with the new or amended rules and it can be demonstrated that the rule, as amended, is not working out as planned and therefore not in the best interests of the amateur community.

The FCC and You

Now, let's talk about your right as a citizen of the United States to participate in the FCC's rule-making process. The ARRL doesn't want to undercut your right to participate in the process, but please exercise common sense and think before you leap. For example, say you've been ragchewing on the same 75-meter frequency at the same time with the same stations for 364 uninterrupted days, and on day 365 you can't complete your contact because of interference from a contest. You should not then run to your computer and draft a petition to the FCC to prohibit contesting. That would be totally out of proportion to such a temporary situation.

A responsibility of Amateur Radio's tradition of self-regulation as discussed in this book means that at all times hams must minimize any tendency to complain or formally petition the FCC for narrow or restrictive rule interpretations, particularly for emotional reasons. Otherwise, unfavorable precedents may be set that will be harmful to the Amateur Radio Service. A call to the FCC may result in a hasty or uninformed legal opinion by a FCC staff member with no real-world operating experience. This opinion would be rendered in good faith, but you can expect that it would be formulated without consideration of all the necessary details. The FCC staff faces a formidable workload and is doing the best it can under the circumstances; the FCC wants hams to resolve operational issues by themselves, as provided for in Part 97.

In terms of a rule making already pending or in a highly important, significant situation where you as a radio amateur feel that it's crucial to submit a Petition for Rule Making on your own, it is best to contact the ARRL first. Although it is a membership organization, the ARRL acts as the clearinghouse for rule-making matters and painstakingly works toward gauging a consensus on an issue before formally contacting the FCC. The ARRL is a representative democracy; when the ARRL determines that a consensus exists, it initiates proposals for the good of the amateur service, such as the ARRL Petition for Rule Making that culminated in Novice Enhancement or the codeless Technician license. The ARRL monitors all FCC proposals, whether they directly or indirectly affect Amateur Radio, publicizes them extensively in *QST*, W1AW bulletins, *ARRLWeb* and elsewhere, and submits comments on behalf of the amateur community on every one, as appropriate. It also encourages individual amateurs to file comments on important matters.

Before you participate in an FCC proceeding, check with the Regulatory Information Branch at ARRL HQ or your ARRL Director to find out more about that particular issue and its status. The ARRL knows how to best approach the FCC—eight decades of crusading for amateurs' rights have given the ARRL unexcelled experience and a clear understanding of government regulatory processes. This is a major reason amateurs support the ARRL and have made it a respected voice in FCC deliberations.

SUMMARY: "IS IT LEGAL?"

Next time you're wondering whether an amateur-related situation is legal, first check Part 97 and also this publication. Hams sometimes comment that Part 97 is too brief—that it doesn't address all of the possible questions amateurs have. True, it does not and that's good because the nature of Amateur Radio as a service provides for experimentation. Part 97 is made up of many rule "pieces." It is the responsibility of amateurs to put together the various applicable rules in order to know how the rules apply to a particular situation.

In some cases, even after lots of research, a situation may still be one of the proverbial "gray areas." In cases like that, check the spirit of the rules. Does the specific activity conform to the Basis and Purpose of the Amateur Radio Service? Use *The FCC Rule Book* to help you decide. ARRL staff has included many interpretations that have evolved over the years to help you apply the rules to your situation. The plain-language discussions should also help. If you still can't decide, contact ARRL HQ's Regulatory Information Branch for help. Its staff is trained in helping amateurs understand and interpret the rules. Contact them at:

ARRL Headquarters
Regulatory Information Branch
225 Main St
Newington, CT 06111
E-mail: **reginfo@arrl.org**
Telephone: 860-594-0200

CONCLUSION

New editions of *The FCC Rule Book* are published to keep pace with changes in the rules. In addition, the ARRL maintains an electronic version of Part 97 on *ARRLWeb*. It is updated once a Part 97 rule change takes effect. Contact the ARRL Regulatory Information Branch for details. The rules have evolved over time and will continue to do so.

The rules are dynamic because Amateur Radio is dynamic—constantly changing to meet and create new methods and technologies to better serve individuals and society at large.

8 A New Era of Enforcement

In the waning years of the past decade, the government issued a new warning label: violating FCC rules causes health problems for Amateur Radio and will no longer be tolerated. In a breathtaking turn of events, the Federal Communications Commission ushered in a revitalized era of amateur rules enforcement. With a change in staff at the FCC's headquarters, and a reprioritization of enforcement activity, festering cases of malicious interference and other serious problems have been addressed with a sweeping (and in many cases, exotic) array of enforcement tools. The FCC has committed the resources for a campaign to bring about higher operating standards and an end to the drought of government monitoring and enforcement in the amateur bands. The recent spate of FCC enforcement action in high visibility, long-standing cases has been nothing short of phenomenal.

And firm indications at the beginning of 2001 are that the FCC's campaign will not only continue for the foreseeable future, but will involve actions even more vigorous and severe. The FCC's Special Counsel for Amateur Radio Enforcement recently explained that poor or lax FCC enforcement in the past led his office to be more forgiving of rulebreakers during the first full calendar year of renewed enforcement. Now, those who persist in operating outside of the stated basis and purpose of Amateur Radio "are beginning to try our patience," FCC said. "I can't say we're going to be as compassionate this year."

As far as the buffet of sanctions available to the FCC is concerned, fines are one of the fastest means of imposing a penalty for a rule violation as they do not require an administrative hearing before the obligation to pay is effective. In addition to the traditional enforcement sanctions of monetary forfeitures, and license suspension and revocation, the FCC has recently adopted innovative tools as well, including short-term license renewal and mandatory retesting. The FCC employed a short-term renewal as a sanction in a recent amateur case where a newly licensed ham was found to be transmitting music on a police frequency using a modified hand-held.

Retesting is another administrative prerogative that the FCC has been employing. The FCC has the authority to request that any amateur who obtained a license through the Volunteer Examiner program retest either at an FCC office or using another Volunteer Examiner Coordinator. In 1999, the FCC notified a Delaware ham that she had to retake her Extra class examination or lose her ticket. The FCC asked a Michigan ham to retake his General and Advanced class examinations. The FCC said that other retesting requests will be going out in cases where licensees either have not responded to a written Warning Notice or where something about the licensee's actions or responses might have raised questions about the individual's qualifications.

The FCC has not only taken numerous actions in malicious interference and other black-and-white serious cases, but the agency has also taken on those involving the *content* of communication, a historically tricky regulatory area. Some groups of amateurs unfortunately feel compelled to discuss topics on the air that are not tolerated by polite society. For example, some nets advance an agenda of racial or religious persecution under the license of the First Amendment right of free speech. They represent a seamy side of Amateur Radio that the rest of us do not care for. Formerly, the prevailing feeling was that while these groups should not have a place on the amateur bands, there was little that could be done about them in view of the fact that their activity was not directly in violation of any rules.

In the past, the best advice was to avoid certain frequencies and groups, and not acknowledge their activity, denying them the attention that they crave. "Turn your VFO," was the best we could do.

This all changed recently when the FCC asked a net control station to justify his net's use of Amateur Radio frequencies. Via a letter to the net, an FCC legal adviser pointed out that Congress has authorized the FCC to seek information to enable it to determine the qualifications of a licensee or applicant. "We are so far unable to determine how the transmissions of this group meet the standards of, or contribute to the purposes of, the allocation of frequencies for the Amateur Radio Service," the FCC legal advisor wrote. The same advisor alluded to the net in comments during an FCC forum, openly questioning the behavior of net participants. "I don't get the connection yet" between what the net participants do on the air and the basis and purpose of Amateur Radio, he said. In his letter to the net control station, the advisor suggested the net explore operation on the Internet or the low-power broadcast service license for pursuit of their discussions. The advisor reminded the net that Part 97 "prohibits communications on the Amateur frequencies that, on a regular basis, 'could reasonably be furnished alternatively through other services.'" He also pointed out that Part 97 prohibits broadcasting.

Although this new tactic has not been tested in judicial venues, it signals a new era of less tolerance on the part of the FCC to any on-the-air activity that could potentially undermine the legitimacy and credibility of the amateur service, and increase the risk of jeopardizing the standing of the service in the global spectrum user community.

FCC BACKS VOLUNTEER MONITORING EFFORT

The FCC said early in 1999 that hams who receive advisory notices from Official Observers (volunteers who monitor and advise amateurs of on-the-air discrepancies) should take them seriously or take the consequences. "Failure to take the notices seriously and to take corrective action where possible will not be tolerated by the Commission," the FCC said. "The volunteer work of these Official Observers is a critical element of the Commission's enforcement program," the agency said, adding that failure to act on an OO notice could lead to fines and other sanctions. The FCC's comments were contained in a station inspection follow-up letter to a subject. The FCC noted that the subject had "apparently ignored notices from Official Observers," and pointed out that the volunteer OOs work "in accordance with an agreement between the Commission and the ARRL and in accordance with our statutory authority."

In the FCC's letter, the subject was told that, although the FCC considers hams to be self-policing, "the success of that regulatory approach depends upon the adherence to notices of possible improper operation from other licensed amateurs who are recognized Official Observers." The FCC asked the subject to list all notices from OOs he had received since the start of his current license term, and any corrective actions taken in response. These statements of support from the FCC are the strongest yet seen from the agency since the inception of the ARRL/FCC volunteer monitoring program.

THE AMATEUR AUXILIARY

In 1984, when the FCC implemented congressionally-authorized volunteer monitoring, the agency recognized the value of the ARRL's Official Observer (OO) program and created the Amateur Auxiliary. The FCC and the ARRL signed an agreement outlining the objectives and nature of the program and the commitment by the ARRL to administer it.

The Amateur Auxiliary addresses both *maintenance monitoring* and *amateur-to-amateur interference*. Maintenance monitoring is conducted through the enhanced OO program, while local amateur-to-amateur interference is handled by *Local Interference Committees* sanctioned by the ARRL Section Manager for the geographical area concerned. The Amateur Auxiliary is administered by the ARRL's Section Managers and OO Coordinators with support from ARRL HQ.

OBJECTIVES

The general objectives of the Amateur Auxiliary are to:

1. Foster a wider knowledge of, and better compliance with, the laws, rules and regulations governing the Amateur Radio Service;

2. Extend the concepts of self-regulation and self-administration of the Service;

3. Enhance the opportunity for individual amateurs to contribute to the public welfare as outlined in the basis and purpose of the Amateur Radio Service; and

4. Enable the FCC to efficiently and effectively utilize its manpower and resources.

The role of the Amateur Auxiliary is to give technical and operational advice and other assistance to amateurs who are receptive. The task is not to find fault but to identify causes and effects, and to find ways to achieve solutions. *The mission is not direct enforcement of the rules.* Because the boundary between observation and enforcement is not always obvious, mature judgment is clearly required of the Auxiliary's members and leadership. The Auxiliary, to be viable and effective, must avoid the appearance of enforcement. It must also avoid the appearance of having a vested interest in any specific type of amateur operations or of being highly sympathetic to amateur groups that advocate specific activities or causes.

The program is restricted to amateurs who have successfully demonstrated thorough knowledge and skill. An applicant must pass a written examination and, ideally, is personally interviewed by local program officials. The applicant should have references from a local club.

EXPECTATIONS

The Amateur Auxiliary cannot solve all problems that affect Amateur Radio. Some are clear violations; others are not. The ability to differentiate is important. Certain cases of malicious interference and harassment are prevalent on repeaters in some parts of the country. These problems cannot be cured swiftly or easily. Much evidence gathering is involved, which is a time-consuming process.

Even more difficult for many amateurs to understand is how to deal with advocates of "free thinking," hams who don't comply with gentlemen's agreements, and so on. These anti-social personalities delight in creating chaos. Unfortunately, such types feed on the ignorance of others and thrive on baiting the listening audience into discussions of who is going to call the monitoring station first, who had the frequency first, and so on. Often the individualists are far better versed in the rules than those who confront them on the air. Too often this leads to frustration manifested by catcalls, whistles, carriers and general chaos on the frequency—exactly the desired effect. This continues to fan the flames, and can lead to the situation where the true violations are now being perpetrated by the hams in the audience. To expect the Auxiliary to solve such problems is not realistic.

TECHNICAL AND OPERATING DISCREPANCIES

The OO program is intended to note discrepancies and call them to the attention of those who very often are unaware of the discrepancy or who do not realize that what they are doing is potentially in violation. For example, it is quite common for an amateur to be unaware of a harmonic or spurious signal outside the amateur bands strong enough to be heard in distant places. Although new entry level licensees are especially prone to this discrepancy, higher-grade licensees, especially those running increased power, are far from immune to excessive harmonic radiation.

Often the operator of a station with key clicks and chirp on his CW signals is unaware they exist. Broad signals, with by-products of splatter and distortion, are frequent on the phone bands, while FM signals are prone to overdeviation. These are all technical difficulties that are watched for and are subject to notification. If you are the recipient of such a notification, please remember that the OO has sent it in a spirit of helpfulness, not fault finding. It is not an FCC notice, and no reply is necessary.

OFFICIAL OBSERVER ADVISORY NOTICE

The primary notification tool of the OO is the Official Observer Advisory Notice, Form FSD-213. This card is used to notify stations of operating discrepancies and usually includes a reference to the appropriate FCC rule.

To avoid the impression that the notice arises from personal interest, Official Observers shouldn't send notices to someone interfering with them or a net or repeater they are operating on. This is not generally good for

OFFICIAL OBSERVER ADVISORY NOTICE

Radio: _____, your call was heard calling/working _____ at _____ UTC.

Date: _____ 19 ___ Frequency _____ kHz. Mode _____. Your RST _____.

The following is noted in the interest of maintaining Amateur Radio's reputation for good operating/technical practices: 1☐ FREQUENCY INSTABILITY 2☐ CHIRP 3☐ SPURIOUS 4☐ HARMONIC 5☐ HUM 6☐ KEY CLICKS 7☐ BROAD SIGNAL 8☐ DISTORTED AUDIO 9☐ OVER DEVIATION 10☐ OUT OF BAND 11☐ IMPROPER ID 12☐ LANGUAGE 13☐ CAUSING INTERFERENCE 15☐ CARRIER 20☐ OTHER

Remarks: _____

Please refer to FCC Regulation _____. Please take a few minutes to determine what equipment factors or operating practices might have contributed to this apparent departure from the rule or the good amateur practice standard. The intent of this notice is to alert you to the above noted operating condition. NO REPLY IS NECESSARY. The undersigned ARRL Official Observer has fulfilled this helping role by simply alerting you, and is not *required* to reply to any correspondence. Thank you for your attention and any cooperative efforts to enhance the high standards of the Amateur Radio Service which we all share with pride.

FSD-213(885)   Signature _____ Call _____

relations with the amateurs the program is trying to serve. On the other hand, there is no harm with an OO asking another Observer to take an independent look if a problem persists.

OOs should project a friendly spirit on their advisory notices. The objective is to bring about compliance with the rules by friendly persuasion.

GOOD OPERATOR REPORT

Official Observers may also report on stations heard that have outstandingly *good* signals or operating procedures. While in today's world of high-quality commercial radio equipment the radio owner is less likely to be responsible for the technical excellence of his signal, operating skill is still a matter of individual cultivation. These reports are not sent out wholesale, but are reserved for those amateurs who set an example for the rest of the community by displaying the *best* that Amateur Radio has to offer.

DIFFICULT CASES

The Official Observer is usually involved with routine maintenance monitoring. Occasionally, OOs will run into an entrenched case of malicious interference or other substantive violation. Consultation with the section's OO Coordinator is in order and, at the discretion of the Coordinator, the ARRL Headquarters staff may be involved. The OO does not initiate direct contact with the FCC. The decision to make such contact is made at a higher level.

Petty cases of interference should be solved by amateurs and not referred to the FCC.

Good Operator Report ■

Radio: _____, your call was heard calling/working _____ at _____ UTC.

Date: _____199 ___Frequency _____kHz. Mode _____. Your RST _____.

We thought you would like to know . . .

That this Official Observer has noted your EXCELLENT radio signal quality/operating procedure as a fine example for all radio amateurs.

Remarks: _____

SAMPLE

_____

This observation by the undersigned ARRL Official Observer is a function of the Amateur Auxiliary to the FCC's Compliance and Information Bureau. This Observer thanks you for your excellent example of good amateur practice for others in the Amateur Radio Service. Keep up the good work.

FSD-15(3/95)   · Signature _____ Call _____

LOCAL INTERFERENCE COMMITTEES

Interference problems generated on VHF or UHF repeaters are primarily local problems requiring local resolution. The Amateur Auxiliary mechanism for dealing with any local amateur-to-amateur interference is the *Local Interference Committee* (LIC). (Note that repeater-to-repeater interference/coordination disputes are generally beyond the scope of the Amateur Auxiliary mission and even FCC enforcement; these problems are best handled through alternative dispute resolution. See the discussion in Chapter 2.)

THE MAKEUP OF THE COMMITTEE

LIC members are amateurs with repeater system expertise and VHF/UHF direction-finding capability. Members of the committee should preferably be selected by an area council of radio clubs, if such an organization exists, or by the clubs particularly interested in VHF, UHF and repeater operations if there is no council. The prime criterion for membership is that the members of the committee must be respected and accepted by the general amateur community in the area.

Complaints of deliberate interference are received and investigated by the committee. The investigation might include preparation of audio tape recordings of the interfering or objectionable transmissions, and results of direction-finding investigations. If such committees are to be effective, their investigations, as well as those of the FCC, must be timely and *confidential*. The committees must be willing and able to *resist demands* for action and confidential information from amateurs who are not familiar with what is being done.

EVIDENCE GATHERING

When all avenues of approach to a difficult, serious case have been exhausted within Auxiliary channels, the matter may be brought to the attention of the ARRL Headquarters staff. If it is deemed appropriate by the Headquarters staff to send the case to the FCC, ARRL HQ will work with the Auxiliary volunteers in properly constructing a basic package of evidence. OOs must conduct monitoring activities and assemble information in such a way that it is useful to the FCC. This involves limiting activities to those prescribed for the program and developing information in accordance with a few basic rules of evidence, discussed in the program training manual.

CONCLUSION

The bottom line is that the Auxiliary can lead a horse to water, and with a nod of thanks, the horse usually drinks as it is in his own best interest to do so. The Auxiliary can't *make* him drink, but if the situation is serious enough, the FCC can and will. While there's always room for improvement, the Amateur Auxiliary continues to work well in helping the amateur community keep its own shop in order. And with renewed government involvement with enforcement and the program itself, it is deserving of every amateur's support. For more information on the Amateur Auxiliary program, contact your ARRL Section Manager (listed on page 12 of recent issues of *QST*), or ARRL Headquarters.

9 Part 97— Amateur Radio Service

Here is the complete text of Part 97 of the FCC regulations, the rules that govern the Amateur Radio Service.

For those who have access to the Internet, the ARRL Regulatory Information Branch maintains the current version of Part 97 on *ARRLWeb* (**http://www.arrl.org/FandES/field/regulations/news/part97/**). It is updated whenever a rule change takes effect.

The sections of Part 97 that were revised since the 11th Edition of *The FCC Rule Book* was published in 1998 are printed in **boldface** type. 35 of 52 pages have been changed by the FCC!

Subpart A—General Provisions

Subpart B—Station Operation Standards

§97.1 Basis and purpose.

The rules and regulations in this Part are designed to provide an amateur radio service having a fundamental purpose as expressed in the following principles:

   (a) Recognition and enhancement of the value of the amateur service to the public as a voluntary noncommercial communication service, particularly with respect to providing emergency communications.

   (b) Continuation and extension of the amateur's proven ability to contribute to the advancement of the radio art.

   (c) Encouragement and improvement of the amateur service through rules which provide for advancing skills in both the communications and technical phases of the art.

   (d) Expansion of the existing reservoir within the amateur radio service of trained operators, technicians, and electronics experts.

   (e) Continuation and extension of the amateur's unique ability to enhance international goodwill.

§97.3 Definitions.

   (a) The definitions of terms used in Part 97 are:

   (1) Amateur operator. A person holding a written authorization to be the control operator of an amateur station.

   (2) Amateur radio services. The amateur service, the amateur-satellite service and the radio amateur civil emergency service.

   (3) Amateur-satellite service. A radiocommunication service using stations on Earth satellites for the same purpose as those of the amateur service.

   (4) Amateur service. A radiocommunication service for the purpose of self-training, intercommunication and technical investigations carried out by amateurs, that is, duly authorized persons interested in radio technique solely with a personal aim and without pecuniary interest.

   (5) Amateur station. A station in an amateur radio service consisting of the apparatus necessary for carrying on radiocommunications.

   (6) Automatic control. The use of devices and procedures for control of a station when it is transmitting so that compliance with the FCC Rules is achieved without the control operator being present at a control point.

   (7) Auxiliary station. An amateur station, other than in a message forwarding system, that is transmitting communications point-to-point within a system of cooperating amateur stations.

   (8) Bandwidth. The width of a frequency band outside of which the mean power of the transmitted signal is attenuated at least 26 dB below the mean power of the transmitted signal within the band.

   (9) Beacon. An amateur station transmitting communications for the purposes of observation of propagation and reception or other related experimental activities.

   (10) Broadcasting. Transmissions intended for reception by the

general public, either direct or relayed.

(11) Call sign system. The method used to select a call sign for amateur station over-the-air identification purposes. The call sign systems are:

(i) *Sequential call sign system.* The call sign is selected by the FCC from an alphabetized list corresponding to the geographic region of the licensee's mailing address and operator class. The call sign is shown on the license. The FCC will issue public announcements detailing the procedures of the sequential call sign system.

(ii) *Vanity call sign system.* The call sign is selected by the FCC from a list of call signs requested by the licensee. The call sign is shown on the license. The FCC will issue public announcements detailing the procedures of the vanity call sign system.

(iii) *Special event call sign system.* The call sign is selected by the station licensee from a list of call signs shown on a common data base coordinated, maintained and disseminated by the amateur station special event call sign data base coordinators. The call sign must have the single letter prefix K, N or W, followed by a single numeral through 9, followed by a single letter A through W or Y or Z (for example K1A). The special event call sign is substituted for the call sign shown on the station license grant while the station is transmitting. The FCC will issue public announcements detailing the procedures of the special event call sign system.

(12) Control operator. An amateur operator designated by the licensee of a station to be responsible for the transmissions from that station to assure compliance with the FCC Rules.

(13) Control point. The location at which the control operator function is performed.

(14) CSCE. Certificate of successful completion of an examination.

(15) CEPT radio-amateur license. A license issued by a country belonging to the European Conference of Postal and Telecommunications Administrations (CEPT) that has adopted Recommendation T/R 61-01 (Nice 1985, revised in Paris 1992 and by correspondence August 1992)

(16) Earth station. An amateur station located on, or within 50 km of the Earth's surface intended for communications with space stations or with other Earth stations by means of one or more other objects in space.

(17) EIC. Engineer in Charge of an FCC Field Facility.

(18) External RF Power Amplifier. A device capable of increasing power output when used in conjunction with, but not an integral part of, a transmitter.

(19) External RF power amplifier kit. A number of electronic parts, which, when assembled, is an external RF power amplifier, even if additional parts are required to complete assembly.

(20) FAA. Federal Aviation Administration.

(21) FCC. Federal Communications Commission.

(22) Frequency coordinator. An entity, recognized in a local or regional area by amateur operators whose stations are eligible to be auxiliary or repeater stations, that recommends transmit/ receive channels and associated operating and technical parameters for such stations in order to avoid or minimize potential interference.

(23) Harmful interference. Interference which endangers the functioning of a radionavigation service or of other safety services or seriously degrades, obstructs or repeatedly interrupts a radiocommunication service operating in accordance with the Radio Regulations.

(24) Indicator. Words, letters or numerals appended to and separated from the call sign during the station identification.

(25) Information bulletin. A message directed only to amateur operators consisting solely of subject matter of direct interest to the amateur service.

(26) International Morse code. A dot-dash code as defined in International Telegraph and Telephone Consultative Committee (CCITT) Recommendation F.1 (1984), Division B, I. Morse Code.

(27) IARP. International Amateur Radio Permit. A document issued pursuant to the terms of the Inter-American Convention on an International Amateur Radio Permit by a country signatory to that Convention, other than the United States. Montrouis, Haiti.

(28) ITU. International Telecommunication Union.

(29) Line A. Begins at Aberdeen, WA, running by great circle arc to the intersection of 48° N, 120° W, thence along parallel 48° N, to the intersection of 95° W, thence by great circle arc through the southernmost point of Duluth, MN, thence by great circle arc to 45° N, 85° W, thence southward along meridian 85° W, to its intersection with parallel 41° N, thence along parallel 41° N, to its intersection with meridian 82° W, thence by great circle arc through the southernmost point of Bangor, ME, thence by great circle arc through the southernmost point of Searsport, ME, at which point it terminates.

(30) Local control. The use of a control operator who directly manipulates the operating adjustments in the station to achieve compliance with the FCC Rules.

(31) Message forwarding system. A group of amateur stations participating in a voluntary, cooperative, interactive arrangement where communications are sent from the control operator of an originating station to the control operator of one or more destination stations by one or more forwarding stations.

(32) National Radio Quiet Zone. The area in Maryland, Virginia and West Virginia bounded by 39° 15' N on the north, 78° 30' W on the east, 37° 30' N on the south and 80° 30' W on the west.

(33) Physician. For the purposes of this Part, a person who is licensed to practice in a place where the amateur service is regulated by the FCC, as either a Doctor of Medicine (MD) or a Doctor of Osteopathy (DO).

(34) Question pool. All current examination questions for a designated written examination element.

(35) Question set. A series of examination questions on a given examination selected from the question pool.

(36) Radio Regulations. The latest ITU *Radio Regulations* to which the United States is a party.

(37) RACES (radio amateur civil emergency service*).* A radio service using amateur stations for civil defense communications during periods of local, regional or national civil emergencies.

(38) Remote control. The use of a control operator who indirectly manipulates the operating adjustments in the station through a control link to achieve compliance with the FCC Rules.

(39) Repeater. An amateur station that simultaneously retransmits the transmission of another amateur station on a different channel or channels.

(40) Space station. An amateur station located more than 50 km above the Earth's surface.

(41) Space telemetry. A one-way transmission from a space station of measurements made from the measuring instruments in a spacecraft, including those relating to the functioning of the spacecraft.

(42) Spurious emission. An emission, on frequencies outside the necessary bandwidth of a transmission, the level of which may be reduced without affecting the information being transmitted.

(43) Telecommand. A one-way transmission to initiate, modify, or terminate functions of a device at a distance.

(44) Telecommand station. An amateur station that transmits communications to initiate, modify, or terminate functions of a space station.

(45) Telemetry. A one-way transmission of measurements at a distance from the measuring instrument.

(46) Third-party communications. A message from the control operator (first party) of an amateur station to another amateur station control operator (second party) on behalf of another person (third party).

(47) ULS (Universal Licensing System). The consolidated database, application filing system and processing system for all Wireless Telecommunications Services.

(48) VE. Volunteer examiner.

(49) VEC. Volunteer-examiner coordinator.

(b) The definitions of technical symbols used in this Part are:

(1) EHF (extremely high frequency). The frequency range 30-300 GHz.

(2) HF (high frequency). The frequency range 3-30 MHz.

(3) Hz. Hertz.

(4) m. Meters.

(5) MF (medium frequency). The frequency range 300-3000 kHz.

(6) PEP (peak envelope power). The average power supplied to the antenna transmission line by a transmitter during one RF cycle at the crest of the modulation envelope taken under normal operating conditions.

(7) RF. Radio frequency.

(8) SHF (super-high frequency). The frequency range 3-30 GHz.

(9) UHF (ultra-high frequency). The frequency range 300-3000 MHz.

(10) VHF (very-high frequency). The frequency range 30-300 MHz.

(11) W. Watts.

(c) The following terms are used in this Part to indicate emission types. Refer to §2.201 of the FCC Rules, *Emission, modulation and transmission characteristics*, for information on emission type designators.

(1) CW. International Morse code telegraphy emissions having designators with A, C, H, J or R as the first symbol; 1 as the second symbol; A or B as the third symbol; and emissions J2A and J2B.

(2) Data. Telemetry, telecommand and computer communications emissions having designators with A, C, D, F, G, H, J or R as the first symbol; 1 as the second symbol; D as the third symbol; and emission J2D. Only a digital code of a type specifically authorized in this Part may be transmitted.

(3) Image. Facsimile and television emissions having designators with A, C, D, F, G, H, J or R as the first symbol; 1, 2 or 3 as the second symbol; C or F as the third symbol; and emissions having B as the first symbol; 7, 8 or 9 as the second symbol; W as the third symbol.

(4) MCW. Tone-modulated international Morse code telegraphy emissions having designators with A, C, D, F, G, H or R as the first symbol; 2 as the second symbol; A or B as the third symbol.

(5) Phone. Speech and other sound emissions having designators with A, C, D, F, G, H, J or R as the first symbol; 1, 2 or 3 as the second symbol; E as the third symbol. Also speech emissions having B as the first symbol; 7, 8 or 9 as the second symbol; E as the third symbol. MCW for the purpose of performing the station identification procedure, or for providing telegraphy practice interspersed with speech. Incidental tones for the purpose of selective calling or alerting or to control the level of a demodulated signal may also be considered phone.

(6) Pulse. Emissions having designators with K, L, M, P, Q, V or W as the first symbol; 0, 1, 2, 3, 7, 8, 9 or X as the second symbol; A, B, C, D, E, F, N, W or X as the third symbol.

(7) RTTY. Narrow-band direct-printing telegraphy emissions having designators with A, C, D, F, G, H, J or R as the first symbol; 1 as the second symbol; B as the third symbol; and emission J2B. Only a digital code of a type specifically authorized in this Part may be transmitted.

(8) *SS.* Spread-spectrum emissions using bandwidth-expansion modulation emissions having designators with A, C, D, F, G, H, J or R as the first symbol; X as the second symbol; X as the third symbol.

(9) *Test.* Emissions containing no information having the designators with N as the third symbol. Test does not include pulse emissions with no information or modulation unless pulse emissions are also authorized in the frequency band.

§97.5 Station license grant required.

(a) **The station apparatus must be under the physical control of a person named in an amateur station license grant on the ULS consolidated license database or a person authorized for alien reciprocal operation by §97.107 of this part, before the station may transmit on any amateur service frequency from any place that is:**

(1) Within 50 km of the Earth's surface and at a place where the amateur service is regulated by the FCC;

(2) Within 50 km of the Earth's surface and aboard any vessel or craft that is documented or registered in the United States; or

(3) More than 50 km above the Earth's surface aboard any craft that is documented or registered in the United States.

(b) **The types of station license grants are:**

(1) **An operator/primary station license grant. One, but only one, operator/primary station license grant may be held by any one person. The primary station license is granted together with the amateur operator license. Except for a representative of a foreign government, any person who qualifies by examination is eligible to apply for an operator/primary station license grant.**

(2) **A club station license grant. A club station license grant may be held only by the person who is the license trustee designated by an officer of the club. The trustee must be a person who holds an Amateur Extra, Advanced, General, Technician Plus, or Technician operator license grant. The club must be composed of at least four persons and must have a name, a document of organization, management, and a primary purpose devoted to amateur service activities consistent with this part.**

(3) **A military recreation station license grant. A military recreation station license grant may be held only by the person who is the license custodian designated by the official in charge of the United States military recreational premises where the station is situated. The person must not be a representative of a foreign government. The person need not hold an amateur operator license grant.**

(4) **A RACES station license grant. A RACES station license grant may be held only by the person who is the license custodian designated by the official responsible for the**

governmental agency served by that civil defense organization. The custodian must be the civil defense official responsible for coordination of all civil defense activities in the area concerned. The custodian must not be a representative of a foreign government. The custodian need not hold an amateur operator license grant.

(c) The person named in the station license grant or who is authorized for alien reciprocal operation by §97.107 of this Part may use, in accordance with the applicable rules of this Part, the transmitting apparatus under the physical control of the person at places where the amateur service is regulated by the FCC.

(d) A CEPT radio-amateur license is issued to the person by the country of which the person is a citizen. The person must not:

(1) Be a resident alien or citizen of the United States, regardless of any other citizenship also held;

(2) Hold an FCC-issued amateur operator license nor reciprocal permit for alien amateur licensee;

(3) Be a prior amateur service licensee whose FCC-issued license was revoked, suspended for less than the balance of the license term and the suspension is still in effect, suspended for the balance of the license term and relicensing has not taken place, or surrendered for cancellation following notice of revocation, suspension or monetary forfeiture proceedings; or

(4) Be the subject of a cease and desist order that relates to amateur service operation and which is still in effect.

(e) An IARP is issued to the person by the country of which the person is a citizen. The person must not:

(1) Be a resident alien or citizen of the United States, regardless of any other citizenship also held;

(2) Hold an FCC-issued amateur operator license nor reciprocal permit for alien amateur licensee;

(3) Be a prior amateur service licensee whose FCC-issued license was revoked, suspended for less than the balance of the license term and the suspension is still in effect, suspended for the balance of the license term and relicensing has not taken place, or surrendered for cancellation following notice of revocation, suspension or monetary forfeiture proceedings; or

(4) Be the subject of a cease and desist order that relates to amateur service operation and which is still in effect.

§97.7 Control operation required.

When transmitting, each amateur station must have a control operator. The control operator must be a person:

(a) For whom an amateur operator/primary station license grant appears on the ULS consolidated licensee database, or

(b) Who is authorized for alien reciprocal operation by §97.107 of this part

§97.9 Operator license.

(a) The classes of amateur operator license grants are: Novice, Technician, Technician Plus (until such licenses expire, a Technician Class license granted before February 14, 1991, is considered a Technician Plus Class license), General, Advanced, and Amateur Extra. The person named in the operator license grant is authorized to be the control operator of an amateur station with the privileges authorized to the operator class specified on the license grant.

(b) The person named in an operator license grant of Novice, Technician, Technician Plus, General or Advanced Class, who has properly submitted to the administering VEs a FCC Form 605 document requesting examination for an operator license grant of a higher class, and who holds a CSCE indicating that the person has completed the necessary examinations within the previous 365 days, is authorized to exercise the rights and privileges of the higher operator class until final disposition of the application or until 365 days following the passing of the examination, whichever comes first.

§97.11 Stations aboard ships or aircraft.

(a) The installation and operation of an amateur station on a ship or aircraft must be approved by the master of the ship or pilot in command of the aircraft.

(b) The station must be separate from and independent of all other radio apparatus installed on the ship or aircraft, except a common antenna may be shared with a voluntary ship radio installation. The station's transmissions must not cause interference to any other apparatus installed on the ship or aircraft.

(c) The station must not constitute a hazard to the safety of life or property. For a station aboard an aircraft, the apparatus shall not be operated while the aircraft is operating under Instrument Flight Rules, as defined by the FAA, unless the station has been found to comply with all applicable FAA Rules.

§97.13 Restrictions on station location.

(a) Before placing an amateur station on land of environmental importance or that is significant in American history, architecture or culture, the licensee may be required to take certain actions prescribed by §§ 1.1305-1.1319 of this chapter.

(b) A station within 1600 m (1 mile) of an FCC monitoring facility must protect that facility from harmful interference. Failure to do so could result in imposition of operating restrictions upon the amateur station by a District Director pursuant to / 97.121 of this Part. Geographical coordinates of the facilities that require protection are listed in / 0.121(c) of this chapter.

(c) Before causing or allowing an amateur station to transmit from any place where the operation of the station could cause human exposure to RF electromagnetic field levels in excess of those allowed under § 1.1310 of this chapter, the licensee is required to take certain actions.

(1) The licensee must perform the routine RF environmental evaluation prescribed by § 1.1307(b) of this chapter, if the power of the licensee's station exceeds the limits given in the following table:

Wavelength Band		Evaluation Required if Power* (watts) Exceeds:
MF	160m	500
HF	80m	500
	75m	500
	40m	500
	30m	425
	20m	225
	17m	125
	15m	100
	12m	75
	10m	50
VHF (all bands)		50
UHF	70cm	70
	33cm	150
	23cm	200
	13cm	250
SHF (all bands)		250
EHF (all bands)		250

Repeater stations (all bands)	non-building-mounted antennas: height above ground level to lowest point of antenna < 10 m and power > 500 W ERP building-mounted antennas: power > 500 W ERP

* Power = PEP input to antenna except, for repeater stations only, power exclusion is based on ERP (effective radiated power).

(2) If the routine environmental evaluation indicates that the RF electromagnetic fields could exceed the limits contained in § 1.1310 of this chapter in accessible areas, the licensee must take action to prevent human exposure to such RF electromagnetic fields. Further information on evaluating compliance with these limits can be found in the FCC's OET Bulletin Number 65, "Evaluating Compliance with FCC Guidelines for Human Exposure to Radiofrequency Electromagnetic Fields."

§97.15 Station antenna structures.

(a) **Owners of certain antenna structures more than 60.96 meters (200 feet) above ground level at the site or located near or at a public use airport must notify the Federal Aviation Administration and register with the Commission as required by Part 17 of this chapter.**

(b) Except as otherwise provided herein, a station antenna structure may be erected at heights and dimensions sufficient to accommodate amateur service communications. [State and local regulation of a station antenna structure must not preclude amateur service communications. Rather, it must reasonably accommodate such communications and must constitute the minimum practicable regulation to accomplish the state or local authority's legitimate purpose. See PRB-1, 101 FCC 2d 952 (1985) for details.]

§97.17 Application for new license grant.

(a) Any qualified person is eligible to apply for a new operator/primary station, club station or military recreation station license grant. No new license grant will be issued for a Novice, Technician Plus, or Advanced Class operator/primary station or RACES station.

(b) Each application for a new amateur service license grant must be filed with the FCC as follows:

(1) Each candidate for an amateur radio operator license which requires the applicant to pass one or more examination elements must present the administering VEs with all information required by the rules prior to the examination. The VEs may collect all necessary information in any manner of their choosing, including creating their own forms.

(2) For a new club or military recreation station license grant, each applicant must present all information required by the rules to an amateur radio organization having tax-exempt status under section 501(c)(3) of the Internal Revenue Code of 1986 that provides voluntary, uncompensated and unreimbursed services in providing club and military recreation station call signs ("Club Station Call Sign Administrator") who must submit the information to the FCC in an electronic batch file. The Club Station Call Sign Administrator may collect the information required by these rules in any manner of their choosing, including creating their own forms. The Club Station Call Sign Administrator must retain the applicants information for at least 15 months and make it available to the FCC upon request. The FCC will issue public announcements listing the qualified organizations that have completed a pilot autogrant batch filing project and are authorized to serve as a Club Station Call Sign Administrator.

(c) No person shall obtain or attempt to obtain, or assist another person to obtain or attempt to obtain, an amateur service license grant by fraudulent means.

(d) One unique call sign will be shown on the license grant of each new primary, club and military recreation station. The call sign will be selected by the sequential call sign system.

§97.19 Application for a vanity call sign.

(a) The person named in an operator/primary station license grant or in a club station license grant is eligible to make application for modification of the license grant, or the renewal thereof, to show a call sign selected by the vanity call sign system. RACES and military recreation stations are not eligible for a vanity call sign.

(b) Each application for a modification of an operator/primary or club station license grant, or the renewal thereof, to show a call sign selected by the vanity call sign system must be filed in accordance with §1.913 of this chapter.

(c) Unassigned call signs are available to the vanity call sign system with the following exceptions:

  (1) A call sign shown on an expired license grant is not available to the vanity call sign system for 2 years following the expiration of the license.

  (2) A call sign shown on a surrendered, revoked, set aside, canceled, or voided license grant is not available to the vanity call sign system for 2 years following the date such action is taken.

  (3) Except for an applicant who is the spouse, child, grandchild, stepchild, parent, grandparent, stepparent, brother, sister, stepbrother, stepsister, aunt, uncle, niece, nephew, or in-law, and except for an applicant who is a club station license trustee acting with the written consent of at least one relative, as listed above, of a person now deceased, the call sign shown on the license of person now deceased is not available to the vanity call sign system for 2 years following the person's death, or for 2 years following the expiration of the license grant, whichever is sooner.

(d) The vanity call sign requested by an applicant must be selected from the group of call signs corresponding to the same or lower class of operator license held by the applicant as designated in the sequential call sign system.

  (1) **The applicant must request that the call sign shown on the license grant be vacated and provide a list of up to 25 call signs in order of preference.**

  (2) The first assignable call sign from the applicant's list will be shown on the license grant. When none of those call signs are assignable, the call sign vacated by the applicant will be shown on the license grant.

  (3) Vanity call signs will be selected from those call signs assignable at the time the application is processed by the FCC.

  (4) A call sign designated under the sequential call sign system for Alaska, Hawaii, Caribbean Insular Areas, and Pacific Insular areas will be assigned only to a primary or club station whose licensee's mailing address is in the corresponding state, commonwealth, or island. This limitation does not apply to an applicant for the call sign as the spouse, child, grandchild, stepchild, parent, grandparent, stepparent, brother, sister,

stepbrother, stepsister, aunt, uncle, niece, nephew, or in-law, of the former holder now deceased.

§97.21 Application for a modified or renewed license.

(a) A person holding a valid amateur station license grant:

(1) Must apply to the FCC for a modification of the license grant as necessary to show the correct mailing address, licensee name, club name, license trustee name or license custodian name in accordance with §1.913 of this chapter. For a club, military recreation or RACES station license grant, it must be presented in document form to a Club Station Call Sign Administrator who must submit the information thereon to the FCC in an electronic batch file. The Club Station Call Sign Administrator must retain the collected information for at least 15 months and make it available to the FCC upon request.

(2) May apply to the FCC for a modification of the operator/ primary station license grant to show a higher operator class. Applicants must present the administering VEs with all information required by the rules prior to the examination. The VEs may collect all necessary information in any manner of their choosing, including creating their own forms.

(3) May apply to the FCC for renewal of the license grant for another term in accordance with §1.913 of this chapter. Application for renewal of a Technician Plus Class operator/primary station license will be processed as an application for renewal of a Technician Class operator/primary station license.

(i) For a station license grant showing a call sign obtained through the vanity call sign system, the application must be filed in accordance with §97.19 of this Part in order to have the vanity call sign reassigned to the station.

(ii) For a primary station license grant showing a call sign obtained through the sequential call sign system, and for a primary station license grant showing a call sign obtained through the vanity call sign system but whose grantee does not want to have the vanity call sign reassigned to the station, the application must be filed with the FCC in accordance with §1.913 of this chapter. When the application has been received by the FCC on or before the license expiration date, the license operating authority is continued until the final disposition of the application.

(iii) For a club station or military recreation station license grant showing a call sign obtained through the sequential call sign system, and for a club or military recreation station license grant showing a call sign obtained through the vanity call sign system but whose grantee does not want to have the vanity call sign reassigned to the station, the application must be presented in document form to a Club Station Call Sign Administrator who must submit the information thereon to the FCC in an electronic batch file. The Club Station Call Sign Administrator must retain the collected information for at least 15 months and make it available to the FCC upon request. RACES station license grants will not be renewed.

(b) A person whose amateur station license grant has expired may apply to the FCC for renewal of the license grant for another term during a 2 year filing grace period. The application must be received at the address specified above prior to the end of the grace period. Unless and until the license grant is renewed, no privileges in this Part are conferred.

(c) A call sign obtained under the sequential or vanity call sign system will be reassigned to the station upon renewal or modification of a station license.

§97.23 Mailing address.

Each license grant must show the grantee's correct name and mailing address. The mailing address must be in an area where the amateur service is regulated by the FCC and where the grantee can receive mail delivery by the United States Postal Service. Revocation of the station license or suspension of the operator license may result when correspondence from the FCC is returned as undeliverable because the grantee failed to provide the correct mailing address.

§97.25 License term.

An amateur service license is normally granted for a 10-year term.

§97.27 FCC modification of station license grant.

(a) The FCC may modify a station license grant, either for a limited time or for the duration of the term thereof, if it determines:

(1) That such action will promote the public interest, convenience, and necessity; or

(2) That such action will promote fuller compliance with the provisions of the Communications Act of 1934, as amended, or of any treaty ratified by the United States.

(b) When the FCC makes such a determination, it will issue an order of modification. The order will not become final until the licensee is notified in writing of the proposed action and the grounds and reasons therefor. The licensee will be given reasonable opportunity of no less than 30 days to protest the modification; except that, where safety of life or property is involved, a shorter period of notice may be provided. Any protest by a licensee of an FCC order of modification will be handled in accordance with the provisions of 47 U.S.C. §316.

§97.29 Replacement license grant document.

Each grantee whose amateur station license grant document is lost, mutilated or destroyed may apply to the FCC for a replacement in accordance with §1.913 of this chapter.

SUBPART B— STATION OPERATION STANDARDS

§97.101 General standards.

(a) In all respects not specifically covered by FCC Rules each amateur station must be operated in accordance with good engineering and good amateur practice.

(b) Each station licensee and each control operator must cooperate in selecting transmitting channels and in making the most effective use of the amateur service frequencies. No frequency will be assigned for the exclusive use of any station.

(c) At all times and on all frequencies, each control operator must give priority to stations providing emergency communications, except to stations transmitting communications for training drills and tests in RACES.

(d) No amateur operator shall willfully or maliciously interfere with or cause interference to any radio communication or signal.

§97.103 Station licensee responsibilities.

(a) The station licensee is responsible for the proper operation of the station in accordance with the FCC Rules. When the control operator is a different amateur operator than the station licensee, both persons are equally responsible for proper operation of the station.

(b) The station licensee must designate the station control operator. The FCC will presume that the station licensee is also the control operator, unless documentation to the contrary is in the station records.

(c) The station licensee must make the station and the station records available for inspection upon request by an FCC representative. When deemed necessary by an EIC to assure compliance with FCC Rules, the station licensee must maintain a record of station operations containing such items of information as the EIC may require in accord with §0.314(x) of the FCC Rules.

§97.105 Control operator duties.

(a) The control operator must ensure the immediate proper operation of the station, regardless of the type of control.

(b) A station may only be operated in the manner and to the extent permitted by the privileges authorized for the class of operator license held by the control operator.

§97.107 Reciprocal operating authority.

A non-citizen of the United States ("alien") holding an amateur service authorization granted by the alien's government is authorized to be the control operator of an amateur station located at places where the amateur service is regulated by the FCC, provided there is in effect a multilateral or bilateral reciprocal operating arrangement, to which the United States and the alien's government are parties, for amateur service operation on a reciprocal basis. The FCC will issue public announcements listing the countries with which the United States has such an arrangement. No citizen of the United States or person holding an FCC amateur operator/primary station license grant is eligible for the reciprocal operating authority granted by this section. The privileges granted to a control operator under this authorization are:

(a) For an amateur service license granted by the Government of Canada:

(1) The terms of the *Convention Between the United States and Canada (TIAS No. 2508) Relating to the Operation by Citizens of Either Country of Certain Radio Equipment or Stations in the Other Country*;

(2) The operating terms and conditions of the amateur service license issued by the Government of Canada; and

(3) The applicable rules of this part, but not to exceed the control operator privileges of an FCC-granted Amateur Extra Class operator license.

(b) For an amateur service license granted by any country, other than Canada, with which the United States has a multilateral or bilateral agreement:

(1) The terms of the agreement between the alien's government and the United States;

(2) The operating terms and conditions of the amateur service license granted by the alien's government;

(3) The applicable rules of this part, but not to exceed the control operator privileges of an FCC-granted Amateur Extra Class operator license; and

(c) At any time the FCC may, in its discretion, modify, suspend or cancel the reciprocal operating authority granted to any person by this section.

§97.109 Station control.

(a) Each amateur station must have at least one control point.

(b) When a station is being locally controlled, the control operator must be at the control point. Any station may be locally controlled.

(c) When a station is being remotely controlled, the control operator must be at the control point. Any station may be remotely controlled.

(d) When a station is being automatically controlled, the control operator need not be at the control point. Only stations specifically designated elsewhere in this Part may be automatically controlled. Automatic control must cease upon notification by an EIC that the station is transmitting improperly or causing harmful interference to other stations. Automatic control must not be resumed without prior approval of the EIC.

(e) No station may be automatically controlled while transmitting third party communications, except a station transmitting a RTTY or data emission. All messages that are retransmitted must originate at a station that is being locally or remotely controlled.

§97.111 Authorized transmissions.

(a) An amateur station may transmit the following types of two-way communications:

(1) Transmissions necessary to exchange messages with other stations in the amateur service, except those in any country whose administration has given notice that it objects to such communications. The FCC will issue public notices of current arrangements for international communications;

(2) Transmissions necessary to exchange messages with a station in another FCC-regulated service while providing emergency communications;

(3) Transmissions necessary to exchange messages with a United States government station, necessary to providing communications in RACES; and

(4) Transmissions necessary to exchange messages with a station in a service not regulated by the FCC, but authorized by the FCC to communicate with amateur stations. An amateur station may exchange messages with a participating United States military station during an Armed Forces Day Communications Test.

(b) In addition to one-way transmissions specifically authorized elsewhere in this Part, an amateur station may transmit the following types of one-way communications:

(1) Brief transmissions necessary to make adjustments to the station;

(2) Brief transmissions necessary to establishing two-way communications with other stations;

(3) Telecommand;

(4) Transmissions necessary to providing emergency communications;

(5) Transmissions necessary to assisting persons learning, or improving proficiency in, the international Morse code;

(6) Transmissions necessary to disseminate information bulletins;

(7) Transmissions of telemetry.

§97.113 Prohibited transmissions.

(a) No amateur station shall transmit:

(1) Communications specifically prohibited elsewhere in this Part;

(2) Communications for hire or for material compensation, direct or indirect, paid or promised, except as otherwise provided in these rules;

(3) Communications in which the station licensee or control operator has a pecuniary interest, including communications on behalf of an employer. Amateur operators may, however, notify other amateur operators of the availability for sale or trade of apparatus normally used in an amateur station, provided that such activity is not conducted on a regular basis;

(4) Music using a phone emission except as specifically provided elsewhere in this Section; communications intended to facilitate a criminal act; messages in codes or ciphers intended to obscure the meaning thereof, except as otherwise provided herein; obscene or indecent words or language; or false or deceptive messages, signals or identification;

(5) Communications, on a regular basis, which could reasonably be furnished alternatively through other radio services.

(b) An amateur station shall not engage in any form of broadcasting, nor may an amateur station transmit one-way communications except as specifically provided in these rules; nor shall an amateur station engage in any activity related to program production or news gathering for broadcasting purposes, except that communications directly related to the immediate safety of human life or the protection of property may be provided by amateur stations to broadcasters for dissemination to the public where no other means of communication is reasonably available before or at the time of the event.

(c) A control operator may accept compensation as an incident of a teaching position during periods of time when an amateur station is used by that teacher as a part of classroom instruction at an educational institution.

(d) The control operator of a club station may accept compensation for the periods of time when the station is transmitting telegraphy practice or information bulletins, provided that the station transmits such telegraphy practice and bulletins for at least 40 hours per week; schedules operations on at least six amateur service MF and HF bands using reasonable measures to maximize coverage; where the schedule of normal operating times and frequencies is published at least 30 days in advance of the actual transmissions; and where the control operator does not accept any direct or indirect compensation for any other service as a control operator.

(e) No station shall retransmit programs or signals emanating from any type of radio station other than an amateur station, except propagation and weather forecast information intended for use by the general public and originated from United States Government stations and communications, including incidental music, originating on United States Government frequencies between a space shuttle and its associated Earth stations. Prior approval for shuttle retransmissions must be obtained from the National Aeronautics and Space Administration. Such retransmissions must be for the exclusive use of amateur operators. Propagation, weather forecasts, and shuttle retransmissions may not be conducted on a regular basis, but only occasionally, as an incident of normal amateur radio communications.

(f) No amateur station, except an auxiliary, repeater or space station, may automatically retransmit the radio signals of other amateur stations.

§97.115 Third party communications.

(a) An amateur station may transmit messages for a third party to:

    (1) Any station within the jurisdiction of the United States.

    (2) Any station within the jurisdiction of any foreign government whose administration has made arrangements with the United States to allow amateur stations to be used for transmitting international communications on behalf of third parties. No station shall transmit messages for a third party to any station within the jurisdiction of any foreign government whose administration has not made such an arrangement. This prohibition does not apply to a message for any third party who is eligible to be a control operator of the station.

(b) The third party may participate in stating the message where:

    (1) The control operator is present at the control point and is continuously monitoring and supervising the third party's participation; and

    (2) The third party is not a prior amateur service licensee whose license was revoked; suspended for less than the balance of the license term and the suspension is still in effect; suspended for the balance of the license term and relicensing has not taken place; or surrendered for cancellation following notice of revocation, suspension or monetary forfeiture proceedings. The third party may not be the subject of a cease and desist order which relates to amateur service operation and which is still in effect.

(c) At the end of an exchange of international third party communications, the station must also transmit in the station identification procedure the call sign of the station with which a third party message was exchanged.

§97.117 International communications.

Transmissions to a different country, where permitted, shall be made in plain language and shall be limited to messages of a technical nature relating to tests, and, to remarks of a personal character for which, by reason of their unimportance, recourse to the public telecommunications service is not justified.

§97.119 Station identification.

(a) Each amateur station, except a space station or telecommand station, must transmit its assigned call sign on its transmitting channel at the end of each communication, and at least every ten minutes during a communication, for the purpose of clearly making the source of the transmissions from the station known to those receiving the transmissions. No station may transmit unidentified communications or signals, or transmit as the station call sign, any call sign not authorized to the station.

(b) The call sign must be transmitted with an emission authorized for the transmitting channel in one of the following ways:

(1) By a CW emission. When keyed by an automatic device used only for identification, the speed must not exceed 20 words per minute;

(2) By a phone emission in the English language. Use of a standard phonetic alphabet as an aid for correct station identification is encouraged;

(3) By a RTTY emission using a specified digital code when all or part of the communications are transmitted by a RTTY or data emission;

(4) By an image emission conforming to the applicable transmission standards, either color or monochrome, of §73.682(a) of the FCC Rules when all or part of the communications are transmitted in the same image emission.

(c) One or more indicators may be included with the call sign. Each indicator must be separated from the call sign by the slant mark (/) or by any suitable word that denotes the slant mark. If an indicator is self-assigned, it must be included before, after, or both before and after, the call sign. No self-assigned indicator may conflict with any other indicator specified by the FCC Rules or with any prefix assigned to another country.

(d) When transmitting in conjunction with an event of special significance, a station may substitute for its assigned call sign a special event call sign as shown for that station for that period of time on the common data base coordinated, maintained and disseminated by the special event call sign data base coordinators. Additionally, the station must transmit its assigned call sign at least once per hour during such transmissions.

(e) When the operator license class held by the control operator exceeds that of the station licensee, an indicator consisting of the call sign assigned to the control operator's station must be included after the call sign.

(f) When the control operator who is exercising the rights and privileges authorized by §97.9(b) of this Part, an indicator must be included after the call sign as follows:

(1) For a control operator who has requested a license modification from Novice to Technician Class: KT;

(2) For a control operator who has requested a license modification from Novice, Technician **or Technician Plus** Class to General Class: AG;

(3) For a control operator who has requested a license modification from Novice, Technician, **Technician Plus**, General, or Advanced Class operator to Amateur Extra Class: AE.

(g) When the station is transmitting under the authority of §97.107 of this part, an indicator consisting of the appropriate letter-numeral designating the station location must be included before the call sign that was issued to the station by the country granting the license. For an amateur service license granted by the Government of Canada, however, the indicator must be

included after the call sign. At least once during each intercommunication, the identification announcement must include the geographical location as nearly as possible by city and state, commonwealth or possession.

§97.121 Restricted operation.

(a) If the operation of an amateur station causes general interference to the reception of transmissions from stations operating in the domestic broadcast service when receivers of good engineering design, including adequate selectivity characteristics, are used to receive such transmissions, and this fact is made known to the amateur station licensee, the amateur station shall not be operated during the hours from 8 p.m. to 10:30 p.m., local time, and on Sunday for the additional period from 10:30 a.m. until 1 p.m., local time, upon the frequency or frequencies used when the interference is created.

(b) In general, such steps as may be necessary to minimize interference to stations operating in other services may be required after investigation by the FCC.

SUBPART C—SPECIAL OPERATIONS

§97.201 Auxiliary station.

(a) **Any amateur station licensed to a holder of a Technician, Technician Plus, General, Advanced or Amateur Extra Class operator license may be an auxiliary station. A holder of a Technician, Technician Plus, General, Advanced or Amateur Extra Class operator license may be the control operator of an auxiliary station, subject to the privileges of the class of operator license held.**

(b) An auxiliary station may transmit only on the 1.25 m and shorter wavelength bands, except the 219-220 MHz, 222.000-222.150 MHz, 431-433 MHz and 435-438 MHz segments.

(c) Where an auxiliary station causes harmful interference to another auxiliary station, the licensees are equally and fully responsible for resolving the interference unless one station's operation is recommended by a frequency coordinator and the other station's is not. In that case, the licensee of the non-coordinated auxiliary station has primary responsibility to resolve the interference.

(d) An auxiliary station may be automatically controlled.

(e) An auxiliary station may transmit one-way communications.

§97.203 Beacon station.

(a) **Any amateur station licensed to a holder of a Technician, Technician Plus, General, Advanced or Amateur Extra Class operator license may be a beacon. A holder of a Technician, Technician Plus, General, Advanced or Amateur Extra Class operator license may be the control operator of a beacon, subject to the privileges of the class of operator license held.**

(b) A beacon must not concurrently transmit on more than 1 channel in the same amateur service frequency band, from the same station location.

(c) The transmitter power of a beacon must not exceed 100 W.

(d) A beacon may be automatically controlled while it is transmitting on the 28.20-28.30 MHz, 50.06-50.08 MHz, 144.275-144.300 MHz, 222.05-222.06 MHz, or 432.300-432.400 MHz segments, or on the 33 cm and shorter wavelength bands.

(e) Before establishing an automatically controlled beacon in the National Radio Quiet Zone or before changing the transmitting frequency, transmitter power, antenna height or directivity, the station licensee must give written notification thereof to the Interference Office, National Radio Astronomy Observatory, P.O. Box 2, Green Bank, WV 24944.

   (1) The notification must include the geographical coordinates of the antenna, antenna ground elevation above mean sea level (AMSL), antenna center of radiation above ground level (AGL), antenna directivity, proposed frequency, type of emission, and transmitter power.

   (2) If an objection to the proposed operation is received by the FCC from the National Radio Astronomy Observatory at Green Bank, Pocahontas County, WV, for itself or on behalf of the Naval Research Laboratory at Sugar Grove, Pendleton County, WV, within 20 days from the date of notification, the FCC will consider all aspects of the problem and take whatever action is deemed appropriate.

(f) A beacon must cease transmissions upon notification by an EIC that the station is operating improperly or causing undue interference to other operations. The beacon may not resume transmitting without prior approval of the EIC.

(g) A beacon may transmit one-way communications.

(h) The provisions of this paragraph do not apply to beacons that transmit on the 1.2 cm or shorter wavelength bands. Before establishing an automatically controlled beacon within 16 km (10 miles) of the Arecibo Observatory or before changing the transmitting frequency, transmitter power, antenna height or directivity of an existing beacon, the station licensee must give written notification thereof to the Interference Office, Arecibo Observatory, Post Office Box 995, Arecibo, Puerto Rico 00613, in writing or electronically, of the technical parameters of the proposal. Licensees who choose to transmit information electronically should e-mail to prcz@naic.edu

   (1) The notification shall state the geographical coordinates of the antenna (NAD-83 datum), antenna height above mean sea level (AMSL), antenna center of radiation above ground level (AGL), antenna directivity and gain, proposed frequency and FCC Rule Part, type of emission, effective radiated power, and whether the proposed use is itinerant. Licensees may wish to consult interference guidelines provided by Cornell University.

   (2) If an objection to the proposed operation is received by the FCC

from the Arecibo Observatory, Arecibo, Puerto Rico, within 20 days from the date of notification, the FCC will consider all aspects of the problem and take whatever action is deemed appropriate.

§97.205 Repeater stations.

(a) Any amateur station licensed to a holder of a Technician, General, Advanced or Amateur Extra Class operator license may be a repeater. A holder of a Technician, General, Advanced or Amateur Extra Class operator license may be the control operator of a repeater, subject to the privileges of the class of operator license held.

(b) A repeater may receive and retransmit only on the 10 m and shorter wavelength frequency bands except the 28.0-29.5 MHz, 50.0-51.0 MHz, 144.0-144.5 MHz, 145.5-146.0 MHz, 222.00-222.15 MHz, 431.0-433.0 MHz and 435.0-438.0 MHz segments.

(c) Where the transmissions of a repeater cause harmful interference to another repeater, the two station licensees are equally and fully responsible for resolving the interference unless the operation of one station is recommended by a frequency coordinator and the operation of the other station is not. In that case, the licensee of the noncoordinated repeater has primary responsibility to resolve the interference.

(d) A repeater may be automatically controlled.

(e) Ancillary functions of a repeater that are available to users on the input channel are not considered remotely controlled functions of the station. Limiting the use of a repeater to only certain user stations is permissible.

(f) [Reserved]

(g) The control operator of a repeater that retransmits inadvertently communications that violate the rules in this Part is not accountable for the violative communications.

§97.207 Space station.

(a) Any amateur station may be a space station. A holder of any class operator license may be the control operator of a space station, subject to the privileges of the class of operator license held by the control operator.

(b) A space station must be capable of effecting a cessation of transmissions by telecommand whenever such cessation is ordered by the FCC.

(c) The following frequency bands and segments are authorized to space stations:
   (1) The 17 m, 15 m, 12 m and 10 m bands, 6 mm, 4 mm, 2 mm and 1 mm bands; and
   (2) The 7.0-7.1 MHz, 14.00-14.25 MHz, 144-146 MHz, 435-438 MHz, 1260-1270 MHz and 2400-2450 MHz, 3.40-3.41 GHz, 5.83-5.85 GHz, 10.45-10.50 GHz and 24.00-24.05 GHz segments.

(d) A space station may automatically retransmit the radio signals of Earth stations and other space stations.

(e) A space station may transmit one-way communications.

(f) Space telemetry transmissions may consist of specially coded messages intended to facilitate communications or related to the function of the spacecraft.

(g) The license grantee of each space station must make two written pre-space station notifications to the International Bureau, FCC, Washington, DC 20554. Each notification must be in accord with the provisions of Articles 11 and 13 of the Radio Regulations.

(1) The first notification is required no less than 27 months prior to initiating space station transmissions and must specify the information required by Appendix 4, and Resolution No. 642 of the Radio Regulations.

(2) The second notification is required no less than 5 months prior to initiating space station transmissions and must specify the information required by Appendix 3 and Resolution No. 642 of the Radio Regulations.

(h) The license grantee of each space station must make a written in-space station notification to the International Bureau no later than 7 days following initiation of space station transmissions. The notification must update the information contained in the pre-space notification.

(i) The license grantee of each space station must make a written post-space station notification to the International Bureau no later than 3 months after termination of the space station transmissions. When the termination is ordered by the FCC, notification is required no later than 24 hours after termination.

§97.209 Earth station.

(a) Any amateur station may be an Earth station. A holder of any class operator license may be the control operator of an Earth station, subject to the privileges of the class of operator license held by the control operator.

(b) The following frequency bands and segments are authorized to Earth stations:

(1) The 17 m, 15 m, 12 m and 10 m bands, 6 mm, 4 mm, 2 mm and 1 mm bands; and

(2) The 7.0-7.1 MHz, 14.00-14.25 MHz, 144-146 MHz, 435-438 MHz, 1260-1270 MHz and 2400-2450 MHz, 3.40-3.41 GHz, 5.65-5.67 GHz, 10.45-10.50 GHz and 24.00-24.05 GHz segments.

§97.211 Space telecommand station.

(a) Any amateur station designated by the licensee of a space station is eligible to transmit as a telecommand station for that space station, subject to the privileges of the class of operator license held by the control operator.

(b) A telecommand station may transmit special codes intended to obscure the meaning of telecommand messages to the station in space operation.

(c) The following frequency bands and segments are authorized to telecommand stations:
  (1) The 17 m, 15 m, 12 m and 10 m bands, 6 mm, 4 mm, 2 mm and 1 mm bands; and
  (2) The 7.0-7.1 MHz, 14.00-14.25 MHz, 144-146 MHz, 435-438 MHz, 1260-1270 MHz and 2400-2450 MHz, 3.40-3.41 GHz, 5.65-5.67 GHz, 10.45-10.50 GHz and 24.00-24.05 GHz segments.
(d) A telecommand station may transmit one-way communications.

§97.213 Telecommand of an amateur station.

An amateur station on or within 50 km of the Earth's surface may be under telecommand where:
  (a) There is a radio or wireline control link between the control point and the station sufficient for the control operator to perform his/her duties. If radio, the control link must use an auxiliary station. A control link using a fiber optic cable or another telecommunication service is considered wireline.
  (b) Provisions are incorporated to limit transmission by the station to a period of no more than 3 minutes in the event of malfunction in the control link.
  (c) The station is protected against making, willfully or negligently, unauthorized transmissions.
  (d) A photocopy of the station license and a label with the name, address, and telephone number of the station licensee and at least one designated control operator is posted in a conspicuous place at the station location.

§97.215 Telecommand of model craft.

An amateur station transmitting signals to control a model craft may be operated as follows:
  (a) The station identification procedure is not required for transmissions directed only to the model craft, provided that a label indicating the station call sign and the station licensee's name and address is affixed to the station transmitter.
  (b) The control signals are not considered codes or ciphers intended to obscure the meaning of the communication.
  (c) The transmitter power must not exceed 1 W.

§97.217 Telemetry.

Telemetry transmitted by an amateur station on or within 50 km of the Earth's surface is not considered to be codes or ciphers intended to obscure the meaning of communications.

§97.219 Message forwarding system.

(a) Any amateur station may participate in a message forwarding system, subject to the privileges of the class of operator license held.
(b) For stations participating in a message forwarding system, the control

operator of the station originating a message is primarily accountable for any violation of the rules in this Part contained in the message.

(c) Except as noted in paragraph (d) of this section, for stations participating in a message forwarding system, the control operators of forwarding stations that retransmit inadvertently communications that violate the rules in this Part are not accountable for the violative communications. They are, however, responsible for discontinuing such communications once they become aware of their presence.

(d) For stations participating in a message forwarding system, the control operator of the first forwarding station must:

(1) Authenticate the identity of the station from which it accepts communication on behalf of the system; or

(2) Accept accountability for any violation of the rules in this Part contained in messages it retransmits to the system.

§97.221 Automatically controlled digital station.

(a) This rule section does not apply to an auxiliary station, a beacon station, a repeater station, an earth station, a space station, or a space telecommand station.

(b) A station may be automatically controlled while transmitting a RTTY or data emission on the 6 m or shorter wavelength bands, and on the 28.120-28.189 MHz, 24.925-24.930 MHz, 21.090-21.100 MHz, 18.105-18.110 MHz, 14.0950-14.0995 MHz, 14.1005-14.112 MHz, 10.140-10.150 MHz, 7.100-7.105 MHz, or 3.620-3.635 MHz segments.

(c) A station may be automatically controlled while transmitting a RTTY or data emission on any other frequency authorized for such emission types provided that:

(1) The station is responding to interrogation by a station under local or remote control; and

(2) No transmission from the automatically controlled station occupies a bandwidth of more than 500 Hz.

SUBPART D—TECHNICAL STANDARDS

§97.301 Authorized frequency bands.

The following transmitting frequency bands are available to an amateur station located within 50 km of the Earth's surface, within the specified ITU Region, and outside any area where the amateur service is regulated by any authority other than the FCC.

(a) **For a station having a control operator who has been granted a Technician, Technician Plus, General, Advanced, or Amateur Extra Class operator license or who holds a CEPT radio-amateur license or IARP of any class:**

Wavelength band	ITU Region 1	ITU Region 2	ITU Region 3	Sharing requirements See §97.303, Paragraph:
VHF	*MHz*	*MHz*	*MHz*	
6 m	—	50-54	50-54	(a)
2 m	144-146	144-148	144-148	(a)
1.25 m	—	219-220	—	(a), (e)
-do-	—	222-225	—	(a)
UHF	*MHz*	*MHz*	*MHz*	
70 cm	430-440	420-450	420-450	(a), (b), (f)
33 cm	—	902-928	—	(a), (b), (g)
23 cm	1240-1300	1240-1300	1240-1300	(h), (i)
13 cm	2300-2310	2300-2310	2300-2310	(a), (b), (j)
-do-	2390-2450	2390-2450	2390-2450	(a), (b), (j)
SHF	*GHz*	*GHz*	*GHz*	
9 cm	—	3.3-3.5	3.3-3.5	(a), (b), (k), (l)
5 cm	5.650-5.850	5.650-5.925	5.650-5.850	(a), (b), (m)
3 cm	10.00-10.50	10.00-10.50	10.00-10.50	(b), (c), (i), (n)
1.2 cm	24.00-24.25	24.00-24.25	24.00-24.25	(a), (b), (h), (o)
EHF	*GHz*	*GHz*	*GHz*	
6 mm	47.0-47.2	47.0-47.2	47.0-47.2	
4 mm	75.5-81.0	75.5-81.0	75.5-81.0	(b), (c), (h)
2.5 mm	119.98-120.02	119.98-120.02	119.98-120.02	(k), (p)
2 mm	142-149	142-149	142-149	(b), (c), (h), (k)
1 mm	241-250	241-250	241-250	(b), (c), (h), (q)
—	above 300	above 300	above 300	(k)

(b) For a station having a control operator who has been granted an Amateur Extra Class operator license or who holds a CEPT radio-amateur license Class 1 license or Class 1 IARP:

Wavelength band	ITU Region 1	ITU Region 2	ITU Region 3	Sharing requirements See §97.303, Paragraph:
MF	*kHz*	*kHz*	*kHz*	
160 m	1810-1850	1800-2000	1800-2000	(a), (b), (c)
HF	*MHz*	*MHz*	*MHz*	
80 m	3.50-3.75	3.50-3.75	3.50-3.75	(a)
75 m	3.75-3.80	3.75-4.00	3.75-3.90	(a)
40 m	7.0-7.1	7.0-7.3	7.0-7.1	(a)
30 m	10.10-10.15	10.10-10.15	10.10-10.15	(d)
20 m	14.00-14.35	14.00-14.35	14.00-14.35	

Wavelength band	ITU Region 1	ITU Region 2	ITU Region 3
17 m	18.068-18.168	18.068-18.168	18.068-18.168
15 m	21.00-21.45	21.00-21.45	21.00-21.45
12 m	24.89-24.99	24.89-24.99	24.89-24.99
10 m	28.0-29.7	28.0-29.7	28.0-29.7

(c) For a station having a control operator who has been granted an operator license of Advanced Class:

Wavelength band	ITU Region 1	ITU Region 2	ITU Region 3	Sharing requirements See §97.303, Paragraph:
MF	*kHz*	*kHz*	*kHz*	
160 m	1810-1850	1800-2000	1800-2000	(a), (b), (c)
HF	*MHz*	*MHz*	*MHz*	
80 m	3.525-3.750	3.525-3.750	3.525-3.750	(a)
75 m	3.775-3.800	3.775-4.000	3.775-3.900	(a)
40 m	7.025-7.100	7.025-7.300	7.025-7.100	(a)
30 m	10.10-10.15	10.10-10.15	10.10-10.15	(d)
20 m	14.025-14.150	14.025-14.150	14.025-14.150	
-do-	14.175-14.350	14.175-14.350	14.175-14.350	
17 m	18.068-18.168	18.068-18.168	18.068-18.168	
15 m	21.025-21.200	21.025-21.200	21.025-21.200	
-do-	21.225-21.450	21.225-21.450	21.225-21.450	
12 m	24.89-24.99	24.89-24.99	24.89-24.99	
10 m	28.0-29.7	28.0-29.7	28.0-29.7	

(d) For a station having a control operator who has been granted an operator license of General Class:

Wavelength band	ITU Region 1	ITU Region 2	ITU Region 3	Sharing requirements See §97.303, Paragraph:
MF	*kHz*	*kHz*	*kHz*	
160 m	1810-1850	1800-2000	1800-2000	(a), (b), (c)
HF	*MHz*	*MHz*	*MHz*	
80 m	3.525-3.750	3.525-3.750	3.525-3.750	(a)
75 m	—	3.85-4.00	3.85-3.90	(a)
40 m	7.025-7.100	7.025-7.150	7.025-7.100	(a)
-do-	—	7.225-7.300	—	(a)
30 m	10.10-10.15	10.10-10.15	10.10-10.15	(d)
20 m	14.025-14.150	14.025-14.150	14.025-14.150	
-do-	14.225-14.350	14.225-14.350	14.225-14.350	
17 m	18.068-18.168	18.068-18.168	18.068-18.168	
15 m	21.025-21.200	21.025-21.200	21.025-21.200	
-do-	21.30-21.45	21.30-21.45	21.30-21.45	
12 m	24.89-24.99	24.89-24.99	24.89-24.99	
10 m	28.0-29.7	28.0-29.7	28.0-29.7	

(e) For a station having a control operator who has been granted an operator license of Novice Class or Technician Class and who has received credit for proficiency in telegraphy in accordance with the international requirements.

Wavelength band	ITU Region 1	ITU Region 2	ITU Region 3	Sharing requirements See §97.303, Paragraph:
HF	*MHz*	*MHz*	*MHz*	
80 m	3.675-3.725	3.675-3.725	3.675-3.725	(a)
40 m	7.050-7.075	7.10-7.15	7.050-7.075	(a)
15 m	21.10-21.20	21.10-21.20	21.10-21.20	
10 m	28.10-28.50	28.10-28.50	28.10-28.50	
VHF	*MHz*	*MHz*	*MHz*	
1.25 m	—	222-225	—	(a)
UHF	*MHz*	*MHz*	*MHz*	
23 cm	1270-1295	1270-1295	1270-1295	(h) (i)

§97.303 Frequency sharing requirements.

The following is a summary of the frequency sharing requirements that apply to amateur station transmissions on the frequency bands specified in §97.301 of this Part. (For each ITU Region, each frequency band allocated to the amateur service is designated as either a secondary service or a primary service. A station in a secondary service must not cause harmful interference to, and must accept interference from, stations in a primary service. See §§2.105 and 2.106 of the FCC Rules, *United States Table of Frequency Allocations* for complete requirements.)

(a) Where, in adjacent ITU Regions or Subregions, a band of frequencies is allocated to different services of the same category, the basic principle is the equality of right to operate. The stations of each service in one region must operate so as not to cause harmful interference to services in the other Regions or Subregions. (See ITU *Radio Regulations*, No. 346 (Geneva, 1979).)

(b) No amateur station transmitting in the 1900-2000 kHz segment, the 70 cm band, the 33 cm band, the 13 cm band, the 9 cm band, the 5 cm band, the 3 cm band, the 24.05-24.25 GHz segment, the 76-81 GHz segment, the 144-149 GHz segment and the 241-248 GHz segment shall cause harmful interference to, nor is protected from interference due to the operation of, the Government radiolocation service.

(c) No amateur station transmitting in the 1900-2000 kHz segment, the 3 cm band, the 76-81 GHz segment, the 144-149 GHz segment and the 241-248 GHz segment shall cause harmful interference to, nor is protected from interference due to the operation of, stations in the non-Government radiolocation service.

(d) No amateur station transmitting in the 30 meter band shall cause harmful interference to stations authorized by other nations in the fixed service. The licensee of the amateur station must make all necessary adjustments, including termination of transmissions, if harmful interference is caused.

(e) In the 1.25 m band:

  (1) Use of the 219-220 MHz segment is limited to amateur stations participating, as forwarding stations, in point-to-point fixed digital message forwarding systems, including intercity packet backbone networks. It is not available for other purposes.

  (2) No amateur station transmitting in the 219-220 MHz segment shall cause harmful interference to, nor is protected from interference due to operation of Automated Maritime Telecommunications Systems (AMTS), television broadcasting on channels 11 and 13, Interactive Video and Data Service systems, Land Mobile Services systems, or any other service having a primary allocation in or adjacent to the band.

  (3) No amateur station may transmit in the 219-220 MHz segment unless the licensee has given written notification of the station's specific geographic location for such transmissions in order to be incorporated into a data base that has been made available to the public. The notification must be given at least 30 days prior to making such transmissions. The notification must be given to:

  The American Radio Relay League
  225 Main Street
  Newington, CT 06111-1494

  (4) No amateur station may transmit in the 219-220 MHz segment from a location that is within 640 km of an AMTS Coast Station that uses frequencies in the 217-218/219-220 MHz AMTS bands unless the amateur station licensee has given written notification of the station's specific geographic location for such transmissions to the AMTS licensee. The notification must be given at least 30 days prior to making such transmissions. The location of AMTS Coast Stations using the 217-218/219-220 MHz channels may be obtained from either:

  The American Radio Relay League
  225 Main Street
  Newington, CT 06111-1494

or

  Interactive Systems, Inc.
  Suite 1103
  1601 North Kent Street
  Arlington, VA 22209
  Fax: (703) 812-8275
  Phone: (703) 812-8270

  (5) No amateur station may transmit in the 219-220 MHz segment from a location that is within 80 km of an AMTS Coast Station that uses frequencies in the 217-218/219-220 MHz AMTS bands

unless that amateur station licensee holds written approval from that AMTS licensee. The location of AMTS Coast Stations using the 217-218/219-220 MHz channels may be obtained as noted in paragraph (e)(4) of this section.

(f) In the 70 cm band:

(1) No amateur station shall transmit from north of Line A in the 420-430 MHz segment.

(2) The 420-430 MHz segment is allocated to the amateur service in the United States on a secondary basis, and is allocated in the fixed and mobile (except aeronautical mobile) services in the International Table of allocations on a primary basis. No amateur station transmitting in this band shall cause harmful interference to, nor is protected from interference due to the operation of, stations authorized by other nations in the fixed and mobile (except aeronautical mobile) services.

(3) The 430-440 MHz segment is allocated to the amateur service on a secondary basis in ITU Regions 2 and 3. No amateur station transmitting in this band in ITU Regions 2 and 3 shall cause harmful interference to, nor is protected from interference due to the operation of, stations authorized by other nations in the radiolocation service. In ITU Region 1, the 430-440 MHz segment is allocated to the amateur service on a co-primary basis with the radiolocation service. As between these two services in this band in ITU Region 1, the basic principle that applies is the equality of right to operate. Amateur stations authorized by the United States and radiolocation stations authorized by other nations in ITU Region 1 shall operate so as not to cause harmful interference to each other.

(4) No amateur station transmitting in the 449.75-450.25 MHz segment shall cause interference to, nor is protected from interference due to the operation of stations in, the space operation service and the space research service or Government or non-Government stations for space telecommand.

(g) In the 33 cm band:

(1) No amateur station shall transmit from within the States of Colorado and Wyoming, bounded on the south by latitude 39° N, on the north by latitude 42° N, on the east by longitude 105° W, and on the west by longitude 108° W.[1] This band is allocated on a secondary basis to the amateur service subject to not causing harmful interference to, and not receiving protection from any interference due to the operation of, industrial, scientific and medical devices, automatic vehicle monitoring systems or Government stations authorized in this band.

(2) No amateur station shall transmit from those portions of the States of Texas and New Mexico bounded on the south by latitude 31° 41' N, on the north by latitude 34° 30' N, on the east by longitude 104°

[[1]In a waiver effective July 2, 1990, the FCC permitted amateurs in the restricted areas to transmit in the following segments: 902.0-902.4, 902.6-904.3, 904.7-925.3, 925.7-927.3, and 927.7-928.0 MHz.]

11' W, and on the west by longitude 107° 30' W.

(h) No amateur station transmitting in the 23 cm band, the 3 cm band, the 24.05-24.25 GHz segment, the 76-81 GHz segment, the 144-149 GHz segment and the 241-248 GHz segment shall cause harmful interference to, nor is protected from interference due to the operation of, stations authorized by other nations in the radiolocation service.

(i) In the 1240-1260 MHz segment, no amateur station shall cause harmful interference to, nor is protected from interference due to the operation of, stations in the radionavigation-satellite service, the aeronautical radio-navigation service, or the radiolocation service.

(j) In the 13 cm band:

(1) The amateur service is allocated on a secondary basis in all ITU Regions. In ITU Region 1, no amateur station shall cause harmful interference to, and is not protected from interference due to the operation of, stations authorized by other nations in the fixed and mobile services. In ITU Regions 2 and 3, no amateur station shall cause harmful interference to, and shall not be protected from interference due to the operation of, stations authorized by other nations in the fixed, mobile and radiolocation services.

(2) In the United States:

(i) The 2300-2305 MHz segment is allocated to the amateur service on a secondary basis. (Currently the 2300-2305 MHz segment is not allocated to any service on a primary basis.);

(ii) The 2305-2310 MHz segment is allocated to the amateur service on a secondary basis to the fixed, mobile, and radiolocation services;

(iii) The 2390-2400 MHz segment is allocated to the amateur service on a primary basis;

(iv) The 2400-2402 MHz segment is allocated to the amateur service on a secondary basis. (Currently the 2400-2402 MHz segment is not allocated to any service on a primary basis.) The 2402-2417 MHz segment is allocated to the amateur service on a primary basis. The 2417-2450 MHz segment is allocated to the amateur service on a co-secondary basis with the Government radiolocation service. Amateur stations operating within the 2400-2450 MHz segment must accept harmful interference that may be caused by the proper operation of industrial, scientific, and medical devices operating within the band.

(k) No amateur station transmitting in the 3.332-3.339 GHz and 3.3458-3525 GHz segments, the 2.5 mm band, the 144.68-144.98 GHz, 145.45-145.75 GHz and 146.82-147.12 GHz segments and the 343-348 GHz segment shall cause harmful interference to stations in the radio astronomy service. No amateur station transmitting in the 300-302 GHz, 324-326 GHz, 345-347 GHz, 363-365 GHz and 379-381 GHz segments shall cause harmful interference to stations in the space research service (passive) or Earth exploration-satellite service (passive).

(l) In the 9 cm band:

(1) In ITU Regions 2 and 3, the band is allocated to the amateur service on a secondary basis.

(2) In the United States, the band is allocated to the amateur service on a co-secondary basis with the non-Government radiolocation service.

(3) In the 3.3-3.4 GHz segment, no amateur station shall cause harmful interference to, nor is protected from interference due to the operation of, stations authorized by other nations in the fixed and fixed-satellite service.

(4) In the 3.4-3.5 GHz segment, no amateur station shall cause harmful interference to, nor is protected from interference due to the operation of, stations authorized by other nations in the fixed and fixed-satellite service.

(m) In the 5 cm band:

(1) In the 5.650-5.725 GHz segment, the amateur service is allocated in all ITU Regions on a co-secondary basis with the space research (deep space) service.

(2) In the 5.725-5.850 GHz segment, the amateur service is allocated in all ITU Regions on a secondary basis. No amateur station shall cause harmful interference to, nor is protected from interference due to the operation of, stations authorized by other nations in the fixed-satellite service in ITU Region 1.

(3) No amateur station transmitting in the 5.725-5.875 GHz segment is protected from interference due to the operation of industrial, scientific and medical devices operating on 5.8 GHz.

(4) In the 5.650-5.850 GHz segment, no amateur station shall cause harmful interference to, nor is protected from interference due to the operation of, stations authorized by other nations in the radiolocation service.

(5) In the 5.850-5.925 GHz segment, the amateur service is allocated in ITU Region 2 on a co-secondary basis with the radiolocation service. In the United States, the segment is allocated to the amateur service on a secondary basis to the non-Government fixed-satellite service. No amateur station shall cause harmful interference to, nor is protected from interference due to the operation of, stations authorized by other nations in the fixed, fixed-satellite and mobile services. No amateur station shall cause harmful interference to, nor is protected from interference due to the operation of, stations in the non-Government fixed-satellite service.

(n) In the 3 cm band:

(1) In the United States, the 3 cm band is allocated to the amateur service on a co-secondary basis with the non-government radiolocation service.

(2) In the 10.00-10.45 GHz segment in ITU Regions 1 and 3, no amateur station shall cause interference to, nor is protected from interference due to the operation of, stations authorized by other nations in the fixed and mobile services.

(o) No amateur station transmitting in the 1.2 cm band is protected from interference due to the operation of industrial, scientific and medical devices on 24.125 GHz. In the United States, the 24.05-24.25 GHz segment is allocated to the amateur service on a co-secondary basis with the non-government radiolocation and Government and non-government Earth exploration-satellite (active) services.

(p) The 2.5 mm band is allocated to the amateur service on a secondary basis. No amateur station transmitting in this band shall cause harmful interference to, nor is protected from interference due to the operation of, stations in the fixed, inter-satellite and mobile services.

(q) No amateur station transmitting in the 244-246 GHz segment of the 1 mm band is protected from interference due to the operation of industrial, scientific and medical devices on 245 GHz.

§97.305 Authorized emission types.

(a) An amateur station may transmit a CW emission on any frequency authorized to the control operator.

(b) A station may transmit a test emission on any frequency authorized to the control operator for brief periods for experimental purposes, except that no pulse modulation emission may be transmitted on any frequency where pulse is not specifically authorized and no SS modulation emission may be transmitted on any frequency where SS is not specifically authorized.

(c) A station may transmit the following emission types on the frequencies indicated, as authorized to the control operator, subject to the standards specified in §97.307(f) of this part.

Wavelength band	Frequencies	Emission Types Authorized	Standards See §97.307(f), paragraph:
MF:			
160 m	Entire band	RTTY, data	(3)
-do-	-do-	Phone, image	(1), (2)
HF:			
80 m	Entire band	RTTY, data	(3), (9)
75 m	Entire band	Phone, image	(1), (2)
40 m	7.000-7.100 MHz	RTTY, data	(3), (9)
-do-	7.075-7.100 MHz	Phone, image	(1), (2), (9), (11)
-do-	7.100-7.150 MHz	RTTY, data	(3), (9)
-do-	7.150-7.300 MHz	Phone, image	(1), (2)
30 m	Entire band	RTTY, data	(3)
20 m	14.00-14.15 MHz	RTTY, data	(3)
-do-	14.15-14.35 MHz	Phone, image	(1), (2)
17 m	18.068-18.110 MHz	RTTY, data	(3)
-do-	18.110-18.168 MHz	Phone, image	(1), (2)
15 m	21.0-21.2 MHz	RTTY, data	(3), (9)
-do-	21.20-21.45 MHz	Phone, image	(1), (2)

Wavelength band	Frequencies	Emission Types Authorized	Standards See §97.307(f), paragraph:
12 m	24.89-24.93 MHz	RTTY, data	(3)
-do-	24.93-24.99 MHz	Phone, image	(1), (2)
10 m	28.0-28.3 MHz	RTTY, data	(4)
-do-	28.3-28.5 MHz	Phone, image	(1), (2), (10)
-do-	28.5-29.0 MHz	Phone, image	(1), (2)
-do-	29.0-29.7MHz	Phone, image	(2)
VHF:			
6 m	50.1-51.0 MHz	RTTY, data	(5)
-do-	-do-	MCW, phone, image	(2)
-do-	51.0-54.0 MHz	RTTY, data, test	(5), (8)
-do-	-do-	MCW, phone, image	(2)
2 m	144.1-148.0 MHz	RTTY, data, test	(5), (8)
-do-	-do-	MCW, phone, image	(2)
1.25 m	219-220 MHz	Data	(13)
-do-	222-225 MHz	MCW, phone, image RTTY, data, test	(2), (6), (8)
UHF:			
70 cm	Entire band	MCW, phone, image, RTTY, data, SS, test	(6), (8)
33 cm	Entire band	MCW, phone, image, RTTY, data, SS, test, pulse	(7), (8), (12)
23 cm	Entire band	MCW, phone, image, RTTY, data, SS, test	(7), (8), (12)
13 cm	Entire band	MCW, phone, image, RTTY, data, SS, test, pulse	(7), (8), (12)
SHF:			
9 cm	Entire band	MCW, phone, image, RTTY, data, SS, test, pulse	(7), (8), (12)
5 cm	Entire band	MCW, phone, image, RTTY, data, SS, test, pulse	(7), (8), (12)
3 cm	Entire band	MCW, phone, image, RTTY, data, SS, test	(7), (8), (12)
1.2 cm	Entire band	MCW, phone, image, RTTY, data, SS, test, pulse	(7), (8), (12)

Wavelength band	Frequencies	Emission Types Authorized	Standards See §97.307(f), paragraph:
EHF:			
6 mm	Entire band	MCW, phone, image, RTTY, data, SS, test, pulse	(7), (8), (12)
4 mm	Entire band	MCW, phone, image, RTTY, data, SS, test, pulse	(7), (8), (12)
2.5 mm	Entire band	MCW, phone, image, RTTY, data, SS, test, pulse	(7), (8), (12)
2 mm	Entire band	MCW, phone, image, RTTY, data, SS, test, pulse	(7), (8), (12)
1 mm	Entire band	MCW, phone, image, RTTY, data, SS, test, pulse	(7), (8), (12)
—	Above 300 GHz	MCW, phone, image, RTTY, data, SS, test, pulse	(7), (8), (12)

§97.307 Emission standards.

(a) No amateur station transmission shall occupy more bandwidth than necessary for the information rate and emission type being transmitted, in accordance with good amateur practice.

(b) Emissions resulting from modulation must be confined to the band or segment available to the control operator. Emissions outside the necessary bandwidth must not cause splatter or keyclick interference to operations on adjacent frequencies.

(c) All spurious emissions from a station transmitter must be reduced to the greatest extent practicable. If any spurious emission, including chassis or power line radiation, causes harmful interference to the reception of another radio station, the licensee of the interfering amateur station is required to take steps to eliminate the interference, in accordance with good engineering practice.

(d) The mean power of any spurious emission from a station transmitter or external RF power amplifier transmitting on a frequency below 30 MHz must not exceed 50 mW and must be at least 40 dB below the mean power of the fundamental emission. For a transmitter of mean power less than 5 W, the attenuation must be at least 30 dB. A transmitter built before April 15, 1977, or first marketed before January 1, 1978, is exempt from this requirement.

(e) The mean power of any spurious emission from a station transmitter or external RF power amplifier transmitting on a frequency between 30-225 MHz must be at least 60 dB below the mean power of the fundamental. For a transmitter having a mean power of 25 W or less, the mean power of any spurious emission supplied to the antenna transmission line must not exceed 25 μW and must be at least 40 dB below the mean power of the fundamental emission, but need not be reduced below the power of 10 μW. A transmitter built before April 15, 1977, or first marketed before January 1, 1978, is exempt from this requirement.

(f) The following standards and limitations apply to transmissions on the frequencies specified in §97.305(c) of this Part.

(1) No angle-modulated emission may have a modulation index greater than 1 at the highest modulation frequency.

(2) No non-phone emission shall exceed the bandwidth of a communications quality phone emission of the same modulation type. The total bandwidth of an independent sideband emission (having B as the first symbol), or a multiplexed image and phone emission, shall not exceed that of a communications quality A3E emission.

(3) Only a RTTY or data emission using a specified digital code listed in §97.309(a) of this Part may be transmitted. The symbol rate must not exceed 300 bauds, or for frequency-shift keying, the frequency shift between mark and space must not exceed 1 kHz.

(4) Only a RTTY or data emission using a specified digital code listed in §97.309(a) of this Part may be transmitted. The symbol rate must not exceed 1200 bauds. For frequency-shift keying, the frequency shift between mark and space must not exceed 1 kHz.

(5) A RTTY, data or multiplexed emission using a specified digital code listed in §97.309(a) of this Part may be transmitted. The symbol rate must not exceed 19.6 kilobauds. A RTTY, data or multiplexed emission using an unspecified digital code under the limitations listed in §97.309(b) of this Part also may be transmitted. The authorized bandwidth is 20 kHz.

(6) A RTTY, data or multiplexed emission using a specified digital code listed in §97.309(a) of this Part may be transmitted. The symbol rate must not exceed 56 kilobauds. A RTTY, data or multiplexed emission using an unspecified digital code under the limitations listed in §97.309(b) of this Part also may be transmitted. The authorized bandwidth is 100 kHz.

(7) A RTTY, data or multiplexed emission using a specified digital code listed in §97.309(a) of this Part or an unspecified digital code under the limitations listed in §97.309(b) of this Part may be transmitted.

(8) A RTTY or data emission having designators with A, B, C, D, E, F, G, H, J or R as the first symbol; 1, 2, 7 or 9 as the second symbol; and D or W as the third symbol is also authorized.

(9) A station having a control operator holding a Novice or Technician Class operator license may only transmit a CW emission using the international Morse code.

(10) A station having a control operator holding a Novice Class operator license or a Technician Class operator license and who has received credit for proficiency in telegraphy in

accordance with the international requirements may only transmit a CW emission using the international Morse code or phone emissions J3E and R3E.

(11) Phone and image emissions may be transmitted only by stations located in ITU Regions 1 and 3, and by stations located within ITU Region 2 that are west of 130° West longitude or south of 20° North latitude.

(12) Emission F8E may be transmitted.

(13) A data emission using an unspecified digital code under the limitations listed in § 97.309(b) of this Part also may be transmitted. The authorized bandwidth is 100 kHz.

§97.309 RTTY and data emission codes.

(a) Where authorized by §97.305(c) and 97.307(f) of this Part, an amateur station may transmit a RTTY or data emission using the following specified digital codes:

(1) The 5-unit, start-stop, International Telegraph Alphabet No. 2, code defined in International Telegraph and Telephone Consultative Committee Recommendation F.1, Division C (commonly known as Baudot).

(2) The 7-unit code, specified in International Radio Consultative Committee Recommendation CCIR 476-2 (1978), 476-3 (1982), 476-4 (1986) or 625 (1986) (commonly known as AMTOR).

(3) The 7-unit code defined in American National Standards Institute X3.4-1977 or International Alphabet No. 5 defined in International Telegraph and Telephone Consultative Committee Recommendation T.50 or in International Organization for Standardization, International Standard ISO 646 (1983), and extensions as provided for in CCITT Recommendation T.61 (Malaga-Torremolinos, 1984) (commonly known as ASCII).

(4) An amateur station transmitting a RTTY or data emission using a digital code specified in this paragraph may use any technique whose technical characteristics have been documented publicly, such as CLOVER, G-TOR, or PacTOR, for the purpose of facilitating communications.

(b) Where authorized by §§97.305(c) and 97.307(f) of this Part, a station may transmit a RTTY or data emission using an unspecified digital code, except to a station in a country with which the United States does not have an agreement permitting the code to be used. RTTY and data emissions using unspecified digital codes must not be transmitted for the purpose of obscuring the meaning of any communication. When deemed necessary by an EIC to assure compliance with the FCC Rules, a station must:

(1) Cease the transmission using the unspecified digital code;

(2) Restrict transmissions of any digital code to the extent instructed;

(3) Maintain a record, convertible to the original information, of all digital communications transmitted.

§97.311 SS emission types.

(a) SS emission transmissions by an amateur station are authorized only for communications between points within areas where the amateur service is regulated by the FCC and between an area where the amateur service is regulated by the FCC and an amateur station in another country that permits such communications. SS emission transmissions must not be used for the purpose of obscuring the meaning of any communication.

(b) A station transmitting SS emissions must not cause harmful interference to stations employing other authorized emissions, and must accept all interference caused by stations employing other authorized emissions.

(c) When deemed necessary by a District Director to assure compliance with this Part, a station licensee must:

   (1) Cease SS emission transmissions;

   (2) Restrict SS emission transmissions to the extent instructed; and

   (3) Maintain a record, convertible to the original information (voice, text, image, etc.) of all spread spectrum communications transmitted.

(d) The transmitter power must not exceed 100 W under any circumstances. If more than 1 W is used, automatic transmitter control shall limit output power to that which is required for the communication. This shall be determined by the use of the ratio, measured at the receiver, of the received energy per user data bit (Eb) to the sum of the received power spectral densities of noise (N0) and co-channel interference (I0). Average transmitter power over 1 W shall be automatically adjusted to maintain an Eb/(N0 + I0) ratio of no more than 23 dB at the intended receiver.

§97.313 Transmitter power standards.

(a) An amateur station must use the minimum transmitter power necessary to carry out the desired communications.

(b) No station may transmit with a transmitter power exceeding 1.5 kW PEP.

(c) No station may transmit with a transmitter power exceeding 200 W PEP on:

   (1) The 3.675-3.725 MHz, 7.10-7.15 MHz, 10.10-10.15 MHz and 21.1-21.2 MHz segments;

   (2) The 28.1-28.5 MHz segment when the control operator is a Novice Class operator or a Technician Class operator who has received credit for proficiency in telegraphy in accordance with the international requirements; or

   (3) The 7.050-7.075 MHz segment when the station is within ITU Regions 1 or 3.

(d) No station may transmit with a transmitter power exceeding 25 W PEP on the VHF 1.25 m band when the control operator is a Novice operator.

(e) No station may transmit with a transmitter power exceeding 5 W PEP on the UHF 23 cm band when the control operator is a Novice operator.

(f) No station may transmit with a transmitter power exceeding 50 W PEP on the UHF 70 cm band from an area specified in footnote US7 to § 2.106 of Part 2, unless expressly authorized by the FCC after mutual agreement, on a case-by-case basis, between the District Director of the applicable field facility and the military area frequency coordinator at the applicable military base. An Earth station or telecommand station, however, may transmit on the 435-438 MHz segment with a maximum of 611 W effective radiated power (1 kW equivalent isotropically radiated power) without the authorization otherwise required. The transmitting antenna elevation angle between the lower half-power (–3 dB relative to the peak or antenna bore sight) point and the horizon must always be greater than 10°.

(g) No station may transmit with a transmitter power exceeding 50 W PEP on the 33 cm band from within 241 km of the boundaries of the White Sands Missile Range. Its boundaries are those portions of Texas and New Mexico bounded on the south by latitude 31° 41' North, on the east by longitude 104° 11' West, on the north by latitude 34° 30' North, and on the west by longitude 107° 30' West.

(h) No station may transmit with a transmitter power exceeding 50 W PEP on the 219-220 MHz segment of the 1.25 m band.

§97.315 Certification of external RF power amplifiers.

(a) No more than 1 unit of 1 model of an external RF power amplifier capable of operation below 144 MHz may be constructed or modified during any calendar year by an amateur operator for use at a station without a grant of **certification**. No amplifier capable of operation below 144 MHz may be constructed or modified by a non-amateur operator without a grant of **certification** from the FCC.

(b) Any external RF power amplifier or external RF power amplifier kit (see §2.815 of the FCC Rules), manufactured, imported or modified for use in a station or attached at any station must be **certificated** for use in the amateur service in accordance with Subpart J of Part 2 of the FCC Rules. This requirement does not apply if one or more of the following conditions are met:

(1) The amplifier is not capable of operation on frequencies below 144 MHz. For the purpose of this part, an amplifier will be deemed to be incapable of operation below 144 MHz if it is not capable of being easily modified to increase its amplification characteristics below 120 MHz and either:

(i) The mean output power of the amplifier decreases, as frequency decreases from 144 MHz, to a point where 0 dB or less gain is exhibited at 120 MHz; or

(ii) The amplifier is not capable of amplifying signals below 120 MHz even for brief periods without sustaining permanent damage to its amplification circuitry.

(2) The amplifier was manufactured before April 28, 1978, and has been issued a marketing waiver by the FCC, or the amplifier was purchased before April 28, 1978, by an amateur operator for use at that amateur operator's station.

(3) The amplifier was:

(i) Constructed by the licensee, not from an external RF power amplifier kit, for use at the licensee's station; or

(ii) Modified by the licensee for use at the licensee's station.

(4) The amplifier is sold by an amateur operator to another amateur operator or to a dealer.

(5) The amplifier is purchased in used condition by an equipment dealer from an amateur operator and the amplifier is further sold to another amateur operator for use at that operator's station.

(c) Any external RF power amplifier appearing in the Commission's database as certificated for use in the amateur service may be marketed for use in the amateur service.

§97.317 Standards for certification of external RF power amplifiers.

(a) To receive a grant of **certification**, the amplifier must satisfy the spurious emission standards of §97.307(d) or (e) of this Part, as applicable, when the amplifier is:

(1) Operated at its full output power;

(2) Placed in the "standby" or "off" positions, but still connected to the transmitter; and

(3) Driven with at least 50 W mean RF input power (unless higher drive level is specified).

(b) To receive a grant of **certification**, the amplifier must not be capable of operation on any frequency or frequencies between 24 MHz and 35 MHz. The amplifier will be deemed incapable of such operation if it:

(1) Exhibits no more than 6 dB gain between 24 MHz and 26 MHz and between 28 MHz and 35 MHz. (This gain will be determined by the ratio of the input RF driving signal (mean power measurement) to the mean RF output power of the amplifier); and

(2) Exhibits no amplification (0 dB gain) between 26 MHz and 28 MHz.

(c) Certification may be denied when denial would prevent the use of these amplifiers in services other than the amateur service. The following features will result in dismissal or denial of an application for **certification**:

(1) Any accessible wiring which, when altered, would permit operation of the amplifier in a manner contrary to the FCC Rules;

(2) Circuit boards or similar circuitry to facilitate the addition of components to change the amplifier's operating characteristics in a manner contrary to the FCC Rules;

(3) Instructions for operation or modification of the amplifier in a manner contrary to the FCC Rules;

(4) Any internal or external controls or adjustments to facilitate operation of the amplifier in a manner contrary to the FCC Rules;

(5) Any internal RF sensing circuitry or any external switch, the purpose of which is to place the amplifier in the transmit mode;

(6) The incorporation of more gain in the amplifier than is necessary to operate in the amateur service; for purposes of this paragraph, the amplifier must:

    (i) Not be capable of achieving designed output power when driven with less than 40 W mean RF input power;

    (ii) Not be capable of amplifying the input RF driving signal by more than 15 dB, unless the amplifier has a designed transmitter power of less than 1.5 kW (in such a case, gain must be reduced by the same number of dB as the transmitter power relationship to 1.5 kW; This gain limitation is determined by the ratio of the input RF driving signal to the RF output power of the amplifier where both signals are expressed in peak envelope power or mean power);

    (iii) Not exhibit more gain than permitted by paragraph (c)(6)(ii) of this Section when driven by an RF input signal of less than 50 W mean power; and

    (iv) Be capable of sustained operation at its designed power level.

(7) Any attenuation in the input of the amplifier which, when removed or modified, would permit the amplifier to function at its designed transmitter power when driven by an RF frequency input signal of less than 50 W mean power; or

(8) Any other features designed to facilitate operation in a telecommunication service other than the Amateur Radio Services, such as the Citizens Band (CB) Radio Service.

SUBPART E—PROVIDING EMERGENCY COMMUNICATIONS

§97.401 Operation during a disaster.

(a) When normal communication systems are overloaded, damaged or disrupted because a disaster has occurred, or is likely to occur, in an area where the amateur service is regulated by the FCC, an amateur station may make transmissions necessary to meet essential communication needs and facilitate relief actions.

(b) When normal communication systems are overloaded, damaged or disrupted because a natural disaster has occurred, or is likely to occur, in an area where the amateur service is not regulated by the FCC, a station assisting in meeting essential communication needs and facilitating relief actions may do so only in accord with ITU Resolution No. 640 (Geneva, 1979). The 80 m, 75 m, 40 m, 30 m, 20 m, 17 m, 15 m, 12 m, and 2 m bands may be used for these purposes.

(c) When a disaster disrupts normal communication systems in a particular area, the FCC may declare a temporary state of communication emergency. The declaration will set forth any special conditions and special rules to be observed by stations during the communication emergency. A request for a declaration of a temporary state of emergency should be directed to the EIC in the area concerned.

(d) A station in, or within 92.6 km of, Alaska may transmit emissions J3E and R3E on the channel at 5.1675 MHz for emergency communications. The channel must be shared with stations licensed in the Alaska-private fixed service. The transmitter power must not exceed 150 W.

§97.403 Safety of life and protection of property.

No provision of these rules prevents the use by an amateur station of any means of radiocommunication at its disposal to provide essential communication needs in connection with the immediate safety of human life and immediate protection of property when normal communication systems are not available.

§97.405 Station in distress.

(a) No provision of these rules prevents the use by an amateur station in distress of any means at its disposal to attract attention, make known its condition and location, and obtain assistance.

(b) No provision of these rules prevents the use by a station, in the exceptional circumstances described in paragraph (a), of any means of radiocommunications at its disposal to assist a station in distress.

§97.407 Radio Amateur Civil Emergency Service (RACES).

(a) No station may transmit in RACES unless it is an FCC-licensed primary, club, or military recreation station and it is certified by a civil defense organization as registered with that organization, or it is an FCC-licensed RACES station. No person may be the control operator of a RACES station, or may be the control operator of an amateur station transmitting in RACES unless that person holds a FCC-issued amateur operator license and is certified by a civil defense organization as enrolled in that organization.

(b) **The frequency bands and segments and emissions authorized to the control operator are available to stations transmitting communications in RACES on a shared basis with the amateur service. In the event of an emergency which necessitates the invoking of the President's War Emergency Powers under the provisions of Section 706 of the Communications Act of 1934, as amended, 47 U.S.C. §606, RACES stations and amateur stations participating in RACES may only transmit on the following frequency segments:**

(1) The 1800-1825 kHz, 1975-2000 kHz, 3.50-3.55 MHz, 3.93-3.98 MHz, 3.984-4.000 MHz, 7.079-7.125 MHz, 7.245-7.255 MHz, 10.10-10.15 MHz, 14.047-14.053 MHz, 14.22-14.23 MHz,

14.331-14.350 MHz, 21.047-21.053 MHz, 21.228-21.267 MHz, 28.55-28.75 MHz, 29.237-29.273 MHz, 29.45-29.65 MHz, 50.35-50.75 MHz, 52-54 MHz, 144.50-145.71 MHz, 146-148 MHz, 2390-2450 MHz segments;

(2) The 1.25 m, 70 cm and 23 cm bands; and

(3) The channels at 3.997 MHz and 53.30 MHz may be used in emergency areas when required to make initial contact with a military unit and for communications with military stations on matters requiring coordination.

(c) A RACES station may only communicate with:

(1) Another RACES station;

(2) An amateur station registered with a civil defense organization;

(3) A United States Government station authorized by the responsible agency to communicate with RACES stations;

(4) A station in a service regulated by the FCC whenever such communication is authorized by the FCC.

(d) An amateur station registered with a civil defense organization may only communicate with:

(1) A RACES station licensed to the civil defense organization with which the amateur station is registered;

(2) The following stations upon authorization of the responsible civil defense official for the organization with which the amateur station is registered:

(i) A RACES station licensed to another civil defense organization;

(ii) An amateur station registered with the same or another civil defense organization;

(iii) A United States Government station authorized by the responsible agency to communicate with RACES stations; and

(iv) A station in a service regulated by the FCC whenever such communication is authorized by the FCC.

(e) All communications transmitted in RACES must be specifically authorized by the civil defense organization for the area served. Only civil defense communications of the following types may be transmitted:

(1) Messages concerning impending or actual conditions jeopardizing the public safety, or affecting the national defense or security during periods of local, regional, or national civil emergencies;

(2) Messages directly concerning the immediate safety of life of individuals, the immediate protection of property, maintenance of law and order, alleviation of human suffering and need, and the combating of armed attack or sabotage;

(3) Messages directly concerning the accumulation and dissemination of public information or instructions to the civilian population essential to the activities of the civil defense organization or other authorized governmental or relief agencies; and

(4) Communications for RACES training drills and tests necessary to ensure the establishment and maintenance of orderly and

efficient operation of the RACES as ordered by the responsible civil defense organizations served. Such drills and tests may not exceed a total time of 1 hour per week. With the approval of the chief officer for emergency planning in the applicable State, Commonwealth, District or territory, however, such tests and drills may be conducted for a period not to exceed 72 hours no more than twice in any calendar year.

SUBPART F—QUALIFYING EXAMINATION SYSTEMS

§97.501 Qualifying for an amateur operator license.

Each applicant must pass an examination for a new amateur operator license grant and for each change in operator class. Each applicant for the class of operator license grant specified below must pass, or otherwise receive examination credit for, the following examination elements:
  (a) Amateur Extra Class operator: Elements 1, 2, 3, and 4;
  (b) General Class operator: Elements 1, 2, and 3;
  (c) Technician Class operator: Element 2.

§97.503 Element standards.

(a) A telegraphy examination must be sufficient to prove that the examinee has the ability to send correctly by hand and to receive correctly by ear texts in the international Morse code at not less than the prescribed speed, using all the letters of the alphabet, numerals 0-9, period, comma, question mark, slant mark and prosigns AR, BT and SK.
  Element 1: 5 words per minute.
(b) A written examination must be such as to prove that the examinee possesses the operational and technical qualifications required to perform properly the duties of an amateur service licensee. Each written examination must be comprised of a question set as follows:
  (1) Element 2: 35 questions concerning the privileges of a Technician Class operator license. The minimum passing score is 26 questions answered correctly.
  (2) Element 3: 35 questions concerning the privileges of a General Class operator license. The minimum passing score is 26 questions answered correctly.
  (3) Element 4: 50 questions concerning the privileges of an Amateur Extra Class operator license. The minimum passing score is 37 questions answered correctly.

§97.505 Element credit.

(a) The administering VEs must give credit as specified below to an examinee holding any of the following license grants or license documents:

(1) An unexpired (or expired but within the grace period for renewal) FCC-granted Advanced Class operator license grant: Elements 1, 2, and 3.

(2) An unexpired (or expired but within the grace period for renewal) FCC-granted General Class operator license grant: Elements 1, 2, and 3.

(3) An unexpired (or expired but within the grace period for renewal) FCC-granted Technician Plus Class operator (including a Technician Class operator license granted before February 14, 1991) license grant: Elements 1 and 2.

(4) An unexpired (or expired but within the grace period for renewal) FCC-granted Technician Class operator license grant: Element 2.

(5) An unexpired (or expired) FCC-granted Novice Class operator license grant: Element 1.

(6) A CSCE: Each element the CSCE indicates the examinee passed within the previous 365 days.

(7) An unexpired (or expired less than 5 years) FCC-issued commercial radiotelegraph operator license or permit: Element 1.

(8) An expired FCC-issued Technician Class operator license document granted before March 21, 1987: Element 3.

(9) An expired or unexpired FCC-issued Technician Class operator license document granted before February 14, 1991: Element 1.

(b) No examination credit, except as herein provided, shall be allowed on the basis of holding or having held any other license grant or document.

§97.507 Preparing an examination.

(a) Each telegraphy message and each written question set administered to an examinee must be prepared by a VE holding an Amateur Extra Class operator license. A telegraphy message or written question set may also be prepared for the following elements by a VE holding an operator license of the class indicated:

(1) Element 3: Advanced Class operator.

(2) Elements 1 and 2: Advanced, General, or Technician (including Technician Plus) Class operators.

(b) Each question set administered to an examinee must utilize questions taken from the applicable question pool.

(c) Each telegraphy message and each written question set administered to an examinee for an amateur operator license must be prepared, or obtained from a supplier, by the administering VEs according to instructions from the coordinating VEC.

(d) A telegraphy examination must consist of a message sent in the international Morse code at no less than the prescribed speed for a minimum of 5 minutes. The message must contain each required telegraphy character at least once. No message known to the examinee may be administered in a telegraphy examination. Each 5 letters of the alphabet must be counted as 1 word. Each numeral, punctuation mark and prosign must be counted as 2 letters of the alphabet.

§97.509 Administering VE requirements.

(a) **Each examination for an amateur operator license must be administered by a team of at least 3 VEs at an examination session coordinated by a VEC. Before the session, the administering VEs or the VE session manager must ensure that a public announcement is made giving the location and time of the session. The number of examinees at the session may be limited.**

(b) Each administering VE must:

(1) Be accredited by the coordinating VEC;

(2) Be at least 18 years of age;

(3) **Be a person who holds an amateur operator license of the class specified below:**

(i) **Amateur Extra, Advanced or General Class in order to administer a Technician Class operator license examination;**

(ii) **Amateur Extra or Advanced Class in order to administer a General Class operator license examination;**

(iii) **Amateur Extra Class in order to administer an Amateur Extra Class operator license examination.**

(4) Not be a person whose grant of an amateur station license or amateur operator license has ever been revoked or suspended.

(c) Each administering VE must be present and observing the examinee throughout the entire examination. The administering VEs are responsible for the proper conduct and necessary supervision of each examination. The administering VEs must immediately terminate the examination upon failure of the examinee to comply with their instructions.

(d) No VE may administer an examination to his or her spouse, children, grandchildren, stepchildren, parents, grandparents, stepparents, brothers, sisters, stepbrothers, stepsisters, aunts, uncles, nieces, nephews, and in-laws.

(e) No VE may administer or certify any examination by fraudulent means or for monetary or other consideration including reimbursement in any amount in excess of that permitted. Violation of this provision may result in the revocation of the grant of the VE's amateur station license and the suspension of the grant of the VE's amateur operator license.

(f) No examination that has been compromised shall be administered to any examinee. Neither the same telegraphy message nor the same question set may be re-administered to the same examinee.

(g) Passing a telegraphy receiving examination is adequate proof of an examinee's ability to both send and receive telegraphy. The administering VEs, however, may also include a sending segment in a telegraphy examination.

(h) Upon completion of each examination element, the administering VEs must immediately grade the examinee's answers. The administering VEs are responsible for determining the correctness of the examinee's answers.

(i) When the examinee is credited for all examination elements required for the operator license sought, 3 VEs must certify that the examinee is qualified for the license grant and that the VEs have complied with these administering VE requirements. The certifying VEs are jointly and individually accountable for the proper administration of each examination element reported. The certifying VEs may delegate to other qualified VEs their authority, but not their accountability, to administer individual elements of an examination.

(j) When the examinee does not score a passing grade on an examination element, the administering VEs must return the application document to the examinee and inform the examinee of the grade.

(k) The administering VEs must accommodate an examinee whose physical disabilities require a special examination procedure. The administering VEs may require a physician's certification indicating the nature of the disability before determining which, if any, special procedures must be used.

(l) The administering VEs must issue a CSCE to an examinee who scores a passing grade on an examination element.

(m) Within 10 days of the administration of a successful examination for an amateur operator license, the administering VEs must submit the application document to the coordinating VEC.

§97.511 Examinee conduct.

Each examinee must comply with the instructions given by the administering VEs.

§97.513 VE session manager requirements.

(a) A VE session manager may be selected by the VE team for each examination session. The VE session manager must be accredited as a VE by the same VEC that coordinates the examination session. The VE session manager may serve concurrently as an administering VE.

(b) The VE session manager may carry on liaison between the VE team and the coordinating VEC.

(c) The VE session manager may organize activities at an examination session.

§97.515 [Reserved]

§97.517 [Reserved]

§97.519 Coordinating examination sessions.

(a) A VEC must coordinate the efforts of VEs in preparing and administering examinations.

(b) **At the completion of each examination session, the coordinating VEC must collect applicant information and tests results from the administering VEs. Within 10 days of collection, the coordinating VEC must:**

(1) **Screen collected information;**

(2) **Resolve all discrepancies and verify that the VE's certifications are properly completed; and**

(3) **For qualified examinees, forward electronically all required data to the FCC. All data forwarded must be retained for at least 15 months and must be made available to the FCC upon request.**

(c) Each VEC must make any examination records available to the FCC, upon request.

(d) The FCC may:

(1) Administer any examination element itself;

(2) Readminister any examination element previously administered by VEs, either itself or under the supervision of a VEC or VEs designated by the FCC; or

(3) Cancel the operator/primary station license of any licensee who fails to appear for readministration of an examination when directed by the FCC, or who does not successfully complete any required element that is readministered. In an instance of such cancellation, the person will be granted an operator/primary station license consistent with completed examination elements that have not been invalidated by not appearing for, or by failing, the examination upon readministration.

§97.521 VEC qualifications.

No organization may serve as a VEC unless it has entered into a written agreement with the FCC. The VEC must abide by the terms of the agreement. In order to be eligible to be a VEC, the entity must:

(a) Be an organization that exists for the purpose of furthering the amateur service;

(b) Be capable of serving as a VEC in at least the VEC region (see Appendix 2) proposed;

(c) Agree to coordinate examinations for any class of amateur operator license;

(d) Agree to assure that, for any examination, every examinee qualified under these rules is registered without regard to race, sex, religion, national origin or membership (or lack thereof) in any amateur service organization.

§97.523 Question pools.

All VECs must cooperate in maintaining one question pool for each written examination element. Each question pool must contain at least 10 times the number of questions required for a single examination. Each question pool must be published and made available to the public prior to its use for making a question set. Each question on each VEC question pool must be prepared by a VE holding the required FCC-issued operator license. See §97.507(a) of this Part.

§97.525 Accrediting VEs.

    (a) No VEC may accredit a person as a VE if:

        (1) The person does not meet minimum VE statutory qualifications or minimum qualifications as prescribed by this Part;

        (2) The FCC does not accept the voluntary and uncompensated services of the person;

        (3) The VEC determines that the person is not competent to perform the VE functions; or

        (4) The VEC determines that questions of the person's integrity or honesty could compromise the examinations.

    (b) Each VEC must seek a broad representation of amateur operators to be VEs. No VEC may discriminate in accrediting VEs on the basis of race, sex, religion or national origin; nor on the basis of membership (or lack thereof) in an amateur service organization; nor on the basis of the person accepting or declining to accept reimbursement.

§97.527 Reimbursement for expenses.

VEs and VECs may be reimbursed by examinees for out-of-pocket expenses incurred in preparing, processing, administering, or coordinating an examination for an amateur operator license.

Appendix 1—Places Where the Amateur Service is Regulated by the FCC

In ITU Region 2, the amateur service is regulated by the FCC within the territorial limits of the 50 United States, District of Columbia, Caribbean Insular areas [Commonwealth of Puerto Rico, United States Virgin Islands (50 islets and cays) and Navassa Island], and Johnston Island (Islets East, Johnston, North and Sand) and Midway Island (Islets Eastern and Sand) in the Pacific Insular areas.

In ITU Region 3, the amateur service is regulated by the FCC within the Pacific Insular territorial limits of American Samoa (seven islands), Baker Island, Commonwealth of Northern Mariannas Islands, Guam Island, Howland Island, Jarvis Island, Kingman Reef, Kure Island, Palmyra Island (more than 50 islets) and Wake Island (Islets Peale, Wake and Wilkes).

Appendix 2—VEC Regions

1. Connecticut, Maine, Massachusetts, New Hampshire, Rhode Island and Vermont.
2. New Jersey and New York.
3. Delaware, District of Columbia, Maryland and Pennsylvania.
4. Alabama, Florida, Georgia, Kentucky, North Carolina, South Carolina, Tennessee and Virginia.
5. Arkansas, Louisiana, Mississippi, New Mexico, Oklahoma and Texas.
6. California.
7. Arizona, Idaho, Montana, Nevada, Oregon, Utah, Washington and Wyoming.
8. Michigan, Ohio and West Virginia.
9. Illinois, Indiana and Wisconsin.
10. Colorado, Iowa, Kansas, Minnesota, Missouri, Nebraska, North Dakota and South Dakota.
11. Alaska.
12. Caribbean Insular areas.
13. Hawaii and Pacific Insular areas.

10 Appendices

§2.1093 Radiofrequency radiation exposure evaluation: portable devices
§2.201 Emission, modulation and transmission characteristics
§2.202 Bandwidths
§2.815 External radio frequency power amplifiers

Appendix 1

EXTRACTS FROM THE COMMUNICATIONS ACT OF 1934, AS AMENDED

The complete text of the Communications Act of 1934, as amended in 1996, occupies a volume larger than this book. The Act, passed by Congress, authorizes the FCC to regulate non-government communications. Only the parts most applicable to Amateur Radio are included here. The entire text can be ordered from the Government Printing Office. You can find it in your nearest Government Document Depository Library; check with your local library.

You can also find the complete text of the Communications Act of 1934, as amended, on the FCC's Web page at http://www.fcc.gov/Reports/1934new.pdf. A brief synopsis of each section of the Communications Act of 1934, as amended, and how it affects amateurs is included before each section. ARRL commentary is in bold.

Section 4 [47 USC 154], provisions relating to the Commission, gives the FCC the authority to make use of unpaid authorized volunteers to give license examinations (Volunteer Examiners) and monitor for violations (Official Observers). This section states:

Section 4. [47 USC 154] PROVISIONS RELATING TO THE COMMISSION.

(4)(A) The Commission, for purposes of preparing any examination for an amateur station operator license, may accept and employ the voluntary and uncompensated services of any individual who holds an amateur station operator license of a higher class than the class license for which the examination is being prepared. In the case of examinations for the highest class of amateur station operator license, the Commission may accept and employ such services of any individual who holds such class of license.

(B)(i) The Commission, for purposes of monitoring violations of any provision of this Act (and of any regulation prescribed by the Commission under this Act) relating to the Amateur Radio Service, may—

(I) recruit and train any individual licensed by the Commission to operate an amateur station; and

(II) accept and employ the voluntary and uncompensated services of such individual.

(ii) The Commission, for purposes of recruiting and training individuals under clause (i) and for purposes of screening, annotating, and summarizing violation reports referred under clause (i), may accept and employ the voluntary and uncompensated services of any amateur station operator organization.

(iii) The functions of individuals recruited and trained under this subparagraph shall be limited to—

(I) the detection of improper Amateur Radio transmissions;

(II) the conveyance to Commission personnel of information which is essential to the enforcement of this Act (or regulations prescribed by the Commission under this Act) relating to the Amateur Radio Service; and

(III) issuing advisory notices, under the general direction of the Commission, to persons who apparently have violated any provision of this Act (or regulations prescribed by the Commission under this Act) relating to the Amateur Radio Service.

Nothing in this clause shall be construed to grant individuals recruited and trained under this subparagraph any authority to issue sanctions to violators or to take any enforcement action other than any action which the Commission may prescribe by rule.

(F) Any person who provides services under this paragraph shall not be considered, by reason of having provided such services, a Federal employee.

(G) The Commission, in accepting and employing services of individuals under subparagraphs (A), (B), and (C), shall seek to achieve a broad representation of individuals and organizations interested in amateur station operation.

(H) The Commission may establish rules of conduct and other regulations governing the service of individuals under this paragraph.

(I) With respect to the acceptance of voluntary uncompensated services for the preparation, processing, or administration of examinations for amateur station operator licenses pursuant to subparagraph (A) of this paragraph, individuals, or organizations which provide or coordinate such authorized volunteer services may recover from examinees reimbursement for out-of-pocket costs. The total amount of allowable cost reimbursement per examinee shall not exceed $4, adjusted annually every January 1 for changes in the Department of Labor Consumer Price Index.

* * * * * * * * * * * * * *

Section 302 [47 USC 302] **gives the FCC the authority to regulate interference the potential and susceptibility of devices capable of causing harmful interference. It also gives the FCC the authority to set minimum performance standards for home entertainment equipment to reduce RF susceptibility. This section states:**

SEC 302 [47 USC 302] DEVICES WHICH INTERFERE WITH RADIO RECEPTION.

(a) The Commission may, consistent with the public interest, convenience, and necessity, make reasonable regulations (1) governing the interference potential of devices which in their operation are capable of emitting radio frequency energy by radiation, conduction, or other means in sufficient degree to cause harmful interference to radio communications; and (2) establishing minimum performance standards for home electronic equipment and systems to reduce their susceptibility to interference from radio frequency energy. Such regulations shall be applicable to the manufacture, import, sale, offer for sale, or shipment of such devices and home electronic equipment and systems, and to the use of such devices.

(b) No person shall manufacture, import, sell, offer for sale, or ship devices or home electronic equipment and systems, or use devices, which fail to comply with regulations promulgated pursuant to this section.

* * * * * * * * * * * * * *

Section 303 [47 USC 303] **General Requirements of the Commission, gives the FCC broad authority to regulate non-government communications, including prescribing licensing requirements of the various classes of license and the associated frequency privileges for each class. It also gives the Commission authority to regulate the spectral purity of licensee's stations. It gives the FCC the authority to issue call letters and prevents interference from licensees. This**

is the authority statement often mentioned in FCC Orders. All of this has been incorporated into Part 97. Some sections have been deleted where there is no relationship to Amateur Radio.

SEC 303 [47 USC 303] GENERAL POWERS OF COMMISSION.

Except as otherwise provided in this Act, the Commission from time to time, as public convenience, interest, or necessity requires shall—

(a) Classify radio stations;

(b) Prescribe the nature of the service to be rendered by each class of licensed stations and each station within any class;

(c) Assign bands of frequencies to the various classes of stations, and assign frequencies for each individual station and determine the power which each station shall use and the time during which it may operate;

(d) Determine the location of classes of stations or individual stations;

(e) Regulate the kind of apparatus to be used with respect to its external effects and the purity and sharpness of the emissions from each station and from the apparatus therein;

(f) Make such regulations not inconsistent with law as it may deem necessary to prevent interference between stations and to carry out the provisions of this Act: *Provided, however,* that changes in the frequencies, authorized power, or in the times of operation of any station, shall not be made without the consent of the station licensee unless the Commission shall determine that such changes will promote public convenience or interest or will serve public necessity, or the provisions of this Act will be more fully complied with;

(g) Study new uses for radio, provide for experimental uses of frequencies, and generally encourage the larger and more effective use of radio in the public interest;

(h) Have authority to establish areas or zones to be served by any station;

(j) Have authority to make general rules and regulations requiring stations to keep such records of programs, transmissions of energy, communications or signals as it may deem desirable;

(l)(3) In addition to amateur operator licenses which the Commission may issue to aliens pursuant to paragraph (2) of this subsection, and notwithstanding section 301 of this Act and paragraph (1) of this subsection, the Commission may issue authorizations, under such conditions and terms as it may prescribe, to permit an alien licensed by his government as an amateur radio operator to operate his amateur radio station licensed by his government in the United States, its possessions, and the Commonwealth of Puerto Rico provided there is in effect a multilateral or bilateral agreement, to which the United States and the alien's government are parties, for such operation on a reciprocal basis by United States amateur radio operators. Other provisions of this Act and of the Administrative Procedure Act shall not be applicable to any request or application for or modification, suspension or cancellation of any such authorization.

(m)(1) Have authority to suspend the license of any operator upon proof sufficient to satisfy the Commission that the licensee—

(A) Has violated, or caused, aided, or abetted the violation of, any provision of any Act, treaty, or convention binding on the United States, which the Commission is authorized to administer, or any regulation made by the Commission under any such Act, treaty, or convention; or

(B) Has failed to carry out a lawful order of the master or person lawfully in charge of the ship or aircraft on which he is employed; or

(C) Has willfully damaged or permitted radio apparatus or installations to be damaged; or

(D) Has transmitted superfluous radio communications or signals or communications containing profane or obscene words, language, or meaning, or has knowingly transmitted—

(1) False or deceptive signals or communications; or

(2) A call signal or letter which has not been assigned by proper authority to the station he is operating; or

(E) Has willfully or maliciously interfered with any other radio communications or signals; or

(F) Has obtained or attempted to obtain, or has assisted another to obtain or attempt to obtain, an operator's license by fraudulent means.

(2) No order of suspension of any operator's license shall take effect until fifteen days' notice in writing thereof, stating the cause for the proposed suspension, has been given to the operator licensee who may make written application to the Commission at any time within said fifteen days for hearing upon such order. The notice to the operator licensee shall not be effective until actually received by him, and from that time he shall have fifteen days in which to mail the said application. In the event that physical conditions prevent mailing of the application at the expiration of the fifteen-day period, the application shall then be mailed as soon as possible thereafter, accompanied by a satisfactory explanation of the delay. Upon receipt by the Commission of such application for hearing, said order of suspension shall be held in abeyance until the conclusion of the hearing which shall be conducted under such rules as the Commission may prescribe. Upon the conclusion of said hearing the Commission may affirm, modify, or revoke said order of suspension.

(n) Have authority to inspect all radio installations associated with stations required to be licensed by any Act, or which the Commission by rule has authorized to operate without a license under section 307(e)(1), or which are subject [to] the provisions of any Act, treaty, or convention binding on the United States, to ascertain whether in construction, installation, and operation they conform to the requirements of the rules and regulations of the Commission, the provisions of any Act, the terms of any treaty or convention binding on the United States and the conditions of the license or other instrument of authorization under which they are constructed, installed, or operated.

(o) Have authority to designate call letters of all stations;

(p) Have authority to cause to be published such call letters and such other announcements and data as in the judgment of the Commission may be required for the efficient operation of radio stations subject [to] the jurisdiction of the United States and for the proper enforcement of this Act;

(q) Have authority to require the painting and/or illumination of radio towers if and when in its judgment such towers constitute, or there is a reasonable possibility that they may constitute, a menace to air navigation. The permittee or licensee, and the tower owner in any case in which the owner is not the permittee or licensee, shall maintain the painting and/or illumination of the tower as prescribed by the Commission pursuant to this section. In the event that the tower ceases to be licensed by the Commission for the transmission of radio energy, the owner of the tower shall maintain the prescribed painting and/or illumination of such tower until it is dismantled, and the Commission may require the owner to dismantle and remove the tower when the administrator of the Federal Aviation Agency determines that there is a reasonable possibility that it may constitute a menace to air navigation.

(r) Make such rules and regulations and prescribe such restrictions and conditions, not inconsistent with law, as may be necessary to carry out the provisions of this Act, or any international radio or wire communications treaty or convention, or regulations annexed thereto, including any treaty or convention insofar as it relates to the use of radio, to which the United States is or may hereafter become a party.

＊ ＊ ＊ ＊ ＊ ＊ ＊ ＊ ＊ ＊ ＊ ＊ ＊ ＊

Section 310 [47 USC 310] **Limitation on Holding and Transfer of Licenses. Much of this section has nothing to do with Amateur Radio, but this section allows the FCC to permit foreign amateur licensees to operate their stations in the US as long as the US and the foreign government share a bilateral or multilateral agreement. The FCC no longer issues reciprocal permits to foreign amateurs. The section applicable to amateurs states:**

SEC 310 [47 USC 310] LIMITATION ON HOLDING AND TRANSFER OF LICENSES.

(*a*) The station license required under this Act shall not be granted to or held by any foreign government or the representative thereof.

(c) In addition to amateur station licenses which the Commission may issue to aliens pursuant to this Act, the Commission may issue authorizations, under such conditions and terms as it may prescribe, to permit an alien licensed by his government as an Amateur Radio operator to operate his Amateur Radio station licensed by his government in the United States, its possessions, and the Commonwealth of Puerto Rico provided there is in effect a multilateral or bilateral agreement, to which the United States and the alien's government are parties, for such operation on a reciprocal basis by United States Amateur Radio operators. Other provisions of this Act and of the Administrative Procedure Act shall not be applicable to any request or application for or modification, suspension or cancellation of any such authorization.

Section 333 [47 USC 333] **involves willful or malicious interference. This is frequently cited by the FCC ordering licensees to stop causing interference:**

SEC 333 [47 USC 333] WILLFUL OR MALICIOUS INTERFERENCE.

No person shall willfully or maliciously interfere with or cause interference to any radio communications of any station licensed or authorized by or under this Act or operated by the United States Government.

＊ ＊ ＊ ＊ ＊ ＊ ＊ ＊ ＊ ＊ ＊ ＊ ＊ ＊

Section 503(b) of the Communications Act of 1934 requires that the Commission take into account the nature, circumstances, extent and gravity of any violation and, with respect to the violator, the degree of culpability, any history of any prior offenses, ability to pay, and other such matters as justice may require. Sections which do not apply to Amateur Radio at all have been deleted.

SEC. 503. FORFEITURES IN CASES OF REBATES AND OFFSETS.

(a) Any person who shall deliver messages for interstate or foreign transmission to any carrier, or for whom as sender or receiver, any such carrier shall transmit any interstate or foreign wire or radio communication, who shall knowingly by employee, agent, officer, or otherwise, directly or indirectly, by or through any means or device whatsoever, receive or accept from such common carrier any sum of money or any other valuable consideration as a rebate or offset against the regular charges for transmission of such messages as fixed by the schedules of charges provided for in this Act, shall in addition to any other penalty provided by this Act forfeit to the United States a sum of money three times the amount of money so received or accepted and three times the value of any other consideration so received or accepted, to be ascertained by the trial court; and in the trial of said action all such rebates or other considerations so received or accepted for a period of six years prior to the commencement of the action, may be included therein, and the amount recovered shall be three times the total amount of money, or three times the total value of such consideration, so received or accepted, or both, as the case may be.

(b)(1) Any person who is determined by the Commission, in accordance with paragraph (3) or (4) of this subsection, to have—

(A) willfully or repeatedly failed to comply substantially with the terms and conditions of any license, permit, certificate, or other instrument or authorization issued by the Commission;

(B) willfully or repeatedly failed to comply with any of the provisions of this Act or of any rule, regulation, or order issued by the Commission under this Act or under any treaty convention, or other agreement to which the United States is a party and which is binding upon the United States;

(C) violated any provision of Section 317(c) or 508(a) of this Act; or

(D) violated any provision of Sections 1304; 1343, or 1464 of Title 18, United States Code; shall be liable to the United States for a forfeiture penalty. A forfeiture penalty under this subsection shall be in addition to any other penalty provided for by this Act; except that this subsection shall not apply to any conduct which is subject to forfeiture under Title II, Part II or III of Title III, or Section 506 of this Act.

(2)(C) In any case not covered in subparagraph (A) or (B), the amount of any forfeiture penalty determined under this subsection shall not exceed $10,000 for each violation or each day of a continuing violation, except that the amount assessed for any continuing violation shall not exceed a total of $75,000 for any single act or failure to act described in paragraph (1) of this subsection.

(D) The amount of such forfeiture penalty shall be assessed by the Commission, or its designee, by written notice, In determining the amount of such a forfeiture penalty, the Commission or its designee shall take into account the nature, circumstances, extent, and gravity of the violation and, with respect to the violator, the degree of culpability, any history of prior offenses, ability to pay, and such other matters as justice may require.

(3)(A) At the discretion of the Commission, a forfeiture penalty may be determined against a person under this subsection after notice and an opportunity for a hearing before the Commission or an administrative law judge thereof in accordance with Section 554 of Title 5, United States Code. Any person against whom a forfeiture penalty is determined under this paragraph may obtain review thereof pursuant to Section 402(a).

(B) If any person fails to pay an assessment of a forfeiture penalty determined under subparagraph (A) of this paragraph, after it has become a final and unappealable order or after the appropriate court has entered final judgment in favor of the Commission, the Commission shall refer the matter to the Attorney General of the United States, who shall recover the amount assessed in any appropriate district court of the United States. In such action, the validity and appropriateness of the final order imposing the forfeiture penalty shall not be subject to review.

(4) Except as provided in paragraph (3) of this subsection, no forfeiture penalty shall be imposed under this subsection against any person unless and until—

(A) the Commission issues a notice of apparent liability, in writing, with respect to such person;

(B) such notice has been received by such person, or until the Commission has sent such notice to the last known address of such person, by registered or certified mail; and

(C) such person is granted an opportunity to show, in writing, within such reasonable period of time as the Commission prescribes by rule or regulation, why no such forfeiture penalty should be imposed.

Such a notice shall (i) identify each specific provision, term, and condition of any Act, rule, regulation, order, treaty, convention, or other agreement, license, permit, certificate, instrument, or authorization which such person apparently violated or with which such person apparently failed to comply; (ii) set forth the nature of the act or omission charged against such person and the facts upon which such charge is based; and (iii) state the date on which such conduct occurred. Any forfeiture penalty determined under this paragraph shall be recoverable pursuant to Section 504(a) of this Act.

(5) No forfeiture liability shall be determined under this subsection against any person, if such person does not hold a license, permit, certificate, or other authorization issued by the Commission and if such person is not an applicant for a license, permit, certificate, or other authorization issued by the Commission, unless, prior to the notice required by paragraph (3) of this subsection or the notice of apparent liability required by paragraph (4) of this subsection, such person (A) is sent a citation of the violation charged; (B) is given a reasonable opportunity for a personal interview with an official of the Commission, at the field office of the Commission which is nearest to such person's place of residence; and (C) subsequently engages in conduct of the type described in such citation. The provisions of this paragraph shall not apply, however, if the person involved is engaging in activities for which a license, permit, certificate, or other authorization is required, or is a cable television system operator, if the person involved is transmitting on frequencies assigned for use in a service in which individual station operation is authorized by rule pursuant to Section 307(e) or in the case of violations of section 303(q), if the person involved is a nonlicensee tower owner who has previously received notice of the obligations imposed by section 303(q) from the Commission or the permittee or licensee who uses that tower. Whenever the requirements of this paragraph are satisfied with respect to a particular person, such person shall not be entitled to receive any additional citation of the violation charged, with respect to any conduct of the type described in the citation sent under this paragraph.

(6) No forfeiture penalty shall be determined or imposed against any person under this subsection if—

(6)(B) such person does not hold a broadcast station license issued under Title III of this Act and if the violation charged occurred more than 1 year prior to the date of issuance of the required notice or notice of apparent liability.

For purposes of this paragraph, "date of commencement of the current term of such license" means the date of commencement of the last term of license for which the licensee has been granted a license by the Commission. A separate license term shall not be deemed to have commenced as a result of continuing a license in effect under section 307(c) pending decision on an application for renewal of the license.

* * * * * * * * * * * * * *

Section 705(a) [47 USC 605] documents the prohibition on divulging contents of communications. Although amateur communications are exempted, this issue can arise due to telephone interference problems. For the FCC's fact sheet, see http://www.fcc.gov/Bureaus/Common_Carrier/Factsheets/investigation.html.

SEC 705 [47 USC 605] UNAUTHORIZED PUBLICATION OF COMMUNICATIONS.

(a) Except as authorized by chapter 119, title 18, United States Code, no person receiving, assisting in receiving, transmitting, or assisting in transmitting, any interstate or foreign communication by wire or radio shall divulge or publish the existence, contents, substance, purport, effect, or meaning thereof, except through authorized channels of transmission or reception, (1) to any person other than the addressee, his agent, or attorney, (2) to a person employed or authorized to forward such communication to its destination, (3) to proper accounting or distributing officers of the various communicating centers over which the communication may be passed, (4) to the master of a ship under whom he is serving, (5) in response to a subpoena issued by a court of competent jurisdiction, or (6) on demand of other lawful authority. No person not being authorized by the sender shall intercept any radio communication and divulge or publish the existence, contents, substance, purport, effect, or meaning of such intercepted communication to any person. No person not being entitled thereto shall receive or assist in receiving any interstate or foreign communication by radio and use such communication (or any information therein contained) for his own benefit or for the benefit of another not entitled thereto. No person having received any intercepted radio communication or having become acquainted with the contents, substance, purport, effect, or meaning of such communication (or any part thereof) knowing that such communication was intercepted, shall divulge or publish the existence, contents, substance, purport, effect, or meaning of such communication (or any part thereof) or use such communication (or any information therein contained) for his own benefit or for the benefit of another not entitled thereto. This section shall not apply to the receiving, divulging, publishing, or utilizing the contents of any radio communication which is transmitted by any station for the use of the general public, which relates to ships, aircraft, vehicles, or persons in distress, or which is transmitted by an amateur radio station operator or by a citizens band radio operator.

Appendix 2

EXTRACTS FROM TITLE 47 CODE
OF FEDERAL REGULATIONS

Title 47 (Telecommunications) of the Code of Federal Regulations occupies five volumes. Sections 0-300 can be ordered from the Government Printing Office. For information on obtaining FCC rule parts, see Appendix 13 at the end of this book. The Code of Federal Regulations can also be found at *http://www.fcc.gov/Bureaus/Engineering_Technology/Documents/cfr/1998/*.

✳ ✳ ✳ ✳ ✳ ✳ ✳ ✳ ✳ ✳ ✳ ✳ ✳ ✳

The FCC regulations for filing an FCC Form 605 manually or electronically appear below. The only forms that apply to Amateur Radio for manual filing are the FCC Forms 159 and 605. The FCC 159 is used to send the $14 fee for a vanity call to the FCC Bank in Pittsburgh (there is no fee for non-vanity applications). Applicants filing a Vanity Call Sign application must also file a Schedule D in addition to FCC Form 605. Club applicants applying for a Club Call Sign must obtain an FCC sequentially assigned call sign by completing NCVEC Form 605, which must be sent to a Club Station Call Sign Administrator, not the FCC. Two members of the club, the trustee and another member of the club, must sign the form and then obtain an Assigned Taxpayer Identification Number from the FCC License Support Staff at 202-414-1250 or electronically at *ulscomm@fcc.gov*. Sections that do not involve Amateur Radio have been deleted. For additional information on filing applications, see Chapter 1. Other sections mentioned in this section can be found electronically at *http://www.access.gpo.gov/cgi-bin/cfrassemble.cgi?title=199947*.

Sec. 1.913 Application forms; electronic and manual filing.

(a) Application forms. Applicants and licensees in the Wireless Radio Services shall use the following forms and associated schedules for all applications:

(4) FCC Form 605, Quick-form Application for Authorization for Wireless Radio Services. FCC Form 605 is used to apply for Amateur, Ship, Aircraft, and General Mobile Radio Service (GMRS) authorizations, as well as Commercial Radio Operator Licenses.

(b) Electronic filing. Except as specified in paragraph (d) of this section or elsewhere in this chapter, all applications and other filings using FCC Forms 601 through 605 or associated schedules must be filed electronically in accordance with the electronic filing instructions provided by ULS. For each Wireless Radio Service that is subject to mandatory electronic filing, this subparagraph is effective on (1) July 1, 1999, or (2) six months after the Commission begins use of ULS to process applications in the service, whichever is later. The Commission will announce by public notice the deployment date of each service in ULS.

(1) Attachments to applications should be uploaded along with the electronically filed application whenever possible. The files, other than the ASCII table of contents, should be in Adobe Acrobat Portable Document Format (PDF) whenever possible.

(2) Any associated documents (see Sec. 1.211(a) of this part) submitted with

an application must be uploaded as attachments to the application whenever possible. The attachment should be uploaded via ULS in Adobe Acrobat Portable Document Format (PDF) whenever possible.

(c) Auctioned license applications. Auctioned license applications, as defined in Sec. 1.907 of this part, shall also comply with the requirements of subpart Q of this part and the applicable Commission orders and public notices issued with respect to each auction for a particular service and spectrum.

(d) Manual filing. (1) ULS Forms 601, 603 and 605 may be filed manually or electronically by applicants and licensees in the following services:

(ii) The part 97 Amateur Radio Service, except those filed by Volunteer Examination Coordinators;

(2) Manually filed applications must be submitted to the Commission at the appropriate address with the appropriate filing fee. The addresses for filing and the fee amounts for particular applications are listed in Subpart G of this part, and in the appropriate fee filing guide for each service available from the Commission's Forms Distribution Center by calling 1-800-418-FORM (3676).

(3) Manually filed applications requiring fees as set forth at Subpart G of this part must be filed in accordance with Sec. 0.401(b).

(4) Manually filed applications that do not require fees must be addressed and sent to Federal Communications Commission, 1270 Fairfield Road, Gettysburg, Pennsylvania 17325-7245.

(5) Standard forms may be reproduced and the copies used in accordance with the provisions of Sec. 0.409 of this chapter.

(6) Attachments to manually filed applications may be filed on a standard 3.5 magnetic diskette formatted to be readable by high density floppy drives operating under MS-DOS (version 3.X or later compatible versions). Each diskette submitted must contain an ASCII text file listing each filename and a brief description of the contents of each file and format for each document on the diskette. The files on the diskette, other than the table of contents, should be in Adobe Acrobat Portable Document Format (PDF) whenever possible. All diskettes submitted must be legibly labelled referencing the application and its filing date.

(e) Applications requiring prior coordination. Parties filing applications that require frequency coordination shall, prior to filing, complete all applicable frequency coordination requirements in service-specific rules contained within this chapter. After appropriate frequency coordination, such applications may be electronically filed via ULS or, if filed manually, must be forwarded to the appropriate address with the appropriate filing fee (if applicable) in accordance with subparagraph (d). Applications filed by the frequency coordinator on behalf of the applicant must be filed electronically.

(f) Applications for Amateur licenses. Each candidate for an amateur radio operator license which requires the applicant to pass one or more examination elements must present the administering Volunteer Examiners (VE) with all information required by the rules prior to the examination. The VEs may collect the information required by these rules in any manner of their choosing, including creating their own forms. Upon completion of the examination, the administering VEs will immediately grade the test papers and will then issue a certificate for successful completion of an amateur radio operator examination (CSCE) if the applicant is successful. The VEs will send all necessary information regarding a candidate to the Volunteer-Examiner Coordinator (VEC) coordinating the examination session. Applications filed with the Commission by VECs must be filed electronically via ULS. All other applications for amateur service licenses may be submitted manually to FCC, 1270 Fairfield Road, Gettysburg, PA 17325-7245, or may be electronically filed via ULS. Feeable requests for vanity call signs must be filed in accordance with Sec. 0.401 of this chapter or electronically filed via ULS.

[Revised as of October 1, 2000]

∗ ∗ ∗ ∗ ∗ ∗ ∗ ∗ ∗ ∗ ∗ ∗ ∗ ∗ ∗ ∗

Throughout this book, we have mentioned instances in which amateurs are not permitted to cause interference to other users in other services to protect FCC Field Offices, the National Radio Quiet Zone in West Virginia and the Arecibo Observatory in Puerto Rico. While not specified in Part 97, amateurs must know which other FCC rule sections affect amateur operations, such as protecting users in these services from interference. The specifics appear in §1.924. Some sections have been eliminated since they do not deal with Amateur Radio:

Sec. 1.924 Quiet zones.

Quiet zones are those areas where it is necessary to restrict radiation so as to minimize possible impact on the operations of radio astronomy or other facilities that are highly sensitive to interference. The areas involved and procedures required are as follows:

(a) NRAO, NRRO. The requirements of this paragraph are intended to minimize possible interference at the National Radio Astronomy Observatory site located at Green Bank, Pocahontas County, West Virginia, and at the Naval Radio Research Observatory site at Sugar Grove, Pendleton County, West Virginia.

Applicants and licensees planning to construct and operate a new or modified station at a permanent fixed location within the area bounded by N 39 deg. 15' 0.4" on the north, W 78 deg. 29' 59.0" on the east, N 37 deg. 30' 0.4" on the south, and W 80 deg. 29' 59.2" on the west must notify the Director, National Radio Astronomy Observatory, Post Office Box No. 2, Green Bank, West Virginia 24944, in writing, of the technical details of the proposed operation. The notification must include the geographical coordinates of the antenna location, the antenna height, antenna directivity (if any), the channel, the emission type and power.

When an application for authority to operate a station is filed with the FCC, the notification required in paragraph (a)(1) of this section should be sent at the same time. The application must state the date that notification in accordance with paragraph (a)(1) of this section was made. After receipt of such applications, the FCC will allow a period of 20 days for comments or objections in response to the notifications indicated.

If an objection is received during the 20-day period from the National Radio Astronomy Observatory for itself or on behalf of the Naval Radio Research Observatory, the FCC will, after consideration of the record, take whatever action is deemed appropriate.

(c) Federal Communications Commission protected field offices. The requirements of this paragraph are intended to minimize possible interference to FCC monitoring activities.

(1) Licensees and applicants planning to construct and operate a new or modified station at a permanent fixed location in the vicinity of an FCC protected field office are advised to give consideration, prior to filing applications, to the need to avoid interfering with the monitoring activities of that office. FCC protected field offices are listed in Sec. 0.121 of this chapter.

(2) Applications for stations (except mobile stations) that could produce on any channel a direct wave fundamental field strength of greater than 10 mV/m (-65.8 dBW/m^2 power flux density assuming a free space characteristic impedance of 120Ω) in the authorized bandwidth at the protected field office may be examined to determine the potential for interference with monitoring activities. After consideration of the effects of the predicted field strength of the proposed station, including the cumulative effects of the signal from the proposed station with other ambient radio field strength levels at the protected field office, the FCC may add a condition restricting radiation toward the protected field office to the station authorization.

(3) In the event that the calculated field strength exceeds 10 mV/m at the protected field office site, or if there is any question whether field strength levels might exceed that level, advance consultation with the FCC to discuss possible measures to avoid interference to monitoring activities should be considered. Prospective applicants may communicate with: Chief, Compliance and Information Bureau, Federal Communications Commission, Washington, DC 20554.

(4) Advance consultation is recommended for applicants that have no reliable data to indicate whether the field strength or power flux density figure indicated would be exceeded by their proposed radio facilities. In general, coordination is recommended for:

Stations located within 2.4 kilometers (1.5 miles) of the protected field office;

Stations located within 4.8 kilometers (3 miles) with 50 watts or more average effective radiated power (ERP) in the primary plane of polarization in the azimuthal direction of the protected field offices.

Stations located within 16 kilometers (10 miles) with 1 kw or more average ERP in the primary plane of polarization in the azimuthal direction of the protected field office.

The FCC will not screen applications to determine whether advance consultation has taken place. However, such consultation may serve to avoid the need for later modification of the authorizations of stations that interfere with monitoring activities at protected field offices.

(d) Notification to the Arecibo Observatory. The requirements in this section are intended to minimize possible interference at the Arecibo Observatory in Puerto Rico. Licensees must make reasonable efforts to protect the Observatory from interference. Licensees planning to construct and operate a new station at a permanent fixed location on the islands of Puerto Rico, Desecheo, Mona, Vieques or Culebra in services in which individual station licenses are issued by the FCC; planning to construct and operate a new station at a permanent fixed location on these islands that may cause interference to the operations of the Arecibo Observatory in services in which individual station licenses are not issued by the FCC; or planning a modification of any existing station at a permanent fixed location on these islands that would increase the likelihood of causing interference to the operations of the Arecibo Observatory must notify the Interference Office, Arecibo

Observatory, Post Office Box 995, Arecibo, Puerto Rico 00613, in writing or electronically (e-mail address: **prcz@naic.edu**), of the technical parameters of the planned operation. Carriers may wish to use the interference guidelines provided by Cornell University as guidance in designing facilities to avoid interference to the Observatory. The notification must include identification of the geographical coordinates of the antenna location (NAD-83 datum), the antenna height, antenna directivity (if any), proposed channel and FCC Rule Part, type of emission, and effective isotropic radiated power.

(1) In the Amateur radio service:

(i) The provisions of paragraph (d) of this section do not apply to repeaters that transmit on the 1.2 cm or shorter wavelength bands; and

(2) The coordination provision of paragraph (d) of this section does not apply to repeaters that are located 16 km or more from the Arecibo observatory.

(ii) In services in which individual station licenses are issued by the FCC, the notification required in paragraph (d) of this section should be sent the same time the application is filed with the FCC, and at least 20 days in advance of the applicant's planned operation. The application must state the date that notification in accordance with paragraph (d) of this section was made. In services in which individual station licenses are not issued by the FCC, the notification required in paragraph (d) of this section should be sent at least 45 days in advance of the applicant's planned operation. In the latter services, the Interference Office must inform the FCC of a notification by an applicant within 20 days if the Office plans to file comments or objections to the notification. After the FCC receives an application from a service applicant or is informed by the Interference Office of a notification from a service applicant, the FCC will allow the Interference Office a period of 20 days for comments or objections in response to the application or notification.

(3) If an objection to any planned service operation is received during the 20-day period from the Interference Office, the FCC will take whatever action is deemed appropriate.

✳ ✳ ✳ ✳ ✳ ✳ ✳ ✳ ✳ ✳ ✳ ✳ ✳ ✳ ✳

REQUIREMENTS FOR FILING AN ENVIRONMENTAL ASSESSMENT

When amateurs complete Form 605 (formerly the FCC Form 610), they must understand and certify by their signature the following statement: "Amateur Applicant certifies that the construction of the station would NOT be an action that is likely to have a significant environmental effect" (see the Commission's Rules 47 CFR Sections 1.1301-1.1319 and Section 97.13(a)).

Almost all amateurs will answer "no" to that question. The only ones who will are those whose stations will be located in an officially designated wildlife area, significant in American history, architecture, archeology, engineering or culture, that are listed, or are eligible for listing, in the National Register of Historic Places, in a wetlands area, those which require tower lighting and for stations which exceed the maximum permitted RF exposure limits.

By completing an FCC Form 605, applicants must also certify that they are in compliance with this statement: "Amateur Applicant certifies that they have READ and WILL COMPLY WITH Section 97.13(c) of the Commission's Rules regarding RADIOFREQUENCY (RF) RADIATION SAFETY and the amateur service section of OST/OET Bulletin Number 65." Section 97.13(c) makes reference to the Part 1 sections mentioned above, so ARRL thought it important that amateurs have a copy of the pertinent regulations. These segments are summarized since some deal with internal FCC actions with respect to Environment Impact Statements and Environmental Assessments. The sections mentioned are the procedures for implementing the National Environmental Policy Act of 1969. The text of 47 CFR Parts 1 and 2 (as well as other Title 47 Parts of the Code of Federal Regulations) can be found on-line at *http:// www.fcc.gov/wtb/rules.html.*

Sections 1.1301-1.1306 are not listed because they are long and of little or no interest to amateurs unless you determine that you must file an Environmental Assessment with the FCC. If you find that you must file an EA, which is a long process requiring FCC notification and public comment of the environmental consequences of the proposed action. You will beed to read these sections of Part 1. You can find these sections at the URL above or contact ARRL HQ.

§1.1307 Actions which may have a significant environmental effect, for which Environmental Assessments (EAs) must be prepared.

(a) Commission actions with respect to the following types of facilities may significantly affect the environment and thus require the preparation of EAs by the applicant (see Secs. 1.1308 and 1.1311) and may require further Commission environmental processing (see Secs. 1.1314, 1.1315 and 1.1317):

(1) Facilities that are to be located in an officially designated wilderness area.

(2) Facilities that are to be located in an officially designated wildlife preserve.

(3) Facilities that: (i) May affect listed threatened or endangered species or designated critical habitats; or (ii) are likely to jeopardize the continued existence of any proposed endangered or threatened species or likely to result in the destruction or adverse modification of proposed critical habitats, as determined by the Secretary of the Interior pursuant to the Endangered Species Act of 1973.

Note: The list of endangered and threatened species is contained in 50 CFR 17.11, 17.22, 222.23(a) and 227.4. The list of designated critical habitats is contained in 50 CFR 17.95, 17.96 and part 226. To ascertain the status of proposed species and habitats, inquiries may be directed to the Regional Director of the Fish and Wildlife Service, Department of the Interior.

(4) Facilities that may affect districts, sites, buildings, structures or objects, significant in American history, architecture, archeology, engineering or culture, that are listed, or are eligible for listing, in the National Register of Historic Places. (See 16 U.S.C. 470w(5); 36 CFR 60 and 800.)

Note: The National Register is updated and re-published in the Federal Register each year in February. To ascertain whether a proposal affects a historical property of national significance, inquiries also may be made to the appropriate State Historic Preservation Officer, see 16 U.S.C. 470a(b); 36 CFR parts 63 and 800.

(5) Facilities that may affect Indian religious sites.

(6) Facilities to be located in a flood Plain (See Executive Order 11988.)

(7) Facilities whose construction will involve significant change in surface features (e.g., wetland fill, deforestation or water diversion). (In the case of wetlands on Federal property, see Executive Order 11990.)

(8) Antenna towers and/or supporting structures that are to be equipped with

high intensity white lights which are to be located in residential neighborhoods, as defined by the applicable zoning law.

(b) In addition to the actions listed in paragraph (a) of this section, Commission actions granting construction permits, licenses to transmit or renewals thereof, equipment authorizations or modifications in existing facilities, require the preparation of an Environmental Assessment (EA) if the particular facility, operation or transmitter would cause human exposure to levels of radiofrequency radiation in excess of the limits in §1.1310 and §2.1093 of this chapter. Applications to the Commission for construction permits, licenses to transmit or renewals thereof, equipment authorizations or modifications in existing facilities must contain a statement confirming compliance with the limits unless the facility, operation, or transmitter is categorically excluded, as discussed below. Technical information showing the basis for this statement must be submitted to the Commission upon request.

(1) The appropriate exposure limits in §1.1310 and §2.1093 are generally applicable to all facilities, operations and transmitters regulated by the Commission. However, a determination of compliance with the exposure limits in §1.1310 or §2.1093 (routine environmental evaluation), and preparation of an EA if the limits are exceeded, is necessary only for facilities, operations and transmitters that fall into the categories listed in Table 1, or those specified in paragraph (b)(2) of this section. All other facilities, operations and transmitters are categorically excluded from making such studies or preparing an EA, except as indicated in paragraphs (c) and (d) of this section. For purposes of Table 1, "building-mounted antennas" means antennas mounted in or on a building structure that is occupied as a workplace or residence. The term "power" in column 2 of Table 1 refers to total operating power of the transmitting operation in question in terms of effective radiated power (ERP), equivalent isotropically radiated power (EIRP), or peak envelope power (PEP), as defined in § 2.1 of this chapter. For the case of the Cellular Radiotelephone Service, subpart H of part 22 of this chapter; the Personal Communications Service, part 24 of this chapter and the Specialized Mobile Radio Service, part 90 of this chapter, the phrase "total power of all channels" in column 2 of Table 1 means the sum of the ERP or EIRP of all co-located simultaneously operating transmitters owned and operated by a single licensee. When applying the criteria of Table 1, radiation in all directions should be considered. For the case of transmitting facilities using sectorized transmitting antennas, applicants and licensees should apply the criteria to all transmitting channels in a given sector, noting that for a highly directional antenna there is relatively little contribution to ERP or EIRP summation for other directions.

(2) Mobile and portable transmitting devices that operate in the Cellular Radiotelephone Service, the Personal Communications Services (PCS), the Satellite Communications Services, the General Wireless Communications Service, the Wireless Communications Service, the Maritime Services (ship earth stations only) and the Specialized Mobile Radio Service authorized under subpart H of part 22, part 24, part 25, part 26, part 27, part 80, and part 90 of this chapter are subject to routine environmental evaluation for RF exposure prior to equipment authorization or use, as specified in §§2.1091 and 2.1093 of this chapter. Unlicensed PCS, unlicensed NII and millimeter wave devices are also subject to routine environmental evaluation for RF exposure prior to equipment authorization or use, as specified in §§15.253(f), 15.255(g), and 15.319(i) and 15.407(f) of this chapter. All other mobile, portable, and unlicensed transmitting devices are categorically excluded from routine environ-

mental evaluation for RF exposure under §§2.1091 and 2.1093 of this chapter except as specified in paragraphs (c) and (d) of this section.

(3) In general, when the guidelines specified in §1.1310 are exceeded in an accessible area due to the emissions from multiple fixed transmitters, actions necessary to bring the area into compliance are the shared responsibility of all licensees whose transmitters produce, at the area in question, power density levels that exceed 5% of the power density exposure limit applicable to their particular transmitter or field strength levels that, when squared, exceed 5% of the square of the electric or magnetic field strength limit applicable to their particular transmitter. Owners of transmitter sites are expected to allow applicants and licensees to take reasonable steps to comply with the requirements contained in §1.1307(b) and, where feasible, should encourage co-location of transmitters and common solutions for controlling access to areas where the RF exposure limits contained in §1.1310 might be exceeded.

(i) Applicants for proposed (not otherwise excluded) transmitters, facilities or modifications that would cause non-compliance with the limits specified in §1.1310 at an accessible area previously in compliance must submit an EA if emissions from the applicant's transmitter or facility would result, at the area in question, in a power density that exceeds 5% of the power density exposure limit applicable to that transmitter or facility or in a field strength that, when squared, exceeds 5% of the square of the electric or magnetic field strength limit applicable to that transmitter [or] facility.

(ii) Renewal applicants whose (not otherwise excluded) transmitters or facilities contribute to the field strength or power density at an accessible area not in compliance with the limits specified in §1.1310 must submit an EA if emissions from the applicant's transmitter or facility results, at the area in question, in a power density that exceeds 5% of the power density exposure limit applicable to that transmitter or facility or in a field strength that, when squared, exceeds 5% of the square of the electric or magnetic field strength limit applicable to that transmitter or facility.

(4) Transition Provisions. Applications filed with the Commission prior to October 15, 1997 (or January 1, 1998, for the Amateur Radio Service only), for construction permits, licenses to transmit or renewals thereof, modifications in existing facilities or other authorizations or renewals thereof require the preparation of an Environmental Assessment if the particular facility, operation or transmitter would cause human exposure to levels of radiofrequency radiation that are in excess of the requirements contained in paragraphs (b)(4)(i)-(4)(iii) of this section. In accordance with section 1.1312, if no new application or Commission action is required for a license to construct a new facility or physically modify an existing facility, e.g., geographic area licensees, and construction begins on or after October 15, 1997, the licensee will be required to prepare an Environmental Assessment if construction or modification of the facility would not comply with the provisions of paragraph (b)(1) of this section. These transition provisions do not apply to applications for equipment authorization or use of mobile, portable and unlicensed devices specified in paragraph (2) of this section.

(5) Existing transmitting facilities, devices and operations: All existing transmitting facilities, operations and devices regulated by the Commission must be in compliance with the requirements of paragraphs (1) - (3) of this section by September 1, 2000, or, if not in compliance, file an Environmental Assessment as specified in 47 CFR §1.1311.

(c) If an interested person alleges that a particular action, otherwise categorically excluded, will have a significant environmental effect, the person shall submit to the Bureau responsible for processing that action a written petition setting forth in detail the reasons justifying or circumstances necessitating environmental consideration in the decision-making process. (See §1.1313.) The Bureau shall review the petition and consider the environmental concerns that have been raised. If the Bureau determines that the action may have a significant environmental impact, the Bureau will require the applicant to prepare an EA (see §§1.1308 and 1.1311), which will serve as the basis for the determination to proceed with or terminate environmental processing.

(d) If the Bureau responsible for processing a particular action, otherwise categorically excluded, determines that the proposal may have a significant environmental impact, the Bureau, on its own motion, shall require the applicant to submit an EA. The Bureau will review and consider the EA as in paragraph (c) of this section.

✳ ✳ ✳ ✳ ✳ ✳ ✳ ✳ ✳ ✳ ✳ ✳ ✳ ✳ ✳

§1.1308 Consideration of environmental assessments (EAs); findings of no significant impact.

(a) Applicants shall prepare EAs for actions that may have a significant environmental impact (see §1.1307). An EA is described in detail in §1.1311 of this part of the Commission rules.

(b) The EA is a document which shall explain the environmental consequences of the proposal and set forth sufficient analysis for the Bureau or the Commission to reach a determination that the proposal will or will not have a significant environmental effect. To assist in making that determination, the Bureau or the Commission may request further information from the applicant, interested persons, and agencies and authorities which have jurisdiction by law or which have relevant expertise.

(c) If the Bureau or the Commission determines, based on an independent review of the EA and any applicable mandatory consultation requirements imposed upon federal agencies (see note above), that the proposal will have a significant environmental impact upon the quality of the human environment, it will so inform the applicant. The applicant will then have an opportunity to amend its application so as to reduce, minimize, or eliminate environmental problems. See §1.1309. If the environmental problem is not eliminated, the Bureau will publish in the Federal Register a Notice of Intent (see §1.1314) that EISs will be prepared (see §1.1315 and 1.1317), or

(d) If the Bureau or Commission determines, based on an independent review of the EA, and any mandatory consultation requirements imposed upon federal agencies (see the note to paragraph (b) of this section), that the proposal would not have a significant impact, it will make a finding of no significant impact. Thereafter, the application will be processed without further documentation of environmental effect. Pursuant to CEQ regulations, see 40 CFR 1501.4 and 1501.6, the applicant must provide the community notice of the Commission's finding of no significant impact.

§1.1309 Application amendments.

Applicants are permitted to amend their applications to reduce, minimize or eliminate potential environmental problems. As a routine matter, an applicant will be permitted to amend its application within thirty (30) days after the Commission or the Bureau informs the applicant that the proposal will have a significant impact upon the quality of the human environment (see §1.1308(c)). The period of thirty (30) days may be extended upon a showing of good cause.

§1.1310 Radiofrequency radiation exposure limits.

The criteria listed in table 1 shall be used to evaluate the environmental impact of human exposure to radiofrequency (RF) radiation as specified in §1.1307(b), except in the case of portable devices which shall be evaluated according to the provisions of §2.1093 of this chapter. Further information on evaluating compliance with these limits can be found in the FCC's OST/OET Bulletin Number 65, "Evaluating Compliance with FCC-Specified Guidelines for Human Exposure to Radio-frequency Radiation."

NOTE TO INTRODUCTORY PARAGRAPH: These limits are generally based on recommended exposure guidelines published by the National Council on Radiation Protection and Measurements (NCRP) in "Biological Effects and Exposure Criteria for Radiofrequency Electromagnetic Fields," NCRP Report No. 86, Sections 17.4.1, 17.4.1.1, 17.4.2 and 17.4.3. Copyright NCRP, 1986, Bethesda, Maryland 20814. In the frequency range from 100 MHz to 1500 MHz, exposure limits for field strength and power density are also generally based on guidelines recommended by the American National Standards Institute (ANSI) in Section 4.1 of "IEEE Standard for Safety Levels with Respect to Human Exposure to Radio Frequency Electromagnetic Fields, 3 kHz to 300 GHz," ANSI/IEEE C95.1-1992, Copyright 1992 by the Institute of Electrical and Electronics Engineers, Inc., New York, New York 10017.

§1.1311 Environmental information to be included in the environmental assessment (EA).

(a) The applicant shall submit an EA with each application that is subject to environmental processing (see §1.1307). The EA shall contain the following information:

(1) For antenna towers and satellite earth stations, a description of the facilities as well as supporting structures and appurtenances, and a description of the site as well as the surrounding area and uses. If high intensity white lighting is proposed or utilized within a residential area, the EA must also address the impact of this lighting upon the residents.

(2) A statement as to the zoning classification of the site, and communications with, or proceedings before and determinations (if any) made by zoning, planning, environmental or other local, state or federal authorities on matters relating to environmental effect.

(3) A statement as to whether construction of the facilities has been a source of controversy on environmental grounds in the local community.

(4) A discussion of environmental and other considerations which led to the

---

Table 1

Transmitters, Facilities and Operations Subject to Routine Environmental Evaluation Service (Title 47 CFR Rule Part) Evaluation Required If:

Amateur Radio Service (Part 97)	transmitter output power > levels specified in §97.13(c)(1) of this chapter

selection of the particular site and, if relevant, the particular facility; the nature and extent of any unavoidable adverse environmental effects, and any alternative sites or facilities which have been or might reasonably be considered.

(5) Any other information that may be requested by the Bureau or Commission.

(6) If endangered or threatened species or their critical habitats may be affected, the applicant's analysis must utilize the best scientific and commercial data available, see 50 CFR 402.14(c).

(b) The information submitted in the EA shall be factual (not argumentative or conclusory) and concise with sufficient detail to explain the environmental consequences and to enable the Commission or Bureau, after an independent review of the EA, to reach a determination concerning the proposal's environmental impact, if any. The EA shall deal specifically with any feature of the site which has special environmental significance (e.g., wilderness areas, wildlife preserves, natural migration paths for birds and other wildlife, and sites of historic, architectural, or archeological value). In the case of historically significant sites, it shall specify the effect of the facilities on any district, site, building, structure or object listed, or eligible for listing, in the National structure or object listed, or eligible for listing, in the National Register of Historic Places. It shall also detail any substantial change in the character of the land utilized (e.g., deforestation, water diversion, wetland fill, or other extensive change of surface features). In the case of wilderness areas, wildlife preserves, or other like areas, the statement shall discuss the effect of any continuing pattern of human intrusion into the area (e.g., necessitated by the operation and maintenance of the facilities).

(c) The EA shall also be accompanied with evidence of site approval which has been obtained from local or federal land use authorities.

(d) To the extent that such information is submitted in another part of the application, it need not be duplicated in the EA, but adequate cross-reference to such information shall be supplied.

(e) An EA need not be submitted to the Commission if another agency of the Federal Government has assumed responsibility for determining whether the facilities in question will have a significant effect on the quality of the human environment and, if it will, for invoking the environmental impact statement process.

§1.1312 Facilities for which no pre-construction authorization is required.

(a) In the case of facilities for which no Commission authorization prior to construction is required by the Commission's rules and regulations the licensee or applicant shall initially ascertain whether the proposed facility may have a significant environmental impact as defined in §1.1307 of this part or is categorically excluded from environmental processing under §1.1306 of this part.

(b) If a facility covered by paragraph (a) of this section may have a significant environmental impact, the information required by §1.1311 of this part shall be submitted by the licensee or applicant and ruled on by the Commission, and environmental processing (if invoked) shall be completed, see §1.1308 of this part, prior to the initiation of construction of the facility.

(c) If a facility covered by paragraph (a) of this section is categorically excluded from environmental processing, the licensee or applicant may proceed with construction and operation of the facility in accordance with the applicable licensing rules and procedures.

(d) If, following the initiation of construction under this section, the licensee or applicant discovers that the proposed facility may have a significant environmental effect, it shall immediately cease construction which may have that effect, and submit the information required by §1.1311 of this part. The Commission shall rule on that submission and complete further environmental processing (if invoked), §1.1308 of this part, before such construction is resumed.

(e) Paragraphs (a) through (d) of this section shall not apply to the construction of mobile stations.

§§1.1313, 1.1314, 1.1315, 1.1317, and 1.1319 detail the specific FCC requirements for filing environmental impact statements (EISs), Draft Environmental Impact Statement (DEIS) Comments, and Final Environmental Impact Statement (FEIS). If you find that you are required to file one of these documents, and almost all amateurs won't, then you should read these sections in detail.

PART 2—FREQUENCY ALLOCATIONS AND RADIO TREATY MATTERS; GENERAL RULES AND REGULATIONS

§2.1091 Radiofrequency radiation exposure evaluation: mobile devices.

✳ ✳ ✳ ✳ ✳ ✳ ✳ ✳ ✳ ✳ ✳ ✳ ✳ ✳ ✳ ✳

(b) For purposes of this section mobile devices are defined as transmitters designed to be used in other than fixed locations and to generally be used in such a way that a separation distance of at least 20 centimeters is normally maintained between radiating antennas and the body of the user or nearby persons.

(c) Mobile devices that operate in the Cellular Radiotelephone Service, the Personal Communications Services, the Satellite Communications Services, the Maritime Services and the Specialized Mobile Radio Service authorized under subpart H of part 22 of this chapter, part 24 of this chapter, part 25 of this chapter, part 80 of this chapter (ship earth station devices only) and part 90 of this chapter ("covered" SMR devices only, as defined in the note to Table 1 of §1.1307(b)(1) of this chapter), are subject to routine environmental evaluation for RF exposure prior to equipment authorization or use if their effective radiated power (ERP) is 1.5 watts or more. Unlicensed personal communications service and unlicensed millimeter wave devices authorized under §15.253, §15.255 and subpart D of part 15 of this chapter are also subject to routine environmental evaluation for RF exposure prior to equipment authorization or use, regardless of their power used, unless they meet the definition of a portable device as specified in §2.1093(b). All other mobile and unlicensed transmitting devices are categorically excluded from routine environmental evaluation for RF exposure prior to equipment authorization, except as specified in §§1.1307(c) and 1.1307(d) of this chapter. Applications for equipment authorization of mobile and unlicensed transmitting devices subject to routine environmental evaluation must contain a statement confirming compliance with the limits specified in paragraph (d) of this section as part of their application. Technical information showing the basis for this statement must be submitted to the Commission upon request.

(d)(3) If appropriate, compliance with exposure guidelines for devices in this section can be accomplished by the use of warning labels and by providing users with information concerning minimum separation distances from transmitting structures and proper installation of antennas.

(4) In some cases, e.g., modular or desktop transmitters, the potential conditions of use of a device may not allow easy classification of that device as either mobile or portable (also see 47 CFR 2.1093). In such cases, applicants are responsible for determining minimum distances for compliance for the intended use and installation of the device based on evaluation of either specific absorption rate (SAR), field strength or power density, whichever is most appropriate.

§2.1093 Radiofrequency radiation exposure evaluation: portable devices.

(b) For purposes of this section, a portable device is defined as a transmitting device designed to be used so that the radiating structure(s) of the device is/are within 20 centimeters of the body of the user.

(c) Portable devices that operate in the Cellular Radiotelephone Service, the Personal Communications Services, the Satellite Communications services, the

---

Table A.1
Maximum Permissible Exposure (MPE) Limits

Controlled Exposure (6-Minute Average)

Frequency Range (MHz)	Electric Field Strength (V/m)	Magnetic Field Strength (A/m)	Power Density (mW/cm^2)
0.3-3.0	614	1.63	(100)*
3.0-30	1842/f	4.89/f	(900/f^2)*
30-300	61.4	0.163	1.0
300-1500	—	—	f/300
1500-100,000	—	—	5

Uncontrolled Exposure (30-Minute Average)

Frequency Range (MHz)	Electric Field Strength (V/m)	Magnetic Field Strength (A/m)	Power Density (mW/cm^2)
0.3-1.34	614	1.63	(100)*
1.34-30	824/f	2.19/f	(180/f^2)*
30-300	27.5	0.073	0.2
300-1500	—	—	f/1500
1500-100,000	—	—	1.0

f = frequency in MHz
* = Plane-wave equivalent power density

NOTE 1 TO TABLE 1: Occupational/controlled limits apply in situations in which persons are exposed as a consequence of their employment provided those persons are fully aware of the potential for exposure and can exercise control over their exposure. Limits for occupational/controlled exposure also apply in situations when an individual is transient through a location where occupational/controlled limits apply provided he or she is made aware of the potential for exposure.

NOTE 2 TO TABLE 1: General population/uncontrolled exposures apply in situations in which the general public may be exposed, or in which persons that are exposed as a consequence of their employment may not be fully aware of the potential for exposure or cannot exercise control over their exposure.

General Wireless Communications Service, the Wireless Communications Service, the Maritime Services and the Specialized Mobile Radio Service authorized under subpart H of part 22 of this chapter, part 24 of this chapter, part 25 of this chapter, part 26 of this chapter, part 27 of this chapter, part 80 of this chapter (ship earth station devices only), part 90 of this chapter, and portable unlicensed personal communication service, unlicensed NII devices and millimeter wave devices authorized under §15.253, §15.255 or subparts D and E of part 15 of this chapter are subject to routine environmental evaluation for RF exposure prior to equipment authorization or use. All other portable transmitting devices are categorically excluded from routine environmental evaluation for RF exposure prior to equipment authorization or use, except as specified in §§1.1307(c) and 1.1307(d) of this chapter. Applications for equipment authorization of portable transmitting devices subject to routine environmental evaluation must contain a statement confirming compliance with the limits specified in paragraph (d) of this section as part of their application. Technical information showing the basis for this statement must be submitted to the Commission upon request.

(d) The limits to be used for evaluation are based generally on criteria published by the American National Standards Institute (ANSI) for localized specific absorption rate ("SAR") in Section 4.2 of "IEEE Standard for Safety Levels with Respect to Human Exposure to Radio Frequency Electromagnetic Fields, 3 kHz to 300 GHz," ANSI/IEEE C95.1-1992, Copyright 1992 by the Institute of Electrical and Electronics Engineers, Inc., New York, New York 10017. These criteria for SAR evaluation are similar to those recommended by the National Council on Radiation Protection and Measurements (NCRP) in "Biological Effects and Exposure Criteria for Radiofrequency Electromagnetic Fields," NCRP Report No. 86, Section 17.4.5. Copyright NCRP, 1986, Bethesda, Maryland 20814. SAR is a measure of the rate of energy absorption due to exposure to an RF transmitting source. SAR values have been related to threshold levels for potential biological hazards. The criteria to be used are specified in paragraphs (d)(1) and (d)(2) of this section and shall apply for portable devices transmitting in the frequency range from 100 kHz to 6 GHz. Portable devices that transmit at frequencies above 6 GHz are to be evaluated in terms of the MPE limits specified in §1.1310 of this chapter. Measurements and calculations to demonstrate compliance with MPE field strength or power density limits for devices operating above 6 GHz should be made at a minimum distance of 5 cm from the radiating source.

✳ ✳ ✳ ✳ ✳ ✳ ✳ ✳ ✳ ✳ ✳ ✳ ✳ ✳ ✳

Classification of Emission Designators

Emission designators generally consist of a three character designator, such as J3E. These are discussed in Chapter 4. Emission Designators can be more specific and can give more information about the emission, but they are not required by the FCC. The classification of emission designators is found in Part 2. See http://www.itu.int/radioclub/rr/aps01.htm or contact ARRL HQ.

§2.201 Emission, modulation and transmission characteristics.

The following system of designating emission, modulation and transmission characteristics shall be employed.

(a) Emissions are designated according to their classification and their necessary bandwidth.

(b) A minimum of three symbols are used to describe the basic characteristics of radio waves. Emissions are classified and symbolized according to the following characteristics:

    (1) First symbol—type of modulation of the main carrier;

    (2) Second symbol—nature of signal(s) modulating the main carrier;

    (3) Third symbol—type of information to be transmitted.

Note: A fourth and fifth symbol are provided for additional information and are shown in Appendix 6, Part A of the ITU Radio Regulations. Use of the fourth and fifth symbol is optional. Therefore, the symbols may be used as described in Appendix 6, but are not required by the Commission.

(c) First symbol—types of modulation of the main carrier:

(1) Emission of an unmodulated carrier .... N

(2) Emission in which the main carrier is amplitude-modulated (including cases where subcarriers are angle-modulated):

    —Double sideband .... A

    —Single sideband, full carrier .... H

    —Single sideband, reduced or variable level carrier .... R

    —Single sideband, suppressed carrier .... J

    —Independent sidebands .... B

    —Vestigial sideband C

(3) Emission in which the main carrier is angle-modulated:

    —Frequency modulation .... F

    —Phase modulation .... G

Note: Whenever frequency modulation (F) is indicated, phase modulation (G) is also acceptable.

(4) Emission in which the main carrier is amplitude and angle-modulated either simultaneously or in a pre-established sequence .... D

(5) Emission of pulses[1]

    —Sequence of unmodulated pulses . ... P

    —A sequence of pulses:

    —Modulated in amplitude .... K

    —Modulated in width/duration L

    —Modulated in position/phase .... M

    —In which the carrier is angle-modulated during the period of the pulse ... Q

    —Which is a combination of the foregoing or is produced by other means V

(6) Cases not covered above, in which an emission consists of the main carrier modulated, either simultaneously or in a pre-established sequence in a combination of two or more of the following modes: amplitude, angle, pulse. W

(7) Cases not otherwise covered X

(d) Second Symbol—nature of signal(s) modulating the main carrier:

(1) No modulating signal 0

(2) A single channel containing quantized or digital information without the use of a modulating subcarrier, excluding time-division multiplex 1

(3) A single channel containing quantized or digital information with the use of a modulating subcarrier, excluding time-division multiplex 2

(4) A single channel containing analog information 3

(5) Two or more channels containing quantized or digital information 7

(6) Two or more channels containing analog information 8

(7) Composite system with one or more channels containing quantized or digital information, together with one or more channels containing analog information 9

(8) Cases not otherwise covered X

(e) Third Symbol—type of information to be transmitted:[2]

(1) No information transmitted .... N
(2) Telegraphy, for aural reception .... A
(3) Telegraphy, for automatic reception .... B
(4) Facsimile C
(5) Data transmission, telemetry, telecommand .... D
(6) Telephony (including sound broadcasting) .... E
(7) Television (video) .... F
(8) Combination of the above .... W
(9) Cases not otherwise covered X

(f) Type *B* emission: As an exception to the above principles, damped waves are symbolized in the Commission's rules and regulations as type *B* emission. The use of type B emissions is forbidden.

(g) Whenever the full designation of an emission is necessary, the symbol for that emission, as given above, shall be preceded by the necessary bandwidth of the emission as indicated in §2.202(b)(1).

[1]Emissions where the main carrier is directly modulated by a signal which has been coded into quantized form (e.g., pulse code modulation) should be designated under (2) or (3):

[2]In this context the word "information" does not include information of a constant, unvarying nature such as is provided by standard frequency emissions, continuous wave and pulse radars, etc.

✱ ✱ ✱ ✱ ✱ ✱ ✱ ✱ ✱ ✱ ✱ ✱ ✱ ✱ ✱

§2.202 Bandwidths.

(a) *Occupied bandwidth.* The frequency bandwidth such that, below its lower and above its upper frequency limits, the mean powers radiated are each equal to 0.5 percent of the total mean power radiated by a given emission. In some cases, for example multi-channel frequency-division systems, the percentage of 0.5 percent may lead to certain difficulties in the practical application of the definitions of occupied and necessary bandwidth; in such cases a different percentage may prove useful.

(b) *Necessary bandwidth.* For a given class of emission, the minimum value of the occupied bandwidth sufficient to ensure the transmission of information at the rate and with the quality required for the system employed, under specified conditions. Emissions useful for the good functioning of the receiving equipment as, for example, the emission corresponding to the carrier of reduced carrier systems, shall be included in the necessary bandwidth.

✱ ✱ ✱ ✱ ✱ ✱ ✱ ✱ ✱ ✱ ✱ ✱ ✱ ✱ ✱

§2.815 External radio frequency power amplifiers.

(a) As used in this Part, an external radio frequency power amplifier is any device which, (1) when used in conjunction with a radio transmitter as a signal source is capable of amplification of that signal, and (2) is not an integral part of a radio transmitter as manufactured.

(b) After April 27, 1978, no person shall manufacture, sell or lease, offer for sale or lease (including advertising for sale or lease), or import, ship, or distribute for the purpose of selling or leasing or offering for sale or lease, any external radio frequency power amplifier or amplifier kit capable of operation on any frequency or frequencies between 24 and 35 MHz.

NOTE: For purposes of this part, the amplifier will be deemed incapable of operation between 24 and 35 MHz if:

(1) The amplifier has no more than 6 decibels of gain between 24 and 26 MHz and between 28 and 35 MHz. (This gain is determined by the ratio of the input RF driving signal (mean power measurement) to the mean RF output power of the amplifier.); and

(2) The amplifier exhibits no amplification (0 decibels of gain) between 26 and 28 MHz.

(c) No person shall manufacture, sell or lease, offer for sale or lease (including advertising for sale or lease) or import, ship or distribute for the purpose of selling or leasing or offering for sale or lease, any external radio frequency power amplifier or amplifier kit capable of operation on any frequency or frequencies below 144 MHz unless the amplifier has received a grant of type acceptance in accordance with Subpart J of this part and Subpart C of Part 97 or other relevant parts of this chapter. No more than 10 external radio frequency power amplifiers or amplifier kits may be constructed for evaluation purposes in preparation for the submission of an application for a grant of type acceptance.

NOTE: For the purposes of this part, an amplifier will be deemed incapable of operation below 144 MHz if the amplifier is not capable of being easily modified to increase its amplification characteristics below 120 MHz, and either:

(1) The mean output power of the amplifier decreases, as frequency decreases from 144 MHz, to a point where 0 decibels or less gain is exhibited at 120 MHz and below 120 MHz, or

(2) The amplifier is not capable of even short periods of operation below 120 MHz without sustaining permanent damage to its amplification circuitry.

(d) The proscription in paragraph (b) of this section shall not apply to the marketing, as defined in that paragraph, by a licensed amateur radio operator to another licensed amateur radio operator of an external radio frequency power amplifier fabricated in not more than one unit of the same model in a calendar year by that operator provided the amplifier is for the amateur operator's personal use at his licensed amateur radio station and the requirements of §§97.315 and 97.317 of this chapter are met.

(e) The proscription in paragraph (c) of this section shall not apply in the marketing, as defined in that paragraph, by a licensed amateur radio operator to another licensed amateur radio operator of an external radio frequency power amplifier if the amplifier is for the amateur operator's personal use at his licensed amateur radio station and the requirements of §§97.315 and 97.317 of this chapter are met.

Appendix 3

REPORTS AND ORDERS CHANGING PART 97 SINCE 1989

EFFECTIVE DATE	DOCKET	SUBJECT
Sep 1,'89	88-139	Reorganization and Deregulation of Part 97 of the Rules Governing the Amateur Radio Service. Complete Part 97 rewrite
Sep 7,'89	88-139	Errata—corrects index, §§97.5, 97.15, 97.109, 97.119, 97.207, 97.209.
Jul 2,'90		Waiver of Parts 2 and 97 of the Rules Concerning Frequency Sharing Requirements Applicable to the Amateur service in Portions of Colorado and Wyoming. Not a Report & Order—suspends but does not change parts of §97.303(g).
Sep 10,'90	88-139	Minor & technical amendments & clarifications to §§97.19, 97.21, 97.119, 97.301, 97.305.
Feb 14,'91	90-55	Amendment of Part 97 of the Commission's Rules Concerning the Establishment of a Codeless Class of Amateur Operator License. §§97.119, 97.301, 97.501.
Feb 14, '91	90-356	Amendment of the Amateur Radio Service Rules to Make the Service More Accessible to Persons with Handicaps. §§97.3. 97.505, 97.511.
Mar 16,'91	90-100	Amendment of the Amateur Service Rules to Relocate the Novice and Technician Operator Class Frequency Segment within the Amateur Service 80 Meter Band. §§97.301, 97.313.
May 29,'91	89-552	Amendment of Part 90 of the Commission's Rules to Provide for the Use of the 220-222 MHz Band by the Private Land Mobile Radio Services. §§97.201, 97.203, 97.205, 97.301, 97.303.
May 3,'91	—	Editorial Amendment of §97.303
Sep 30,'91		Nonsubstantive Amendment of Part 97 of the Commission's Rules Governing the Amateur Radio Services. §97.301 & 97.303
Oct 31,'91	90-356	Amendment of the Amateur Radio Service Rules to Make the Service More Accessible to Persons with Handicaps. §97.505.
Aug 29,'91	—	Erratum—corrects §97.301
Dec 16,'91	90-561	Miscellaneous Amendments to Part 97 of the Rules Governing the Amateur Radio Services. §§97.3, 97.111, 97.113, 97.201, 97.207, 97.211, 97.213, 97.215, 97.216, 97.309.

Jul 15, '92	90-356	Nonsubstantive amendment of the Amateur Radio Service Rules Concerning Examination Credit for Handicapped Persons. §97.505.
Sep 23,'92	92-310	Amendment of the Amateur Radio Services Rules (Part 97) Concerning Space Station Operations. §97.207.
Oct 30,'92		Editorial Amendment: spelling correction & FCC address change.
Jul 1,'93	92-154	Amendment of the Amateur Service Rules to Include Novice Class Operator License Examinations in the Volunteer-Examiner Coordinator Examination System. §§97.507, 97.511, 97.527.
Jul 19,'93		Amendment of the Amateur Service Rules to Establish Station Call Sign Administrators for Club and Military Recreation Stations. Program never implemented.
Jul 28,'93	92-136	Amendment of Part 97 of the Commission's Rules to Relax Restrictions on the Scope of Permissible Communications in the Amateur Service. §97.113
Oct 7,'93		Amendment of Part 97 of the Commission's Rules Regarding the Amateur Service. §97.21-deletes station location requirement.
Feb 1,'94	92-289	Amendment of the Amateur Service Rules Concerning the 222-225 MHz and 1240-1300 MHz Frequency Bands. 222-222.15 subband created. Novices not granted repeater control op. privileges on 1.25 m or 23 cm bands. §§97.201, 97.205, 97.301.
Dec 29,'93		Amendment of the Amateur Service Rules to Establish Station Call Sign Administrators for Club and Military Recreation Stations. Cancellation of program concurrent with vanity NPRM
Jun 1,'94	93-85	Amendment of Part 97 of the Commission's Rules Concerning Message Forwarding Systems in the Amateur Service. §§97.3, 97.109, 97.205, 97.219.
Dec 20,'94		Amendment of the Amateur Service Rules to Change Procedures for Filing an Amateur Service License Application and to Make Other Procedural Changes. Creates Tech Plus class; allows electronic filing, Form 610-R; adds requirement to change address; drops requirement for license document in hand. §§97.5, 97.7, 97.9, 97.17, 97.21, 97.23, 97.25, 97.27, 97.29, 97.301, 97.501, 97.505, 97.507, 97.509, 97.511, 97.519.

Mar 24,'95	93-305	Amendment of the Amateur Service Rules to Implement a Vanity Call Sign System. §§97.3, 97.17, 97.19, 97.21.
Feb 6,'95 —	93-61	Amendment of Part 90 of the Commission's Rules to Adopt Regulations for Automatic Vehicle Monitoring Systems. Does not modify Part 97, but changes AVMS to Location and Monitoring Service (LMS) and expands its subbands to cover the entire amateur band at 902-928 MHz. We are still secondary to the LMS.
Feb 17,'95 —	94-32	Allocation of Spectrum Below 5 GHz Transferred from Federal Government Use. This does not modify Part 97, but does modify §2.106 and Part 15 to, among other things, give amateurs primary status in the 2390-2400 and 2402-2417 MHz bands.
Apr 26,'95	93-40	Allocation of the 219-220 MHz Band for Use by the Amateur Radio Service. §§2.106, 97.201, 97.301, 97.303, 97.305, 97.307, 97.313.
Jul 1,'95	94-59	Amendment of Part 97 of the Commission's Rules Concerning HF Digital Communications in the Amateur Service. §§97.109, 97.221
Oct 31, '95	—	Amendment of Parts 80, 90 and 97 of the Commission's Rules to reflect Bureau name changes and to make other editorial changes. Changes "Private Radio" to "Wireless Telecommunications" §§97.15, 97.19, 97.207
Oct 2, '95	93-305	Amendment of the Amateur Service Rules to Implement a Vanity Call Sign System. Limits requests for call signs reflecting Region 11, 12, & 13. Requires applicant seeking deceased relative's call to have appropriate class of license. Fixes a renewal problem. §§97.17, 97.19, 97.21.
Nov 1, '95	—	Amendment of the Amateur Service Rules to Clarify Use of CLOVER, G-TOR, and PacTOR Digital Codes. §97.309.
Mar 7,'96	95-473	In the Matter of Streamlining the Commission's Antenna Structure Clearance Procedure and Revision of Part 17 of the Commission's Rules Concerning Construction, Marking, and Lighting of Antenna Structures.
Apr 11, '96	96-74	In the Matter of Amendment of Part 97 of the Commission's Rules to Conform the Amateur Service Rules to the Provisions of the Telecommunications Act of 1996. Drops VE and VEC Conflict of interest and reimbursement rules. §§97.509, 97.521, 97.527.

Mar 22, '96	93-40	Allocation of the 219-220 MHz Band for Use by the Amateur Radio Service. Minor amendment of §97.303.
Apr 1, '97	95-57	Amendments to improve eligibility standards for a club station license; Recognize the role of VE teams and session managers; Establish a special event call sign system and Authorize a self-assigned indicator in the station identification announcement.
Oct 15, '97	96-2	Amendment of the Commission's Rules to Establish a Radio Astronomy Coordination Zone in Puerto Rico. §97.203 (h).
Oct 5, '98	98-94	Streamlining the Equipment Authorization Process; FCC Type Acceptance process is replaced by FCC Certification. §§97.315, 97.317
Oct 21, '98	98-20	Biennial Regulatory Review of Parts 0, 1, 13, 22, 24, 26, 27, 80, 87, 90, 95, 97 and 101 of the Commission's Rules to Facilitate the Development and Use of the Universal Licensing System in the Wireless Telecommunications Services. §§97.3, 97.5, 97.7, 97.9, 97.13, 97.15, 97.17, 97.19, 97.21, 97.23, 97.25, 97.27, 97.29, 97.107, 97.119, 97.201, 97.203, 97.205, 97.207, 97.301, 97.505, 97.509, 97.519.
June 28, ' 99	98-20	Memorandum Opinion and Order on Reconstruction. 97.15, 97.17, 97.21.
Oct 21, '98	96-188	Amendment of the Amateur Service Rules to Authorize Visiting Foreign Amateur Operators to Operate Stations in the United States
Nov 1, '99	97-12	Amendment of the Amateur Service Rules to Provide for Greater Use of Spread Spectrum Communication Technologies (for a copy, see **http://www.arrl.org/ announce/regulatory/wt97-12/**). §§97.3, 97.305, 97.311.
Apr 15, '00	98-143	1998 Biennial Review—Part 97 of the Commission's Amateur Service Rules (see **http://www.arrl.org/announce/regulatory/ wt98-143ro.pdf**). §§97.9, 97.13, 97.17, 97.21, 97.301, 97.307, 97.313, 97.407, 97.501, 97.503, 97.505, 97.507, 97.509.
Jul 1, '01	98-143	1998 Biennial Review of Part 97 (plus denials of filed petitions) §§ 97.119 (f)(2), (3); 97.527 (see **http://www.arrl.org/FandES/Field/ regulations/**.)

Appendix 4

RECIPROCAL OPERATING AGREEMENT WITH CANADA

Convention Between Canada and the United States of America, Relating to the operation by Citizens of Either Country of Certain Radio Equipment or Stations in the Other Country (Effective May 15, 1952)

Article III

It is agreed that persons holding appropriate amateur licenses issued by either country may operate their amateur stations in the territory of the other country under the following conditions:

(a) Each visiting amateur may be required to register and receive a permit before operating any amateur station licensed by his government.

(b) The visiting amateur will identify his station by:

(1) Radiotelegraph operation. The amateur call sign issued to him/her by the licensing country followed by a slant (/) sign and the amateur call sign prefix and call area number of the country he is visiting.

(2) Radiotelephone operation. The amateur call sign in English issued to him by the licensing country followed by the words, "fixed" "portable" or "mobile," as appropriate, and the amateur call sign prefix and call area number of the country he is visiting.

(c) Each amateur station shall indicate at least once during each contact with another station its geographical location as nearly as possible by city and state or city and province.

(d) In other respects the amateur station shall be operated in accordance with the laws and regulations of the country in which the station is temporarily located.

Appendix 5

EXTRACTS FROM THE INTERNATIONAL RADIO REGULATIONS

Among other things, ITU Article S25 states that amateurs must be able to send and receive texts in Morse code before HF operation can start. A copy of these international Radio Regulations can be found at *http://www.itu.int/ plweb-cgi/fastweb?getdoc+view1+www+5151+7++s25* or from ARRL HQ.

ARTICLE S25

Section I. Amateur Service

S25.1 § 1. Radiocommunications between amateur stations of different countries shall be forbidden if the administration of one of the countries concerned has notified that it objects to such radiocommunications.

S25.2 § 2. 1) When transmissions between amateur stations of different countries are permitted, they shall be made in plain language and shall be limited to messages of a technical nature relating to tests and to remarks of a personal character for which, by reason of their unimportance, recourse to the public telecommunications service is not justified.

S25.3 2) It is absolutely forbidden for amateur stations to be used for transmitting international communications on behalf of third parties.

S25.4 3) The preceding provisions may be modified by special arrangements between the administrations of the countries concerned.

S25.5 § 3. 1) Any person seeking a license to operate the apparatus of an amateur station shall prove that he is able to send correctly by hand and to receive correctly by ear, texts in Morse code signals. The administrations concerned may, however, waive this requirement in the case of stations making use exclusively of frequencies above 30 MHz.

S25.6 2) Administrations shall take such measures as they judge necessary to verify the operational and technical qualifications of any person wishing to operate the apparatus of an amateur station.

S25.7 § 4. The maximum power of amateur stations shall be fixed by the administrations concerned, having regard to the technical qualifications of the operators and to the conditions under which these stations are to operate.

S25.8 § 5. 1) All the general rules of the Convention, the Convention and of these Regulations shall apply to amateur stations. In particular, the emitted frequency shall be as stable and as free from spurious emissions as the state of technical development for such stations permits.

S25.9 2) During the course of their transmissions, amateur stations shall transmit their call sign at short intervals.

Section II. Amateur-Satellite Service

S25.10 § 6. The provisions of Section I of this Article shall apply equally, as appropriate, to the amateur-satellite service.

S25.11 § 7. Space stations in the amateur-satellite service operating in bands shared with other services shall be fitted with appropriate devices for controlling emissions in the event that harmful interference is reported in accordance with the procedure laid down in Article S15. Administrations authorizing such space stations shall inform the Bureau and shall ensure that sufficient earth command stations are established before launch to guarantee that any harmful interference which might be reported can be terminated by the authorizing administration (see No. S22.1).

Section III. Radio Services

§3.34 *Amateur Service:* A radiocommunication service for the purpose of self-training, intercommunication and technical investigations carried out by amateurs, that is, by duly authorized persons interested in radio technique solely with a personal aim and without pecuniary interest.

§3.35 *Amateur-Satellite Service:* A radiocommunication service using space stations on earth satellites for the same purposes as those of the amateur service.

✱ ✱ ✱ ✱ ✱ ✱ ✱ ✱ ✱ ✱ ✱ ✱ ✱ ✱ ✱ ✱

Resolution No. 641

Use of the Frequency Band 7000-7100 kHz

The World Administrative Radio Conference for the Planning of the HF Bands Allocated to the Broadcasting Service (Geneva, 1987),

Considering

a) that the sharing of frequency bands by amateur and broadcasting services is undesirable and should be avoided;

b) that it is desirable to have world-wide exclusive allocations for these services in Band 7;

c) that the band 7000-7100 kHz is allocated on a world-wide basis exclusively to the amateur service;

Resolves

that the broadcasting service shall be prohibited from the band 7000-7100 kHz and that the broadcasting stations operating on frequencies in this band shall cease such operation.

urges

the administrations responsible for the broadcasting stations operating on frequencies in the band 7000-7100 kHz to take the necessary steps to ensure that such operation ceases immediately,

instructs the Secretary-General

to bring this Resolution to the attention of administrations.

✱ ✱ ✱ ✱ ✱ ✱ ✱ ✱ ✱ ✱ ✱ ✱ ✱ ✱ ✱ ✱

Resolution No. 642

Relating to the Bringing into Use of Earth Stations in the Amateur-Satellite Service. The World Administrative Radio Conference, Geneva, 1979,

Recognizing

that the procedures of Articles 11 and 13 are applicable to the Amateur Satellite Service;

Recognizing Further

a) that the characteristics of earth stations in the Amateur-Satellite Service vary widely;

b) that space stations in the Amateur-Satellite Service are intended for multiple access by amateur earth stations in all countries;

c) that coordination among stations in the amateur and Amateur-Satellite Services is accomplished without the need for formal procedures;

d) that the burden of terminating any harmful interference is placed upon the administration authorizing a space station in the Amateur-Satellite Service pursuant to the provisions of No. 2741 of the Radio Regulations;

Notes

that certain information specified in Appendices 3 and 4 cannot reasonably be provided for earth stations in the Amateur-Satellite Service;

Resolves

1. that when an administration (or one acting on behalf of a group of named administrations) intends to establish a satellite system in the Amateur-Satellite Service and wishes to publish information with respect to earth stations in that system it may:

1.1 communicate to the IFRB all or part of the information listed in Appendix 3; the IFRB shall publish such information in a special section of its weekly circular requesting comments to be communicated within a period of four months after the date of publication;

1.2 notify under Nos. 1488 to 1491 all or part of the information listed in Appendix 3; the IFRB shall record it in a special list;

2. that this information shall include at least the characteristics of a typical amateur earth station in the Amateur-Satellite Service having the facility to transmit signals to the space station to initiate, modify, or terminate the functions of the space station.

Appendix 6

PUBLIC LAW 103-408—JOINT RESOLUTION OF CONGRESS TO RECOGNIZE THE ACHIEVEMENTS OF RADIO AMATEURS

PUBLIC LAW 103-408—OCT. 22, 1994

Public Law 103-408
103d Congress
Joint Resolution

To recognize the achievements of radio amateurs, and to establish support for such amateurs as national policy.

Whereas Congress has expressed its determination in section 1 of the Communications Act of 1934 (47 U.S.C. 151) to promote safety of life and property through the use of radio communication;

Whereas Congress, in section 7 of the Communications Act of 1934 (47 U.S.C. 157), established a policy to encourage the provision of new technologies and services;

Whereas Congress, in section 3 of the Communications Act of 1934, defined radio stations to include amateur stations operated by persons interested in radio technique without pecuniary interest;

Whereas the Federal Communications Commission has created an effective regulatory framework through which the amateur radio service has been able to achieve the goals of the service;

Whereas these regulations, set forth in Part 97 of title 47 of the Code of Federal Regulations clarify and extend the purposes of the amateur radio service as a—

(1) voluntary noncommercial communication service, particularly with respect to providing emergency communications;

(2) contributing service to the advancement of the telecommunications infrastructure;

(3) service which encourages improvement of an individual's technical and operating skills;

(4) service providing a national reservoir of trained operators, technicians and electronics experts; and

(5) service enhancing international good will;

Whereas Congress finds that members of the amateur radio service community have provided invaluable emergency communications services following such disasters as Hurricanes Hugo, Andrew, and Iniki, the Mt. St. Helens Eruption, the Loma Prieta earthquake, tornadoes, floods, wild fires, and industrial accidents in great number and variety across the Nation; and

Whereas Congress finds that the amateur radio service has made a contribution to our Nation's communications by its crafting, in 1961, of the first Earth satellite licensed by the Federal Communications Commission, by its proof-of-concept for search rescue satellites, by its continued exploration of the low Earth orbit in particular pointing the way to commercial use thereof in the 1990s, by its pioneering of communications using reflections from meteor trails, a technique now used for certain government and commercial communications, and by its leading role in development of low-cost, practical data transmission by radio which increasingly is being put to extensive use in, for instance, the land mobile service: Now, therefore, be it

Resolved by the Senate and House of Representatives of the United States of America in Congress assembled,

SECTION 1. FINDINGS AND DECLARATIONS OF CONGRESS

Congress finds and declares that—

(1) radio amateurs are hereby commended for their contributions to technical progress in electronics, and for their emergency radio communications in times of disaster;

(2) the Federal Communications Commission is urged to continue and enhance the development of the amateur radio service as a public benefit by adopting rules and regulations which encourage the use of new technologies within the amateur radio service; and

(3) reasonable accommodation should be made for the effective operation of amateur radio from residences, private vehicles and public areas, and that regulation at all levels of government should facilitate and encourage amateur radio operation as a public benefit.

Approved October 22, 1994.

Appendix 7

MEMORANDUM OPINION AND ORDER IN PRB-1

Here's the full text of FCC's Memorandum Opinion and Order in PRB-1. If you require an "official" copy of PRB-1 for use in a legal proceeding, you may cite the *Federal Register*: 50 FR 38813. The ARRL PRB-1 and related material can be found on the Web at: *http://www.arrl.org/FandES/field/regulations/*. The most complete information can be found in the ARRL book Antenna Zoning for the Radio Amateur, which includes a CD of useful documents. It is available from ARRL HQ or Amateur Radio book dealers.

Before the
Federal Communications Commission   FCC 85-506
Washington, DC 20554   36149

In the Matter of   )
Federal Preemption of State and   )   PRB-1
Local Regulations Pertaining   )
to Amateur Radio Facilities.   )

Memorandum Opinion And Order

Adopted: September 16, 1985   Released: September 19, 1985
By the Commission: Commissioner Rivera not participating.

Background

1. On July 16, 1984, the American Radio Relay League, Inc (ARRL) filed a Request for Issuance of a Declaratory Ruling asking us to delineate the limitations of local zoning and other local and state regulatory authority over Federally-licensed radio facilities. Specifically, the ARRL wanted an explicit statement that would preempt all local ordinances which provably preclude or significantly inhibit effective reliable amateur radio communications. The ARRL acknowledges that local authorities can regulate amateur installations to insure the safety and health of persons in the community, but believes that those regulations cannot be so restrictive that they preclude effective amateur communications.

2. Interested parties were advised that they could file comments in the matter.[1] With extension, comments were due on or before December 26, 1984,[2] with reply comments due on or before January 25, 1985.[3] Over sixteen hundred comments were filed.

Local Ordinances

3. Conflicts between amateur operators regarding radio antennas and local authorities regarding restrictive ordinances are common. The amateur operator is governed by the regulations contained in Part 97 of our rules. Those rules do not limit the height of an amateur antenna but they require, for aviation safety reasons, that certain FAA notification and FCC approval procedures must be followed for antennas which exceed 200 feet in height above ground level or antennas which are to be erected near airports. Thus, under FCC rules some antenna support structures require obstruction marking and lighting. On the other hand, local municipalities or governing bodies frequently enact regulations limiting antennas and their support

structures in height and location, e.g. to side or rear yards, for health, safety or aesthetic considerations. These limiting regulations can result in conflict because the effectiveness of the communications that emanate from an amateur radio station are directly dependent upon the location and the height of the antenna. Amateur operators maintain that they are precluded from operating in certain bands allocated for their use if the height of their antennas is limited by a local ordinance.

4. Examples of restrictive local ordinances were submitted by several amateur operators in this proceeding. Stanley J. Cichy, San Diego, California, noted that in San Diego amateur radio antennas come under a structures ruling which limits building heights to 30 feet. Thus, antennas there are also limited to 30 feet. Alexander Vrenios, Mundelein, Illinois, wrote that an ordinance of the Village of Mundelein provides that an antenna must be a distance from the property line that is equal to one and one-half times its height. In his case, he is limited to an antenna tower for his amateur station just over 53 feet in height.

5. John C. Chapman, an amateur living in Bloomington, Minnesota, commented that he was not able to obtain a building permit to install an amateur radio antenna exceeding 35 feet in height because the Bloomington city ordinance restricted "structures" heights to 35 feet. Mr. Chapman said that the ordinance, when written, undoubtedly applied to buildings but was now being applied to antennas in the absence of a specific ordinance regulating them. There were two options open to him if he wanted to engage in amateur communications. He could request a variance to the ordinance by way of a hearing before the City Council, or he could obtain affidavits from his neighbors swearing that they had no objection to the proposed antenna installation. He got the building permit after obtaining the cooperation of his neighbors. His concern, however, is that he had to get permission from several people before he could effectively engage in radio communications for which he had a valid FCC amateur license.

6. In addition to height restrictions, other limits are enacted by local jurisdictions—anti-climb devices on towers or fences around them; minimum distances from high voltage power lines; minimum distances of towers from property lines; and regulations pertaining to the structural soundness of the antenna installation. By and large, amateurs do not find these safety precautions objectionable. What they do object to are the sometimes prohibitive, non-refundable application filing fees to obtain a permit to erect an antenna installation and those provisions in ordinances which regulate antennas for purely aesthetic reasons. The amateurs contend, almost universally, that "beauty is in the eye of the beholder." They assert that an antenna installation is not more aesthetically displeasing than other objects that people keep on their property, e.g. motor homes, trailers, pick-up trucks, solar collectors and gardening equipment.

Restrictive Covenants

7. Amateur operators also oppose restrictions on their amateur operations which are contained in the deeds for their homes or in their apartment leases. Since these restrictive covenants are contractual agreements between private parties, they are not generally a matter of concern to the Commission. However, since some amateurs who commented in this proceeding provided us with examples of restrictive covenants, they are included for information. Mr. Eugene O. Thomas of Hollister, California, included in his comments an extract of the Declaration of Covenants and Restrictions

for Ridgemark Estates, County of San Benito, State of California. It provides:

No antenna for transmission or reception of radio signals shall be erected outdoors for use by any dwelling unit except upon approval of the Directors. No radio or television signals or any other form of electromagnetic radiation shall be permitted to originate from any lot which may unreasonably interfere with the reception of television or radio signals upon any other lot.

Marshall Wilson, Jr. provided a copy of the restrictive covenant contained in deeds for the Bell Martin Addition #2, Irving, Texas. It is binding upon all of the owners or purchasers of the lots in the said addition, his or their heirs, executors, administrators or assigns. It reads:

No antenna or tower shall be erected upon any lot for the purposes of radio operations.

William J. Hamilton resides in an apartment building in Gladstone, Missouri. He cites a clause in his lease prohibiting the erection of an antenna. He states that he has been forced to give up operating amateur radio equipment except a hand-held 2 meter (144-148 MHz) radio transceiver. He maintains that he should not be penalized just because he lives in an apartment.

Other restrictive covenants are less global in scope than those cited above. For example, Robert Webb purchased a home in Houston, Texas. His deed restriction prohibited "transmitting or receiving antennas extending above the roof line."

8. Amateur operators generally oppose restrictive covenants for several reasons. They maintain that such restrictions limit the places that they can reside if they want to pursue their hobby of amateur radio. Some state that they impinge on First Amendment rights of speech. Others believe that a constitutional right is being abridged because, in their view, everyone has a right to access the airwaves regardless of where they live.

9. The contrary belief held by housing subdivision communities and condominium or homeowner's associations is that amateur radio installations constitute safety hazards, cause interference to other electronic equipment which may be operated in the home (television, radio, stereos) or are eyesores that detract from the aesthetic and tasteful appearance of the housing development or apartment complex. To counteract these negative consequences, the subdivisions and associations include in their deeds, leases or by-laws, restrictions and limitations on the location and height of antennas or, in some cases, prohibit them altogether. The restrictive covenants are contained in the contractual agreement entered into at the time of the sale or lease of the property. Purchasers or lessees are free to choose whether they wish to reside where such restrictions on amateur antennas are in effect or settle elsewhere.

Supporting Comments

10. The Department of Defense (DOD) supported the ARRL and emphasized in its comments that continued success of existing national security and emergency preparedness telecommunications plans involving amateur stations would be severely diminished if state and local ordinances were allowed to prohibit the construction and usage of effective amateur transmission facilities. DOD utilizes volunteers in the Military Affiliate Radio Service (MARS),[4] Civil Air Patrol (CAP) and the Radio Amateur Civil Emergency Service (RACES). It points out that these volunteer communicators are operating radio equipment installed in their homes and that undue restrictions on antennas by local authorities adversely affect their

efforts. DOD states that the responsiveness of these volunteer systems would be impaired if local ordinances interfere with the effectiveness of these important national telecommunication resources. DOD favors the issuance of a ruling that would set limits for local and state regulatory bodies when they are dealing with amateur stations.

11. Various chapters of the American Red Cross also came forward to support the ARRL's request for a preemptive ruling. The Red Cross works closely with amateur radio volunteers. It believes that without amateurs' dedicated support, disaster relief operations would significantly suffer and that its ability to serve disaster victims would be hampered. It feels that antenna height limitations that might be imposed by local bodies will negatively affect the service now rendered by the volunteers.

12. Cities and counties from various parts of the United States filed comments in support of the ARRL's request for a Federal preemption ruling. The comments from the Director of Civil Defense, Port Arthur, Texas, are representative:

> The Amateur Radio Service plays a vital role with our Civil Defense program here in Port Arthur and the design of these antennas and towers lends greatly to our ability to communicate during times of disaster.
>
> We do not believe there should be any restrictions on the antennas and towers except for reasonable safety precautions. Tropical storms, hurricanes and tornadoes are a way of life here on the Texas Gulf Coast and good communications are absolutely essential when preparing for a hurricane and even more so during recovery operations after the hurricane has past.

13. The Quarter Century Wireless Association took a strong stand in favor of the Issuance of a declaratory ruling. It believes that Federal preemption is necessary so that there will be uniformity for all Amateur Radio installations on private property throughout the United States.

14. In its comments, the ARRL argued that the Commission has the jurisdiction to preempt certain local land use regulations which frustrate or prohibit amateur radio communications. It said that the appropriate standard in preemption cases is not the extent of state and local interest in a given regulation, but rather the impact of the regulation on Federal goals. Its position is that Federal preemption is warranted whenever local government regulations relate adversely to the operational aspects of amateur communication. The ARRL maintains that localities routinely employ a variety of land use devices to preclude the installation of effective amateur antennas, including height restrictions, conditional use permits, building setbacks and dimensional limitations on antennas. It sees a declaratory ruling of Federal preemption as necessary to cause municipalities to accommodate amateur operator needs in land use planning efforts.

15. James C. O'Connell, an attorney who has represented several amateurs before local zoning authorities, said that requiring amateurs to seek variances or special use approval to erect reasonable antennas unduly restricts the operation of amateur stations. He suggested that the Commission preempt zoning ordinances which impose antenna height limits of less than 65 feet. He said that this height would represent a reasonable accommodation of the communication needs of most amateurs and the legitimate concerns of local zoning authorities.

Opposing Comments

16. The City of La Mesa, California, has a zoning regulation which controls amateur antennas. Its comments reflected an attempt to reach a balanced view.

This regulation has neither the intent, nor the effect, of precluding or inhibiting effective and reliable communications. Such antennas may be built as long as their construction does not unreasonably block views or constitute eyesores. The reasonable assumption is that there are always alternatives at a given site for different placement, and/or methods for aesthetic treatment. Thus, both public objectives of controlling land use for the public health, safety, and convenience, and providing an effective communications network, can be satisfied. A blanket to completely set aside local control, or a ruling which recognizes control only for the purpose of safety of antenna construction, would be contrary to...legitimate local control.

17. Comments from the County of San Diego state:

While we are aware of the benefits provided by amateur operators, we oppose the issuance of a preemption ruling which would elevate "antenna effectiveness" to a position above all other considerations. We must, however, argue that the local government must have the ability to place reasonable limitations upon the placement and configuration of amateur radio transmitting and receiving antennas. Such ability is necessary to assure that the local decision-makers have the authority to protect the public health, safety and welfare of all citizens.

In conclusion, I would like to emphasize an important difference between your regulatory powers and that of local governments. Your Commission's approval of the preemptive requests would establish a "national policy." However, any regulation adopted by a local jurisdiction could be overturned by your Commission or a court if such regulation was determined to be unreasonable.

18. The City of Anderson, Indiana, summarized some of the problems that face local communities:

I am sympathetic to the concerns of these antenna owners and I understand that to gain the maximum reception from their devices, optimal location is necessary. However, the preservation of residential zoning districts as "liveable" neighborhoods is jeopardized by placing these antennas in front yards of homes. Major problems of public safety have been encountered, particularly vision blockage for auto and pedestrian access. In addition, all communities are faced with various building lot sizes. Many building lots are so small that established setback requirements (in order to preserve adequate air and light) are vulnerable to the unregulated placement of antennas. ...the exercise of preemptive authority by the FCC in granting this request would not be in the best interest of the general public.

19. The National Association of Counties (NACO), the American Planning Association (APA) and the National League of Cities (NLC) all opposed the issuance of an antenna preemption ruling. NACO emphasized that federal and state power must be viewed in harmony and warns that Federal intrusion into local concerns of health, safety and welfare could weaken the traditional police power exercised by the state and unduly interfere with the legitimate activities of the states. NLC believed that both Federal and local interests can be accommodated without

preempting local authority to regulate the installation of amateur radio antennas. The APA said that the FCC should continue to leave the issue of regulating amateur antennas with the local government and with the state and Federal courts.

Discussion

20. When considering preemption, we must begin with two constitutional provisions. The tenth amendment provides that any powers which the constitution either does not delegate to the United States or does not prohibit the states from exercising are reserved to the states. These are the police powers of the states. The Supremacy Clause, however, provides that the constitution and the laws of the United States shall supersede any state law to the contrary. Article III, Section 2. Given these basic premises, state laws may be preempted in three ways: First, Congress may expressly preempt the state law. See *Jones v. Rath Packing Co.*, 430 U.S. 519, 525 (1977). Or, Congress may indicate its intent to completely occupy a given field so that any state law encompassed within that field would implicitly be preempted. Such intent to preempt could be found in a congressional regulatory scheme that was so pervasive that it would be reasonable to assume that Congress did not intend to permit the states to supplement it. See *Fidelity Federal Savings & Loan Ass'n v. de la Cuesta,* 458 U.S. 141, 153 (1982). Finally, preemption may be warranted when state law conflicts with federal law. Such conflicts may occur when "compliance with both Federal and state regulations is a physical impossibility," *Florida Lime & Avocado Growers, Inc. v. Paul,* 373 U.S. 132, 142, 143 (1963), or when state law "stands as an obstacle to the accomplishment and execution of the full purposes and objectives of Congress," *Hines v. Davidowitz,* 312 U.S. 52, 67 (1941). Furthermore, federal regulations have the same preemptive effect as federal statutes, *Fidelity Federal Savings & Loan Association v. de la Cuesta,* supra.

21. The situation before us requires us to determine the extent to which state and local zoning regulations may conflict with federal policies concerning amateur radio operators.

22. Few matters coming before us present such a clear dichotomy of viewpoint as does the instant issue. The cities, counties, local communities and housing associations see an obligation to all of their citizens and try to address their concerns. This is accomplished through regulations, ordinances or covenants oriented toward the health, safety and general welfare of those they regulate. At the opposite pole are the individual amateur operators and their support groups who are troubled by local regulations which may inhibit the use of amateur stations or, in some instances, totally preclude amateur communications. Aligned with the operators are such entities as the Department of Defense, the American Red Cross and local civil defense and emergency organizations who have found in Amateur Radio a pool of skilled radio operators and a readily available backup network. In this situation, we believe it is appropriate to strike a balance between the federal interest in promoting amateur operations and the legitimate interests of local governments in regulating local zoning matters. The cornerstone on which we will predicate our decision is that a reasonable accommodation may be made between the two sides.

23. Preemption is primarily a function of the extent of the conflict between federal and state and local regulation. Thus, in considering whether our regulations or policies can tolerate a state regulation, we may consider such factors as the severity of the

conflict and the reasons underlying the state's regulations. In this regard, we have previously recognized the legitimate and important state interests reflected in local zoning regulations. For example, in *Earth Satellite Communications, Inc.*, 95 FCC 2d 1223 (1983), we recognized that

...countervailing state interests inhere in the present situation...For example, we do not wish to preclude a state or locality from exercising jurisdiction over certain elements of an SMATV operation that properly may fall within its authority, such as zoning or public safety and health, provided the regulation in question is not undertaken as a pretext for the actual purpose of frustrating achievement of the preeminent federal objective and so long as the non-federal regulation is applied in a nondiscriminatory manner.

24. Similarly, we recognize here that there are certain general state and local interests which may, in their even-handed application, legitimately affect amateur radio facilities. Nonetheless, there is also a strong federal interest in promoting amateur communications. Evidence of this interest may be found in the comprehensive set of rules that the Commission has adopted to regulate the amateur service.[5] Those rules set forth procedures for the licensing of stations and operators, frequency allocations, technical standards which amateur radio equipment must meet and operating practices which amateur operators must follow. We recognize the amateur radio service as a voluntary, noncommercial communication service, particularly with respect to providing emergency communications. Moreover, the amateur radio service provides a reservoir of trained operators, technicians and electronic experts who can be called on in times of national or local emergencies. By its nature, the Amateur Radio Service also provides the opportunity for individual operators to further international goodwill. Upon weighing these interests, we believe a limited preemption policy is warranted. State and local regulations that operate to preclude amateur communications in their communities are in direct conflict with federal objectives and must be preempted.

25. Because amateur station communications are only as effective as the antennas employed, antenna height restrictions directly affect the effectiveness of amateur communications. Some amateur antenna configurations require more substantial installations than others if they are to provide the amateur operator with the communications that he/she desires to engage in. For example, an antenna array for international amateur communications will differ from an antenna used to contact other amateur operators at shorter distances. We will not, however, specify any particular height limitation below which a local government may not regulate, nor will we suggest the precise language that must be contained in local ordinances, such as mechanisms for special exceptions, variances, or conditional use permits. Nevertheless, local regulations which involve placement, screening, or height of antennas based on health, safety, or aesthetic considerations must be crafted to accommodate reasonably amateur communications, and to represent the minimum practicable regulation to accomplish the local authority's legitimate purpose.[6]

26. Obviously, we do not have the staff or financial resources to review all state and local laws that affect amateur operations. We are confident, however, that state and local governments will endeavor to legislate in a manner that affords appropriate recognition to the important federal interest at stake here and thereby avoid unnecessary conflicts with federal policy, as well as time-consuming and expensive

litigation in this area. Amateur operators who believe that local or state governments have been overreaching and thereby have precluded accomplishment of their legitimate communications goals, may, in addition, use this document to bring our policies to the attention of local tribunals and forums.

27. Accordingly, the Request for Declaratory Ruling filed July 16, 1984, by the American Radio Relay League, Inc., IS GRANTED to the extent indicated herein and in all other respects, IS DENIED.

FEDERAL COMMUNICATIONS COMMISSION
William J. Tricarico
Secretary

Footnotes

[1] Public Notice, August 30, 1984, Mimeo. No. 6299, 49 F.R. 36113, September 14, 1984.

[2] Public Notice, December 19,1984, Mimeo. No. 1498.

[3] Order, November 8, 1984, Mimeo. No. 770.

[4] MARS is solely under the auspices of the military which recruits volunteer amateur operators to render assistance to it. The Commission is not involved in the MARS program.

[5] 47 CFR Part 97.

[6] We reiterate that our ruling herein does not reach restrictive covenants in private contractual agreements. Such agreements are voluntarily entered into by the buyer or tenant when the agreement is executed and do not usually concern this Commission.

Appendix 8

FCC LETTER: LOCAL GOVERNMENTS PROHIBITED FROM REGULATING RFI

FEDERAL COMMUNICATIONS COMMISSION
WASHINGTON, D.C. 20554
FEB 14, 1990

Christopher D. Imlay, Esquire
American Radio Relay League, Inc.
Office of Legal Counsel
Washington, D.C.

Re: Ordinance Regulating Radio Frequency Interference, Pierre, South Dakota

Dear Mr. Imlay:

This is in response to your letter of January 16, 1990, concerning an ordinance enacted in Pierre, South Dakota, empowering the City Inspector to investigate and prohibit emissions by radios and other electronic devices which cause or create interference to television or radio reception. You state that the City Inspector has enforced this ordinance against an amateur radio operator licensed by the Commission, and you seek an opinion concerning the validity of the ordinance.

Congress has preempted any concurrent state or local regulation of radio interference pursuant to the provisions of the Communications Act. See 47 U.S.C. §302(a). Section 302(a)(1) of the Act provides that the "Commission may, consistent with the public interest, convenience, and necessity, make reasonable regulations (1) governing the interference potential of devices which in their operation are capable of emitting radio frequency energy by radiation, conduction, or other means in sufficient degree to cause harmful interference to radio communications . . . ." 47 U.S.C. §302(a)(1). The legislative history of Section 302(a) provides explicitly that the Commission has exclusive authority to regulate radio frequency interference (RFI). In its Conference Report No. 97-765, Congress declared:

> The Conference Substitute is further intended to clarify the reservation of exclusive jurisdiction to the Federal Communications Commission over matters involving RFI. Such matters shall not be regulated by local or state law, nor shall radio transmitting be subject to local or state regulation as part of any effort to resolve an RFI complaint.

H.R. Report No. 765, 97th Cong., 2d Sess. 33 (1982), reprinted at 1982 U.S. Code Cong. & Ad News 2277.

State laws that require amateurs to cease operations or incur penalties as a consequence of radio interference thus have been entirely preempted by Congress.

Of course, any member of the public may seek the Commission's assistance in resolving interference problems. The Commission's Field Operations Bureau (FOB) frequently investigates radio interference complaints and has prepared the enclosed pamphlets describing the various remedies available to address radio interference matters. Members of the public in Pierre experiencing interference may also wish to contact Dennis P. Carlton, Engineer-in-Charge of FOB's Denver Office at (303) 236-8026.

I trust the foregoing is responsive to your inquiry.

Sincerely yours,

Robert L. Pettit
General Counsel

Enclosures
cc: City Inspector, Pierre, South Dakota

Appendix 9

FCC LETTER: LOCAL GOVERNMENTS ARE PROHIBITED FROM DENYING A BUILDING PERMIT BASED SOLELY ON RFI

FEDERAL COMMUNICATIONS COMMISSION
WASHINGTON, D.C. 20554

25 OCT 1994

IN REPLY REFER TO:
7240-F/1700C1

Board of Zoning Appeals
Town of Hempstead
1 Washington Street
Hempstead, New York, 11550-4923

Dear Board Members:

It has come to our attention that the Town of Hempstead's Board of Zoning Appeals (Board) has denied Mr. Hayden M. Nadel's application for a variance permitting him to maintain his amateur radio station's antenna at a height of fifty-five feet (versus the thirty feet permitted by the zoning ordinance). According to the text of the Board's decision (provided by Mr. Nadel), it based its determination largely on its finding that the "proposed and existing antenna height of fifty-five feet" was resulting in interference to the home electronic equipment of Mr. Nadel's neighbors.

Local Governments must reasonably accommodate amateur operations in zoning decisions. See PRB-1, 101 FCC 2d 952 (1985) and Section 97.15(e) of the Commission's Rules, 47 C.F.R. §97.15(e) (copies enclosed). Section 97.15(e) provides that an amateur station antenna structure may be erected at heights and dimensions sufficient to accommodate amateur service communications. Local authorities may adopt regulations pertaining to placement, screening, or height of antennas, if such regulations are based on health, safety, or aesthetic considerations and reasonably accommodate amateur communications. They may not, however, base their regulation of amateur service antenna structures on the causation of interference to home electronic equipment—an area regulated exclusively by the Commission.

The Commission's jurisdiction over interference matters is set forth in Section 302(a) of the Communications Act of 1934, as amended, 47 U.S.C. §302(a) (copy enclosed). It is clear from the report of the Joint Committee of Conference, H.R. Report No. 765, 97th Cong., 2nd Sess. (pertinent excerpts enclosed), that the congress intended that the Commission have exclusive jurisdiction over interference to home electronic equipment.

I would also like to point out that there is no reasonable connection between requiring Mr. Nadel to reduce the height of his antenna and reducing the amount of interference to his neighbor's home electronic equipment. On the contrary, antenna height is inversely related to the strength, in the horizontal plane, of the radio signal that serves as a catalyst for interference in susceptible home electronic equipment. It is a matter of technical fact that the higher an amateur antenna, the less likely it is that radio frequency interference will appear in home electronic equipment.

I hope the information in this letter is helpful

Sincerely,

Ralph A. Haller
Chief, Private Radio Bureau

Enclosures

Appendix 10

LIST OF LANDMARK CASES AFFECTING AMATEUR RADIO

Schroeder v. Municipal Court of Cerritos
    73 Cal. Rptr 3d 841, 141 Cal. Rptr. 85 (1977)
    Appeal dismissed 435 US 990 (1978)

Guske v. Oklahoma City, Oklahoma
    763 F. 2d 379 (10th Cir 1985)

PRB-1 Declaratory Ruling
    Amateur Radio Preemption, 101 FCC 2d 952 (1985)

Satellite Receive Only Earth Stations Preemption Order
    Docket 85-87; Pike and Fischer Radio Regulation 2d 1073 (1986)

John Thernes v. City of Lakeside Park, Kentucky, et al
    779 F. 2d 1187 (6th Cir. 1986)
    Final Judgment; 62 Pike and Fischer Radio Regulation 2d, 284 (E. D. KY, 1987)

Andrew B. Bodony v. Incorporated Village of Sands Point et al (NY)
    681 F. Supp 1009 (E.D. NY 1987)

William F. Bulchis v. City of Edmonds (WA)
    671 F. Supp 1270 (W. D. Wash 1987)

Izzo v. Borough of River Edge, New York, et al
    843 F. 2d 765 (3rd Cir., 1988)

James D. MacMillan v. City of Rocky River, Ohio, et al
    748 F. Supp 1241 (N.D.Ohio 1990)

John F. Williams v. City of Columbia, SC
    707 F. Supp 207 (D.S.C., 1989)
    Affirmed 906 F.2d 994 (4th Cir. 1990)

Vernon Howard v. City of Burlingame (CA)
    726 F. Supp 770 (N.D.Cal. 1989)
    Affirmed 937 F. 2d 1376 (9th Cir. 1991)

Palmer Hotz et al v. James E. Rich (Cov.)
    6 Cal. Rptr. 2d 219 (Cal. Ct. of Appeals 1992)

D. R. Evans v. Board of County Commissioners of the County of Boulder, Colorado, et al
    752 F. Supp 973 (D.Colo. 1990)
    Reversed 994 F. 2d 761 (10th Cir 1993)

Sylvia Pentel v. City of Mendota Heights (MN)
    13 F. 3d 1261 (8th Cir 1994)

Appendix 11

PR DOCKET 91-36: FEDERAL PREEMPTION OF STATE AND LOCAL LAWS CONCERNING AMATEUR USE OF TRANSCEIVERS CAPABLE OF RECEPTION BEYOND AMATEUR ALLOCATIONS.

This preemption allows amateurs to possess a transceiver capable of reception (but not transmission) on frequencies adjoining the amateur VHF/UHF bands. It does not apply to scanners which are separate from an amateur transceiver.

Before the
Federal Communications Commission
Washington, DC 20554
PR Docket 91-36

In the Matter of

Federal Preemption of State
and Local Laws Concerning Amateur
Operator Use of Transceivers
Capable of Reception Beyond
Amateur Service Frequency
Allocations

Memorandum Opinion and Order

Adopted: August 20, 1993;   Released: September 3, 1993
By the Commission:

I. INTRODUCTION

1. On November 14, 1989, the American Radio Relay League, Incorporated (ARRL), filed a *Motion for a Declaratory Ruling*[1] requesting that the Commission preempt certain state statutes and local ordinances affecting transceivers[2] used by Amateur Radio Service Licensees. The laws referenced by the ARRL prohibit the possession of such transceivers if they are capable of the reception of communications on certain frequencies other than amateur service frequencies. On March 15, 1990, we released a public notice[3] inviting comment on ARRL's request. In addition, on February 28, 1991, we released a *Notice of Inquiry*[4] that solicited additional comment to assist us in making a decision in this matter. This *Memorandum Opinion and Order* grants the request to the extent indicated herein.

II. BACKGROUND

2. The ARRL motion discusses state statutes and local ordinances commonly known as "scanner laws," the violation of which may be a criminal misdemeanor with the possibility of equipment confiscation.[5] Specifically, ARRL notes that state statutes in New Jersey and Kentucky (which have subsequently been changed —see paragraph 3, *infra*) prohibit the possession of a mobile short-wave radio capable of receiving frequencies assigned by the Commission for, *inter alia*, police use.[6] In addition, ARRL states that local ordinances exist throughout the United States that similarly prohibit the possession of such mobile short-wave radios without a locally-issued permit.[7] Therefore, ARRL explains, scanner laws can, *inter alia*, render

amateur radio licensees traveling interstate by automobile vulnerable to arrest and to the seizure of their radio equipment by state or local police.[8]

3. Since the ARRL motion was filed with the Commission, New Jersey repealed its statute and substituted a new, narrowly tailored scanner law that only applies in the criminal context.[9] In addition, Kentucky amended its statute by adding an exemption applying to amateur radio licensees.[10] As a result, there no longer appears to be any state scanner law with a deleterious effect on the legitimate operations of amateur radio service licensees. Nonetheless, the preemption issue raised by the ARRL motion remains timely because it appears that some local scanning ordinances remain in effect without safeguards to protect the legitimate use of such radios by our licensees.[11]

III. MOTION, INQUIRY AND COMMENTS

A. The ARRL Motion.

4. ARRL makes two arguments in support of preemption. First, it states that the receiver sections of the majority of commercially available amateur station transceivers can be tuned slightly past the edges of the amateur service bands to facilitate adequate reception up to the end of the amateur service bands. ARRL seeks a preemption ruling that would permit amateur operators to install in vehicles transceivers that are capable of this "incidental" reception.[12] Although ARRL's formal request is couched in terms of this first, technical point, the request focuses almost entirely on a second, broader issue of whether state and local authorities should be permitted, via the scanner laws, to prohibit the capability of radio reception by amateur operators on public safety and special emergency frequencies that are well outside the amateur service bands.

5. Concerning the broader issue, ARRL argues that amateur operators have special needs for broadscale "out-of-band" reception, and that the marketplace has long recognized these needs by offering accommodating transceivers. According to ARRL,[13] all commercially manufactured amateur service HF transceivers and the majority of such VHF and UHF transceivers have non-amateur service frequency reception capability well beyond the "incidental" — they can receive across a broad spectrum of frequencies, including the police and other public safety and special emergency frequencies here at issue. This additional capability, argues ARRL, permits amateur operators to participate in a variety of safety activities, some in conjunction with the military or the National Weather Service. In both cases, reception on non-amateur frequencies is necessary. Such activities benefit the public, according to ARRL, especially in times of emergency,[14] and some require the mobile use of the amateur stations.[15] ARRL states that, in addition, the vast majority of amateur operators take part in these mobile activities, and that the widespread enforcement of scanner laws would render illegal the possession of virtually all modern amateur mobile equipment.[16] ARRL states that, as a result of scanner laws, "several dozen instances of radio seizure and criminal arrest [have been] suffered by licensed amateurs."[17]

B. The Inquiry and Comments.

6. The Commission's February 28, 1991 *Inquiry* solicited additional information concerning the technical and financial feasibility of modifying existing amateur service mobile transceivers to render them incapable of receiving police or other public safety channels. We also asked for information concerning the current and future marketplace availability of mobile equipment meeting the restrictions of the laws and whether there is value in having an available pool of wide-band, mobile amateur equipment in the United States to meet emergency needs.

7. In response to the *Inquiry,* we received 115 comments and reply comments, of which the great majority are from individual amateurs who support the preemption.[18] One commenter, the Michigan Department of State Police, states that although it cooperates with the amateur service during emergencies, it is concerned about isolated incidents of apparently unlawful actions taken by amateur licensees upon receipt of public safety communications outside of the amateur radio band.[19] Therefore, it concludes that "there can be no beneficial need for amateur radio equipment to tune in public safety channels."[20] Of the remaining comments received, only a few address the technical and marketplace questions described above. These comments are from individual amateur operators[21] who state that existing wide-band transceivers cannot be modified to meet the restrictions of the scanner laws without substantial expense and that this situation will continue as new equipment becomes available. Despite our specific request in the *Inquiry* that manufacturers comment on these technical and financial questions, no manufacturer chose to respond on these points. We also received a few comments describing the prevalence of scanner laws nationwide.[22] Finally, the National Communications System (NCS), of the Department of Defense, states in its comment that the federal government utilizes amateur operators in a number of programs requiring mobile, wide-band transceivers.[23]

IV. DISCUSSION

8. There are three ways state and local laws may be preempted. First, Congress may expressly preempt the state or local law. Second, Congress may, through legislation, clearly indicate its intent to occupy the field of regulation, leaving "no room for the States to supplement."[24] Last, and most important for this discussion,

[e]ven where Congress has not completely displaced state regulation in a specific area, state law [may be] nullified to the extent that it actually conflicts with federal law. Such a conflict arises when "compliance with both federal and state regulations is a physical impossibility,"...or when state law "stands as an obstacle to the accomplishment and execution of the full purposes and objectives of Congress."[25]

Furthermore, "[f]ederal regulations have no less preemptive effect than federal statutes."[26]

9. The amateur service is regulated extensively under Part 97 of the Commission's Rules, 47 C.F.R. Part 97. As we have stated in the past:

[T]here is...a strong federal interest in promoting amateur communications. Evidence of this interest may be found in the comprehensive set of rules that the Commission has adopted to regulate the amateur service. Those rules set forth procedures for the licensing of stations and operators, frequency allocations, technical standards which amateur radio equipment must meet and operating practices which amateur operators must follow. We recognize the Amateur Radio Service as a voluntary, noncommercial communication service, particularly with respect to providing emergency communications. Moreover, the Amateur Radio Service provides a reservoir of trained operators, technicians and electronic experts who can be called on in times of national or local emergencies. By its nature, the Amateur Radio Service also provides the opportunity for individual operators to further international goodwill.[27]

This federal interest in the amateur service is also reflected in Section 97.1 of our rules, 47 C.F.R. §97.1, which provides that the amateur service exists to "continu[e] and exten[d]...the amateur's proven ability to contribute to the advancement of the radio art."[28] This regulatory purpose is consistent with the

Communications Act requirement that "[i]t shall be the policy of the United States to encourage the provision of new technologies to the public."[29]

10. The strong federal interest in the preservation and advancement of the amateur service is also demonstrated by Congress's recent recognition of the goals of the amateur service in a "Sense of Congress" provision in which Congress strongly encouraged and supported the amateur service.[30] Congress therein directed all Government agencies to take into account the valuable contribution of amateurs when considering actions affecting the amateur radio service.[31] We believe that the strong federal interest in supporting the emergency services provided by amateurs cannot be fully accomplished unless amateur operators are free to own and operate their stations to the fullest extent permitted by their licenses and are not unreasonably hampered in their ability to transport their radio transmitting stations across state and local boundaries for purposes of transmitting and receiving on authorized frequencies. Indeed, as a result of advances in technology making smaller, lighter weight radios commercially available, the Commission has expressly amended its rules to facilitate and encourage unrestricted mobile amateur operations. As we noted in a recent rule making proceeding to modify the rules governing the amateur radio service,

> In the age of the microprocessor and the integrated circuit [amateur] equipment is highly portable. It is common for amateur operators to carry hand-held transceivers capable of accessing many local repeaters in urban areas and also capable of reasonably good line-of-sight communication. It appears that the concept of fixed station operation no longer carries with it the same connotation it did previously. For this reason, we propose to delete current rules that relate to station operation away from the authorized fixed station location.[32]

As a consequence of these changes, the rules now expressly authorize amateur service operation "at points where the amateur service is regulated by the FCC," that is, at fixed and mobile locations throughout the United States. Furthermore, the Commission's Rules do not in any way prohibit an amateur service transceiver from having out-of-band reception capability.[33]

11. Against this background, we conclude that certain state and local laws, as described below, conflict with the Commission's regulatory scheme designed to promote a strong amateur radio service. Scanner laws that prohibit the use of transceivers that transmit and receive amateur frequencies because they also receive public safety, special emergency or other radio service frequencies frustrate most legitimate amateur service mobile operations through the threat of penalties such as fines and the confiscation of equipment. As noted by ARRL, virtually all modern amateur service equipment in use today can receive transmissions on the public safety and special emergency frequencies at issue, and the majority of amateur stations[34] are operated in a mobile fashion. Consequently, the mobile operations of the vast majority of amateurs are affected by such laws. In addition, the record statements by amateurs that the costs would be substantial to modify existing transceivers are unchallenged. The scanner laws, then, essentially place the amateur operator in the position of either foregoing mobile operations by simply avoiding all use of the equipment in vehicles or other locations specified in the laws, or risking fines, or equipment confiscation. This very significant limitation on amateurs' operating rights runs counter to the express policies of both Congress and the Commission to encourage and support amateur service operations, including mobile operations, and impermissibly encroaches on federal authority over amateur operators.[35] It conflicts directly with the federal interest in amateur operators being able to transmit and receive on authorized amateur service frequencies.[36]

12. For these reasons, we find it necessary to preempt state and local laws that effectively preclude the possession in vehicles or elsewhere of amateur service transceivers by amateur operators merely on the basis that the transceivers are capable of reception on public safety, special emergency, or other radio service frequencies, the reception of which is not prohibited by federal law.[37] We find that, under current conditions and given the types of equipment available in the market today, such laws prevent amateur operators from using their mobile stations to the full extent permitted under the Commission's Rules and thus are in clear conflict with federal objectives of facilitating and promoting the Amateur Radio Service. We recognize the state law enforcement interest present here, and we do not suggest that state regulation in this area that reasonably attempts to accommodate amateur communications is preempted.[38] This decision does not pertain to scanner laws narrowly tailored to the use of such radios, for example, for criminal ends such as to assist flight from law enforcement personnel. We will not, however, suggest the precise language that must be contained in state and local laws. We do find that state and local laws must not restrict the possession of amateur transceivers simply because they are capable of reception of public safety, special emergency or other radio service frequencies, the reception of which is not prohibited by federal law, and that a state or local permit scheme will not save from preemption an otherwise objectionable law.[39] Finally, we note, as stated by APCO in comments filed previously in this proceeding, that any public safety agency that desires to protect the confidentiality of its communications can do so through the use of technology such as scrambling or encryption.[40]

V. CONCLUSION

13. We hold that state and local laws that preclude the possession in vehicles or elsewhere of amateur radio service transceivers by amateur operators merely on the basis that the transceivers are capable of the reception of public safety, special emergency, or other radio service frequencies, the reception of which is not prohibited by federal law, are inconsistent with the federal objectives of facilitating and promoting the amateur radio service and, more fundamentally, with the federal interest in amateur operator's being able to transmit and receive on authorized amateur service frequencies. We therefore hold that such state and local laws are preempted by federal law.

14. Accordingly, IT IS ORDERED that the request for a declaratory ruling filed by the ARRL IS GRANTED to the extent indicated herein and in all other respects IS DENIED.

FEDERAL COMMUNICATIONS COMMISSION
William F. Caton
Acting Secretary

APPENDIX

Comments or reply comments to the *Inquiry* were submitted by the following parties:

70 individual amateur operators, some of whom also operate GMRS equipment or use scanning receivers
2 individual General Mobile Radio Service (GMRS) operators
13 individual scanning receiver users
American Radio Relay League, Inc. (ARRL)
Associated Public-Safety Communications Officers, Inc. (APCO)
Bellcore Pioneers Amateur Radio Association
Big Spring/Howard County, Texas; Hal Boyd, Emergency Coordinator

C. Crane Company
Capital Cities/ABC, Inc.
City of Martinez, California; Gerald W. Boyd, Chief of Police
Communications Electronics, Inc.
County of Sussex, New Jersey; John Ouweleen, Emergency Management
    Coordinator
CO Communications, Inc.
Egyptian Radio Club, Inc.
Grove Enterprises, Inc.
Jessamine Amateur Radio Society
National Communications System (NCS), Department of Defense
Pasco County, Florida; Edith L. Sanders, Disaster Preparedness Coordinator
Personal Radio Steering Group, Inc. (PRSG)
Radio Communications Monitoring Association (RCMA)
Riverside County R.E.A.C.T.
Seminole County, Florida; Kenneth M. Roberts, Emergency Management
    Coordinator
State of Michigan, Department of State Police; David H. Held, Director,
    Communications Section
Tandy Corporation

Footnotes

[1] The American Radio Relay League, Inc., Request for Declaratory Ruling Concerning the Possession of Radio Receivers Capable of Reception of Police or Other Public Safety Communications (November 13, 1989) (ARRL motion).

[2] Transceivers are radio equipment capable of both transmission and reception.

[3] Public Notice, 5 FCC Rcd 1981 (1990). 55 Fed. Reg. 10805 (March 23, 1990). Comments were due by May 16, 1990, and reply comments by May 31, 1990.

[4] 6 FCC Rcd 1305 (1991) (*Inquiry*).

[5] The scanner laws appear to be aimed at promoting the health, safety, and general welfare of the citizenry.

[6] *See generally* ARRL motion (citing N.J. Stat. Ann. §2A:127—4 (West 1985) (noting that a person is guilty of a misdemeanor for possessing or installing a short-wave radio in an automobile capable of receiving, *inter alia*, frequencies assigned for police use unless a permit has been issued therefor by the chief of the county or municipal police wherein such person resides) and Ky. Rev. Stat. Ann. §432.570 (Michie/Bobbs-Merrill 1985) (noting that any person who possesses a mobile short-wave radio capable of receiving frequencies assigned for police use is guilty of a misdemeanor, except that certain users such as radio and television stations, sellers of the "scanner" radios, disaster and emergency personnel, and those using the weather radio service of the National Oceanic and Atmospheric Administration are exempt, while amateur radio licensees are not exempt).

[7] *See generally* ARRL motion (regarding, *inter alia*, a Kansas City, Missouri, scanner law). *See also* note 24, *infra*.

[8] *Id.*

[9] N.J. Stat. Ann. §2C:33-22 (West 1992).

[10] Ky. Rev. Stat. Ann. §432.570(4)(c) (Baldwin 1992).

[11] *See* note 22, *infra*.

[12] ARRL Motion at 1, 3 and 5, "Most commercial Amateur Radio VHF and UHF transceivers...are incidentally capable of reception (but not transmission) on frequencies additional to those allocated to the Amateur Radio Service. These frequencies are adjacent to amateur allocations. This is true even though the equipment is primarily designed for amateur bands, and results from the intentional effort to insure proper operation of the transceiver throughout the entire amateur band in question." *Id*, at 3.

[13] *Id*. at 12.

[14] For example, Amateur Radio licensees were widely recognized as serving a vital role in providing communications from devastated areas of South Florida during

Hurricane Andrew and its aftermath in 1992.

[15]*See generally* House Comm. on the Judiciary, Electronic Communications Privacy Act of 1986, H.R. Rep. No. 647, 99th Cong., 2d Sess, 42.

[16]ARRL motion at 2 and 12. As of February 28, 1993, the Commission's licensing database indicates that there are 598,656 amateur stations in the United States and its territories and possessions.

[17]*Id.* at 11.

[18]A list of commenters is provided in the Appendix. Further, we have accepted a comment from Communications Electronics, Inc., which was filed one day late. *See generally* 47 C.F.R. §1.46(b). We also have considered 45 comments filed previously in this proceeding. *See Inquiry,* 6 FCC Rcd at 1306-1308 (noting that all of the filed comments support the ARRL motion). In addition, we received comments from scanner (receive-only equipment) users, who are not federal licensees and whose interests have not been at issue in the proceeding.

[19]Comment of State of Michigan, Department of State Police, at 2-3 (June 3, 1991). *But see* Reply Comments of Personal Radio Steering Group of Ann Arbor, Michigan (July 8, 1991) (noting that ARRL has not requested the preemption of state and local laws that proscribe unlawful actions taken by amateur licensees).

[20]Comment of State of Michigan, *supra,* at 2-3. *But see* paragraph 12, n. 40, *infra* (noting the comments supporting preemption filed previously in this proceeding by the Associated Public Safety Communications Officers (APCO)).

[21]*See, e.g.,* Comment of John F. Fuhrman at 4 (April 29, 1991), Comment of Joseph Reymann at 9, 14 (May 24, 1991), and Comment of Mark D. Tavaglini at 3 (July 5, 1991).

[22]*See, e.g.,* Comment of ARRL at 12 & n.6, 14 (June 7, 1991); Comment of Association of North American Radio Clubs at 5 (April 30, 1990): Comment of Radio Communications Monitoring Association at 5 (June 6, 1991). With respect to scanner laws at the local level, ARRL has noted that it is difficult to determine the precise number of such ordinances. *See* Comment of ARRL at 12 (June 7, 1991); *See also* Letter from ARRL to the Chief, Private Radio Bureau, Federal Communications Commission, Washington, D.C. (May 26, 1993) (noting local scanner laws in effect in Newton and Overland Park, Kansas, Jersey City, New Jersey, and Kansas City, Missouri).

[23]Comment of National Communications System at 2-4 (June 7, 1991).

[24]Capital Cities Cable, Inc. v. Crisp, 467 U.S. 691, 699-705 (1984) (*quoting* Rice v. Santa Fe Elevator Corp., 331 U.S. 218, 230 (1947)).

[25]Fidelity Fed. Savings & Loan Ass'n v. de la Cuesta, 458 U.S. 141, 153 (1982) (*quoting* Florida Lime & Avocado Growers, Inc. v. Paul, 373 U.S. 132, 142-43 (1963); Hines v. Davidowitz, 312 U.S. 52, 67 (1941)); *see* Capital Cities Cable, Inc. v. Crisp, 467 U.S. at 705-09.

[26]Fidelity Fed. Savings & Loan Ass'n v. de la Cuesta, 458 U.S. at 153.

[27]*Federal Preemption of State and Local Regulations Pertaining to Amateur Radio Facilities,* 101 FCC 2d 952, 959-60 (1985) (concerning Amateur Radio antenna restrictions) (*Amateur Preemption Order*), *See* 47 C.F.R. §97.1. *See also* Note. Federal Preemption of Amateur Radio Antenna Height Regulation: Should the Sky Be the Limit? 9 Cardozo L. Rev. 1501, 1517-19 (1988), Note, Local Regulation of Amateur Radio Antennae and the Doctrine of Federal Preemption: The Reaches of Federalism, 9 Pac. L.J. 1041, 1055-60 (1978).

[28]47 C.F.R. §97.1(b).

[29]47 U.S.C. §157(a).

[30]SENSE OF CONGRESS

SEC. 10

(a) The Congress finds that—

(1) more than four hundred thirty-five thousand four hundred radio amateurs in the United States are licensed by the Federal Communications Commission upon examination in radio regulations, technical principles, and the international Morse code;

(2) by international treaty and the Federal Communications Commission regulation, the amateur is authorized to operate his or her station in a radio service of intercommunications and technical investigations solely with a personal aim and without pecuniary interest;

(3) among the basic purposes for the Amateur Radio Service is the provision of voluntary, noncommercial radio service, particularly emergency communications; and

(4) volunteer amateur radio emergency communications services have consistently and reliably been provided before, during, and after floods, tornadoes, forest fires, earthquakes, blizzards, train wrecks, chemical spills, and other disasters.

(b) It is the sense of Congress that —

(1) it strongly encourages and supports the Amateur Radio Service and its emergency communications efforts; and

(2) Government agencies shall take into account the valuable contributions made by amateur radio operators when considering actions affecting the Amateur Radio Service.

Federal Communications Commission Authorization Act of 1988. Pub. L. No. 100-594, 102 Stat. 3021, 3025 (November 3, 1988); see also Joint Explanatory Statement of the Committee of Conference on H.R. Conf. Rep. No. 386. 101st Cong., 1st Sess. 415, 433 (November 21, 1989), reprinted in 1990 U.S. Code Cong. & Admin. News 3018, 3037 (amateur licensees exempted from new Commission-wide fees program because "[t]he Conferees recognize that amateur licensees do not operate for profit and can play an important public safety role in times of disaster or emergency"). Joint Explanatory Statement of the Committee of Conference on H.R. Conf. Rep. No. 765, 97th Cong., 2d Sess. 18-19 (August 19, 1982), reprinted in 1982 U.S. Code Cong. & Admin. News 2261, 2262-63.

[31] *Id.*

[32] *Reorganization and Deregulation of Part 97 of the Rules Governing the Amateur Radio Services*, Notice of Proposed Rule Making, 3 FCC Rcd 2076, 2077, (1988), final rules adopted in *Report and Order*, 4 FCC Rcd 4719 (1989), aff'd in *Memorandum Opinion and Order*, 5FCC Rcd 4614 (1990).

[33] The rules, however, do prohibit amateur service *transmissions* outside of the allocated amateur service bands. 47 C.F.R §97.307(b); Public Notice, Extended Coverage Transceivers in the Amateur Radio Service, mimeo no. 4114 (July 21, 1987) (noting that "[i]t is a violation of the Commission's regulations to...transmit on a frequency allocated to a licensed service without the appropriate Commission-issued station license.").

[34] *See* para. 5, n.16, supra.

[35] *Cf.* Capital Cities Cable, Inc. v. Crisp, 467 U.S. at 711 (state ban on alcoholic beverages commercials preempted where compliance by cable companies might result in deletion of out-of-state programming, thereby frustrating federal goal of promoting programming variety).

[36] *See Amateur Preemption Order*, 101 FCC 2d at 960 (ordinances that "operate to preclude amateur operations in their communities are in direct conflict with federal objectives and must be preempted").

[37] We note that federal law prohibits unauthorized reception on frequencies of certain radio services, e.g., cellular radio. *See* Electronic Communications Privacy Act of 1986. §§101(a)(1), 101(a)(6), 101(c), 18 U.S.C. §§2510(1), 2510(10), 2510(16)(d), 2511(1). House Comm. on the Judiciary, Electronic Communications Privacy Act of 1986, H.R. Rep. No. 647, 99th Cong., 2d Sess. 31-33, 37.

[38] *See Amateur Preemption Order*, 101 FCC 2d at 960 (state and local regulations regarding amateur antennas based on health, safety or aesthetic considerations "must be crafted to accommodate reasonably amateur communications and to represent the minimum practicable regulation to accomplish the local authority legitimate purpose").

[39] The possibility that an affected licensee might obtain an additional authorization or permit to operate under the state or local law does not ameliorate the conflict, because the state or local issuing authority might choose to deny the amateur operator the permit, or charge a fee for the permit, or require the permit of even a non-resident.

[40] *See* Comments of APCO at 2-3 (May 16, 1990) (summarized in *Inquiry*, 6 FCC Rcd at 1306).

Appendix 12

FCC ENFORCEMENT BUREAU FIELD OFFICES

All calls to the FCC should be directed to the FCC Customer Center in Gettysburg, Pennsylvania. The toll-free number is 1-888-CALL FCC (1-888-225-5322). Amateurs can send e-mail to this address at callctr@fcc.gov. Amateurs can also view the FCC Customer Center Web page at *http://www.fcc.gov/cib/ncc/Welcome.html*. The FCC Customer Center in Gettysburg, PA, is able to answer all questions about FCC Rules.

ATLANTA OFFICE
Federal Communications Commission
District Director: Fred Broce
3575 Koger Blvd, Suite 320
Duluth, GA 30096-4958
Fax: 770-279-4633

BOSTON OFFICE
Federal Communications Commission
District Director: Vincent F. Kajunski
1 Batterymarch Park
Quincy, MA 02169-7495
Fax: 617-770-2408

CHICAGO OFFICE
Federal Communications Commission
District Director: G. Michael Moffitt
Park Ridge Office Center, Room 306
1550 Northwest Hwy
Park Ridge, IL 60068-1460
Fax: 847-298-5403

COLUMBIA OPERATIONS CENTER
Federal Communications Commission
District Director: Charles Magin
9200 Farm House Ln
Columbia, MD 21046
Fax: 301-206-2896

DALLAS OFFICE
Federal Communications Commission
District Director: James D. Wells
9330 LBJ Freeway, Room 1170
Dallas, TX 75243-3429
Fax: 972-907-1738

DENVER OFFICE
Federal Communications Commission
District Director: Leo Cirbo
165 South Union Blvd, Room 860
Lakewood, CO 80228-2213
Fax: 303-969-6556

DETROIT OFFICE
Federal Communications Commission
District Director: James A. Bridgewater
24897 Hathaway St
Farmington Hills, MI 48335-1552
Fax: 248-471-6131

KANSAS CITY OFFICE
Federal Communications Commission
District Director: Robert McKinney
8800 East 63rd St, Room 320
Kansas City, MO 64133-4895
Fax: 816-313-1655

LOS ANGELES OFFICE
Federal Communications Commission
District Director: James R. Zoulek
Cerritos Corporate Tower
18000 Studebaker Rd, Room 660
Cerritos, CA 90703-3130
Fax: 562-865-0736

NEW ORLEANS OFFICE
Federal Communications Commission
District Director: James C. Hawkins
2424 Edenborn Ave, Suite 460
Metarie, LA 70001
Fax: 504-834-9230

NEW YORK OFFICE
Federal Communications Commission
District Director: Alexander Zimney
201 Varick St, Suite 1151
New York, NY 10014-4870
Fax: 212-620-3718

PHILADELPHIA OFFICE
Federal Communications Commission
District Director: John Rahter
One Oxford Valley Office Bldg, Room 404
2300 East Lincoln Hwy
Langhorne, PA 19047-1859
Fax: 215-752-2363

SAN DIEGO OFFICE
Federal Communications Commission
Acting District Director: James R. Zoulek
Interstate Office Park
4542 Ruffner St, Room 370
San Diego, CA 92111-2216
Fax: 619-557-7158

SAN FRANCISCO OFFICE
Federal Communications Commission
District Director: Thomas Van Stevern
3777 Depot Rd, Room 420
Hayward, CA 94545-2756
Fax: 510-732-6015

SEATTLE OFFICE
Federal Communications Commission
District Director: Dennis J. Anderson
11410 NE 122nd Way, Room 312
Kirkland, WA 98034-6927
Fax: 425-820-0126

TAMPA OFFICE
Federal Communications Commission
District Director: Ralph M. Barlow
2203 N. Lois Ave, Room 1215
Tampa, FL 33607-2356
Fax: 813-348-1581

FCC Field Offices in these cities have been closed, but two members of the staff were retained as resident enforcement agents:

Anchorage, Alaska; Buffalo, New York; Honolulu, Hawaii; Houston, Texas; Miami, Florida; Norfolk, Virginia; Portland, Oregon; St. Paul, Minnesota; San Juan, Puerto Rico

The following sites are monitored remotely from the Columbia Operations Center, Maryland:

Allegan, Michigan; Anchorage, Alaska; Canandaigua, New York; Douglas, Arizona; Ferndale, Washington; Grand Island, Nebraska; Kingsville, Texas; Livermore, California; Powder Springs, Georgia; Sabana Seca, Puerto Rico; Santa Isabel, Puerto Rico; Vero Beach, Florida; Waipahu, Hawaii

Appendix 13
FCC INFORMATION AVAILABLE

If you need information on non-amateur rules, contact the Government Printing Office, Superintendent of Documents by mail at PO Box 317954, Pittsburgh, PA 15250-7954, by phone at 1-202-512-1800, by fax at 1-202-512-2250 or through the GPO Web site at **http://www.gpo.gov**. Government publications can be ordered. The Government Printing Office (GPO) operates 24 U.S. Government Bookstores throughout the country. Each bookstore carries a selection of at least 1500 of the most popular federal government publications, subscriptions and electronic products.

The rules mentioned in this book can be found in Title 47 (Telecommunications) of the *Code of Federal Regulations*. An up-to-date copy of Part 97 can be found at: **http://www.arrl.org/field/regulations/news/part97/**. The following Web site allows you to download needed parts of any section of the *Code of Federal Regulations*: **http://www.access.gpo.gov/nara/cfr/cfr-retrieve.html#page1**. A GPO product list can be found at this Web site: **http://www.access.gpo.gov/su_docs/index.html**.

The FCC Web address is: **http://www.fcc.gov**. You can obtain FCC forms via the Internet from the following address: **http://www.arrl.org/fcc/forms.html**. The Amateur Service forms available are the FCC Form 605 and 159 (used with Form 605, Schedule D for vanity applications) to be used with remittance to be submitted to the FCC. Forms are .pdf files and can be read with the free Adobe Acrobat reader software (available at this address: **http://www.arrl.org/acrorget.html**). ARRL members may use NCVEC Form 605 for license renewal, changes of address, changes of name and a club application for a new or modified club license. The NCVEC Form 605 must be sent to a VEC, not the ARRL. The ARRL VEC will process applications from ARRL members at no cost.

Index

366

THE ARRL'S
FCC RULE BOOK

PROOF OF
PURCHASE

Please use this form to give us your comments on this book and what you'd like to see in future editions, or e-mail us at **pubsfdbk@arrl.org** (publications feedback). If you use e-mail, please include your name, call, e-mail address and the book title, edition and printing in the body of your message. Also indicate whether or not you are an ARRL member.

Where did you purchase this book?
☐ From ARRL directly   ☐ From an ARRL dealer

Is there a dealer who carries ARRL publications within:
☐ 5 miles   ☐ 15 miles   ☐ 30 miles   of your location?   ☐ Not sure.

License class:
☐Novice ☐Technician ☐Technician Plus ☐General ☐Advanced ☐Extra

Name	ARRL member? ☐ Yes ☐ No
_____	Call Sign _____
Daytime Phone ( ) _____	Age _____
Address _____	
City, State/Province, ZIP/Postal Code _____	
e-mail address _____	
If licensed, how long? _____	**For ARRL use only** **FCC**
Other hobbies _____	Edition 12 13 14 15 16 17 18
Occupation _____	Printing 3 4 5 6 7 8 9 10 11 12

From _____

_____

_____

EDITOR, THE ARRL'S FCC RULE BOOK
AMERICAN RADIO RELAY LEAGUE
225 MAIN STREET
NEWINGTON CT 06111-1494

———————————— please fold and tape ————————————